Sequence Analysis Primer

UWBC Biotechnical Resource Series

Richard R. Burgess, Series Editor
University of Wisconsin Biotechnology Center
Madison, Wisconsin

M. Gribskov and J. Devereux, eds.	**Sequence Analysis Primer**
In Preparation: G. Grant, ed.	**Synthetic Peptides: Design and Use**
B. Brownstein and D. Nelson, eds.	**YAC Libraries: Construction and Use**
R. Garber	***In Situ* Localization: Analysis of RNA, DNA and Protein Molecules**

Sequence Analysis Primer

Edited by

**Michael Gribskov
and
John Devereux**

**M
stockton
press**

New York   London   Tokyo   Melbourne   Hong Kong

Cover Illustration by Dr. Mark S. Boguski

© Stockton Press, 1991

Published in the United States and Canada by Stockton Press
15 E. 26th Street, New York, NY 10010

Library of Congress Cataloging-in-Publication Data
I. Gribskov, Michael, 1958- . II. Devereux, John, 1947- .
     Sequence analysis primer / Michael Gribskov, John Devereux.
        p.   cm.
     Includes bibliographical references
     Includes index.
     ISBN 1-56159-007-X (soft cover):
       1. Nucleotide sequence--Methodology. 2. Amino
     acid sequence--Methodology
     QP620.S47   1990
     574.87'322--dc20
for Library of Congress
                           90-10164
                             CIP

Published in the United Kingdom by
MACMILLAN PUBLISHERS LTD (Journals Division), 1991
Distributed by Globe Book Services Ltd.,
Brunel Road, Houndmills, Basingstroke,
Hants RG21 2XS, England

British Library Cataloging in Publication Data
Gribskov, Michael
     Sequence analysis primer.
     1. Organisms. DNA. Sequences. Analysis. Applications of computer systems
     I. Title II. Deverux, John
     574.873282
     ISBN 0-333-55092-7

Printed in the United States of America
9 8 7 6 5 4 3 2 1

Contributors

Mark S. Boguski, National Center for Biotechnology Information, National Library of Medicine, National Institutes of Health, Bethesda, MD

Lisa Caballero, Biocomputing Center, Salk Institute, San Diego, CA

David Eisenberg, Molecular Biology Institute and Department of Chemistry and Biochemistry, University of California, Los Angeles, CA

Keith Elliston, Department of Biological Data, Merck Sharp & Dohme Research Laboratory, Rahway, NJ

Roland Lüthy, Molecular Biology Institute and Department of Chemistry and Biochemistry, University of California, Los Angeles, CA

Peter M. Rice, Computing Group, European Molecular Biology Laboratory, Heidelberg, FRG

David J. States, National Center for Biotechnology Information, National Library of Medicine, National Institutes of Health, Bethesda, MD

Contents

2

Protein

3

Similarity and Homology

4

Practical Aspects: Analysis of *Notch*

Foreword

This volume, Sequence Analysis Primer, is the first in the Biotechnical Resource series being produced by the University of Wisconsin Biotechnology Center and published by Stockton Press. Books in this series will cover two broad areas that we refer to as current and emerging technologies. Those books describing current technologies such as this volume will be directed at the beginning or intermediate user of the technology. Emerging technologies will cover topics at a more advanced level. As we see it, many emerging technologies will soon become current and widely used.

Rapid advances in research have paved the way for rapid changes in the ways we do research, leading to more research advances. Once we relied solely on our labs' own power (and possibly shared an ultracentrifuge with other groups). Now many of us have come to rely on core facilities or contract services to provide us with some of the more powerful research tools. We no longer need to be an expert in all areas necessary for modern research, but we do need some familiarity with these services to use them most effectively and efficiently. We hope these books will help provide that familiarity.

We have four main goals we wish to achieve with these books. First, we want to provide information enabling you to understand the principles of the methods. Second, we want to address many of the "common" problems faced by beginners so they do not repeat these mistakes. In addition, we want to describe relevant applications of the technology to help those searching for answers to their research problems. Most of all, we hope these books become helpful references to the labs using the technologies covered.

In this first volume, we hope to familiarize the reader with computer-aided sequence analysis. Our ability to obtain information on the sequences of protein, RNA, and DNA has only developed during the last 40 years. The first sequence information was obtained from proteins in the laboratories of Edman and Sanger in the mid-1950s. Later, in the mid-1960s, the laboratories of Holley and Sanger developed the ability to sequence RNA. Methods for obtaining DNA sequence were not available until 1975, when they were developed by Maxam and Gilbert and in an alternative approach, by Sanger's laboratory.

Now the amount of sequence obtained from DNA vastly overshadows the sequence obtained for proteins and RNA. The databases that contain primary sequence information have grown exponentially over the last 10 years and now, in early 1991, have reached over 50 million nucleotides of DNA sequence available in the GenBank nucleic acid database. Until recently, a majority of the DNA sequencing occurred in individual research groups who were studying a protein or enzyme of interest. They isolated the gene for that protein, and then sequenced the DNA. Therefore they were somewhat familiar with the product coded for by the region they had sequenced. This focus has now shifted, driven by the impetus of the human genome program, a very ambitious program to obtain extremely large amounts of sequence information including the entire DNA sequence of the genomes of the human and a number of major research organisms. Much larger amounts of DNA sequence are now being generated and vastly more will be generated as sequencing techniques continue to improve. But, unlike the earlier sequence work, which focused on a particular gene, most of these data will be raw, uncharacterized sequence where it is not known if it codes for a protein nor what the protein is if one is encoded. The growing availability of DNA sequence information, both that generated in individual labs, that generated by use of centralized DNA sequencing facilities in universities or companies, and that generated by large sequencing projects, opens up tremendous opportunities for the analysis of the coding regions and the proteins that are encoded. No matter how a sequence is accumulated, more and more people will need to analyze sequences.

Fortunately the growth of sequencing technology was paralleled by the increasing sophistication of computer hardware and software that are essential to store and analyze sequence information. Whether researchers carry out computer-aided sequence analysis on their PC in their laboratory or office, whether they use their PC as a terminal to connect to a larger centralized computer, or whether they have access to a computer resource center that will carry out the analysis as needed, they still need to understand the procedures of sequence analysis: what kinds of analysis are available, what are the limitations or caveats associated with each sort of analysis, and what you can and can not conclude based on this analysis.

This volume is designed to help researchers new to protein or DNA sequence analysis, to help them understand the sequence features that can be searched for and identified, to help them understand the assumptions behind the analyses, and to help them better and more accurately interpret what the analysis reveals about their particular sequence. In a lab, for example, that has obtained a DNA sequence, the researcher may ask, "What can I learn from the DNA sequence now that I have it?" Once they have identified the protein coding region within that DNA sequence and have translated it into a protein sequence, they can ask, "What can I learn from the protein sequence about the structure or function or characteristics of that protein?" Finally they can ask, "Is my sequence similar or homologous to sequences that have already been obtained in other labs?" Significant similarity between two sequences implies some common ancestry and makes suggestions about both structural and functional characteristics of an uncharacterized protein.

This volume is divided into four chapters. The first chapter introduces the reader to the computer analyses that can be carried out on DNA or RNA sequences. In the second chapter, one is introduced to the analyses that can be carried out on a protein sequence. In the third chapter, the question of identifying similar sequences and the inference of homology is treated. Finally, in the fourth chapter, all of these forms of analysis are brought to bear on one particular gene, the *Drosophila Notch* gene to show how the various analyses can be combined to learn a great deal about the structure and the function of a gene and the protein that it encodes.

The references for all four chapters are found together in a reference section. This is followed by a series of appendices that are designed to provide in one place useful information about nucleotide base and amino acid designations and characteristics, software and hardware used in sequence analysis, databases and bulletin boards of interest to persons involved in sequence analysis, and a glossary of specialized terms that are used throughout the book.

This book is not designed to be an advanced text on sequence analysis but rather to offer the reader an introduction to the terms, the kinds of computer analyses presently available, the limitations of these analyses, and examples of how these analyses are applied to specific DNA, RNA, and protein sequences. It is our hope that this volume will prove to be both useful and educational and that it will provide a stepping stone to the more advanced literature.

I would like to thank the volume editors Michael Gribskov and John Devereux for suggesting the overall organization of the volume and helping make the individual sections fit together and the chapter authors for their thoughtful contributions. Finally, I want especially to thank Carolyn Stock, series developmental editor at the University of Wisconsin Biotechnology Center, for her massive efforts to actually assemble and refine the volume and take care of the innumerable details that were involved in producing Sequence Analysis Primer.

Richard Burgess, Series Editor
Madison, Wisconsin
March 9, 1991

1 DNA

Peter M. Rice, Keith Elliston and

Michael Gribskov*

SEQUENCING PROJECT MANAGEMENT

Many molecular biology research projects involve the cloning and sequencing of a gene or some other interesting region of nucleic acid. There are many protocols, but all reduce in the end to a set of sequence fragments which must be combined and corrected to produce the finished sequence.

The tasks of collecting, assembling, and correcting the sequence data are generally performed with the help of computer programs. The following sections introduce the features of these sequence assembly programs and provide guidance for the novice user. The advice is based on experience with the sequencing of the human HPRT locus (Edwards et al., 1990), which was a shotgun sequencing project of a 57 kb region of human genomic DNA used to develop and test the EMBL Automated DNA Sequencing Workstation. The discussion is directed towards shotgun sequencing because it represents the most difficult problems in sequence assembly.

Getting Started

Choosing a Software Package

Software packages are available for all common laboratory computer systems. The packages for personal computers (PC or Macintosh) are able

*M.G. Reseach sponsored by the National Cancer Institute, DHHS, under contract N01-CO-74101 with the Advanced Bioscience Laboratories. The contents of this publication do not necessarily reflect the views or policies of the Department of Health and Human Services, nor does mention of trade names, commercial products, or organizations imply endorsement by the U.S. government.

1

assemble and correct the sequence, those for the larger systems (VAX or Unix) are generally able to analyze the sequence in greater detail. Most laboratories will be able to use sequence assembly programs in their favorite sequence analysis software package.

In general, the stages of sequence assembly are gel entry, overlap detection, editing, and reporting. The available programs differ in the ways they handle each of these tasks. No single package is ideal, though all should be adequate for a smaller project such as a single cDNA. Particular attention should be given to the quality and features of the editor, as this is where most time will be spent, and to the possibilities of extending the software to cope with problems that may arise. Good status reports and a choice of methods for overlap detection can save considerable time in resolving ambiguities and correcting errors later. Figure 1 lists some of the commonly used sequence assembly programs. The prices vary widely depending on the features of the package and the options for academic or commercial licenses.

Originally, each package used its own "special" codes to represent ambiguous bases and gaps in sequences. Most packages now use the standard IUB-IUPAC codes (Figure 2) for the nucleotides, though the program documentation should be checked before starting the project.

Sequence Reading Hardware

The task of sequence reading depends on the sequencing protocol used. In many laboratories the sequence is generated on an autoradiograph (Figure 3) from which the sequence is read. Although automated gel readers are on the market, most sequence data is read manually with the aid of a digitizer.

Most sequence assembly programs accept DNA sequence read by a sonic digitizer. An example of a device which is supported by most of the available programs is the GrafBar GP-7 [Science Accessories Corporation, Southport, CT, USA and P.M.S. (Instruments) Ltd., Waldeck House, Reform Road, Maidenhead, Berks, SL6 8BX, UK]. Sonic digitizers have a stylus to point to locations on an autoradiograph, which is illuminated from below by a light box. Pressing the stylus down causes a spark to be produced. There are two microphones at the top of the device that can locate the position of the stylus by triangulation using the time taken for the sound of the spark to arrive. The stylus location is sent to the computer by a normal terminal connection. Programs differ in how the digitizer must be connected to the computer so that a particular digitizer may be usable by only a few of the available packages.

Automated gel readers are now available, which scan an autoradiograph and read the sequence directly into a computer file (Elder and Southern, 1987; Elder et al., 1986). These devices attempt to correct gel problems by using image processing techniques to enhance the quality of the autoradiograph and produce a sequence reading with difficult regions highlighted so that they can be corrected by hand.

Laboratories working on large sequencing projects are now using auto-

System	Program	Contact address
VAX/VMS	GCG Fragment Assembly System	Genetics Computer Group Inc., University Research Park, 575 Science Drive, Suite B, Madison, WI 53711, USA
	GEL	Intelligenetics Inc., 700 E. El Camino Real, Mountain View, CA 94040, USA
	SAP (DB system)	Rodger Staden, MRC Laboratory of Molecular Biology, Hills Road, Cambridge, CB2 2QH, UK.
	GENEUS	Robert Harr, Unit of Applied Cell and Molecular Biology, Umea University, S-901 87 Umea, Sweden
Unix	GEL	Intelligenetics Inc., 700 El Camino Real, Mountain View, CA 94040, USA
	EUGENE	Molecular Biology Information Resource, Department of Cell Biology, Baylor College of Medicine, 1 Baylor Plaza, Houston, TX 77030, USA
IBM-PC	PC-GENE	Intelligenetics Inc., 700 El Camino Real, Mountain View, CA 94040, USA
	IBI Pustell	Blackwell Scientific Software, Blackwell Scientific Publications Ltd, Osney Mead, Oxford, OX2 0EL, UK
		International Biotechnologies, Inc. (IBI), P.O. Box 9558, 25 Science Park, New Haven, CT 06535 USA
	DNA-STAR	DNASTAR Inc., 1228 South Park St., Madison, WI 53705, USA or 105-113, The Broadway, West Ealing, London, W139BL, UK
	MICROGENIE	Beckman Instruments Inc., 2500 Harbor Blvd., Fullerton, CA 92634 USA
	DNASIS	Hitachi Software Engineering Co. Ltd., 2000 Sierra Point Parkway, Brisbane, CA 94005 USA
	The DNA Inspector	Textco, 27 Gilson Road, West Lebanon, NH 03784, USA
Macintosh	MacVector	Blackwell Scientific Software, Blackwell Scientific Publications Ltd, Osney Mead, Oxford, OX2 0EL, UK
		International Biotechnologies, Inc. (IBI), P.O. Box 9588, 25 Science Park, New Haven, CT 06535 USA
	SAP (DB system)	Rodger Staden, MRC Laboratory of Molecular Biology, Hills Road, Cambridge, CB2 2QH, UK.
General Sources	Cambridge DNA Sequencing	D.P. Judge, University of Cambridge, Computer Laboratory, Corn Exchange Street, Cambridge, CB2 3QG, UK
	EMBL File Server	Fuchs et al. (1990)
	GenBank FTP Service	Benton (1990)
	Univ. of Houston Server	Davison and Chappelaar (1990)

Figure 1: Sources of sequence assembly programs for various computer systems.

Code	Bases	Mnemonic
A	A	A-denine
C	C	C-ytosine
G	G	G-uanine
T (or U)	T	T-hymine (or U-racil)
R	A or G	pu-R-ine
Y	C or T	p-Y-rimidine
S	G or C	S-trong (3 H-bonds)
W	A or T	W-eak (2 H-bonds)
K	G or T	K-eto
M	A or C	a-M-ino
B	C or G or T	not-A
D	A or G or T	not-C
H	A or C or T	not-G
V	A or C or G	not-(T or U)
N (or X)	any base	a-N-y (or unknown)
.	gap	

Figure 2: IUB standard nucleotide codes.

mated fluorescent sequencers, such as the ALF from Pharmacia LKB (Ansorge et al., 1987) or the Applied BioSystems 370A (Smith et al., 1986; Connell et al., 1987). These machines produce sequence files which are then transferred to the laboratory computer, typically by some kind of communications link.

Copying the sequence files to the host computer, where the sequence assembly software usually runs, requires a little help from your local computer support staff for the first attempt, but is usually a simple operation. A great advantage of the fluorescent sequencers is that the quality of the original data (Figure 4) that can easily be checked on the screen when resolving ambiguities in the sequence readings. This is both faster and more accurate than rereading old autoradiographs.

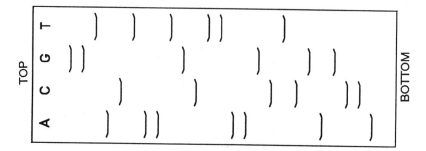

Figure 3: An example of a didcoxy-sequencing autoradiograph. Each column is a lane in the original gel. The sequence is read from the bottom by noting which lane each band is in.

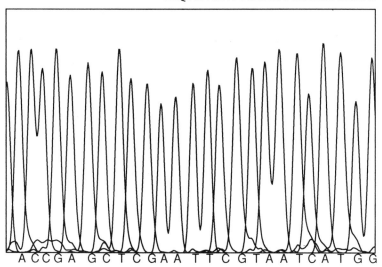

Figure 4: An example of the data produced by an automated fluorescent sequencer. The peaks (normally in a different color for each base) are read directly from left to right to determine the sequence.

Creating a Database

All packages work with sequencing data in a "project database." Several sequencing projects may be in progress at any time, but programs will only use the sequencing data from the currently selected project.

Each package uses its own method of data organization. In the Staden package, for example, all data is stored in a single large "database file" created at the start of the project. In the GCG package, the data from each gel is stored in an individual file which is available for use by the other programs in the package. In other sequence assembly packages, it may be necessary to extract sequences from the project database before other analyses are possible.

Project Standards

In planning a major sequencing project, attention should be given at the very start to ensuring that the computing task will operate smoothly. Ideally, a single member of the group should be delegated the responsibility for the assembly and correction of sequence data.

Before working with real data, a trial project should be assembled using data from a previous sequencing project, or from a tutorial exercise supplied with the software package, to ensure familiarity with the use of the programs.

One often ignored simple step is defining a convention for naming sequence fragments that allows easy access to the original raw data at a later stage when sequence ambiguities are being corrected. This should certainly include the clone number/name, and preferably details of the primer, run

Position(s)	Example	Description
1	C	Single letter for the original lambda/plasmid clone
2-4	126	Shotgun subclone number
5	u	u=universal, r=reverse, abc..=other primers
6	a	run conditions (enzyme, gel, etc.)
7	a	a=first run, bcd...=repeat run
8	a	a=automatic read, p=read by Peter, etc.

Figure 5: Suggested fragment naming convention.

conditions, and reading method.

For the human HPRT sequencing project (Edwards et al., 1990), the clone naming convention used eight letters and numbers, as shown in Figure 5. This convention allowed the later searching of the fragment database for sequences from any specific clone, which proved to be invaluable when checking overlaps and planning strategies for gap closure.

Sequence Entry and Quality Control

Sequence Entry

Using a sonic digitizer, most programs allow a second gel reading to check that the same sequence is produced in each case. This is the simplest way to detect reading errors and should always be employed. If a conflict arises between the two readings of the sequence, they will be highlighted and can be resolved before proceeding further.

The automated gel readers should, of course, give the same results each time. It is wise, however, to read several sequences manually in the project's early stages to check the quality of the sequence produced. If you are able to read (accurately) further than the automated reader, you should consider manually extending the readings of difficult gels.

The automated fluorescent sequencers also allow you to read the sequence manually by viewing the raw data (peaks from the fluorescent detector(s) in the device) and comparing the automatically-read sequence with the size and position of each peak. Because you can use the original peak data in such systems, it is possible to detect and resolve many compressions by closely examining the positions of each peak and checking for changes in the peak separation.

Sequence Checking

A general rule for sequence quality is to allow only 1-2% error in each sequence fragment. Higher error rates make the tasks of sequence assembly and correction more difficult and can delay the completion of the project. The error rate is rapidly apparent when sequence assembly starts. Sequence reading should stop at the point where one or more bases becomes difficult to determine with certainty. Beyond this point, too many errors will be made as the signal quality, whether autoradiographic or fluorescent, deteriorates rapidly. If this rule is applied, the sequence fragments will be of consistent quality, but could vary considerably in length.

In general, the sequence accuracy will be far higher (virtually perfect) at the 5' end. Most errors will be found in the 3' end of a typical fragment. The 3' end is still useful for finding and confirming overlaps, but should be treated with caution when resolving sequence conflicts. For overlap detection, it is important not to miss or insert bases insofar as is possible. Many programs will interpret lower case characters as uncertain assignments, so this convention can be used to highlight difficult read to read regions of a gel. A few sequence assemblers, however, prefer to use lower case throughout for better readability on a terminal screen.

Removing Vector Sequence

The original sequence reading must be checked for the presence of possible vector sequence. For example, when using M13 as a sequencing vector and the universal primer, the first few bases will be part of the polylinker sequence and must be discarded. Further, if the insert is short and the sequence data is good enough to read beyond the end of the insert, the last bases will again be vector (starting in the polylinker again) and must be discarded. If vector sequence is not removed at this stage, it can cause problems later during sequence assembly. The original cloning vector can be similarly screened, although the full sequences of the lambda vectors, for example, may not be known. Several cases are known in the literature where vector sequence of variable quality has found its way into a published sequence.

Some packages automatically check for vector sequences as the data are entered into the computer. Others provide programs to check and exclude vector sequences before assembly begins. Most programs that read gels using a sonic digitizer can highlight vector sequences at the sequence entry stage. Figure 6 shows the detection of an M13 vector sequence by the GCG GelEnter program. Note, however, that the vector sequence is only detected if it is long enough to be clearly identified, and that short (less than 10 bases) regions of vector sequence at either end of a fragment may escape detection by any of the packages.

In general, the automated fluorescent sequencers do not include vector screening directly, although this would be a desirable feature. Vector

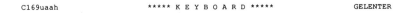

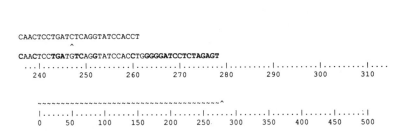

Figure 6: Vector screening during sequence entry using the GCG GelEnter program. In this example, the lower sequence represents the original sequence entry. The GelEnter program has highlighted the M13mp19 vector sequence (from base 262 on) as it was entered, and only the sequence up to base 261 (...CCACCT) should be used from this sequence reading. The upper sequence represents a sequence retyping which checks for typographical errors. Disagreements between the two sequence entries are indicated by a carat (^).

sequences can be screened by using a standard database search program, such as WordSearch in the GCG package (Figure 7), or by including the polylinker sequence on each side of the cloning site as fragments in the project database, and then rejecting any sequence that overlaps with these.

Restriction Site Checking

When sequencing fragments produced by sonication of circular DNA, it is usually necessary to split any sequence fragments containing the originally ligated restriction site. Sequence entry programs generally provide checking of one or more restriction sites during sequence reading. Sequences read automatically can be checked using the standard search programs (see Sequence Patterns). Remember that a reading error may prevent the restriction site in one or more fragments from being detected until later in the assembly process.

Sequence Assembly

Finding Overlaps and Building Contigs[1]

The next step is to find overlaps between fragments which can be used to build contigs. Each package differs in the ways overlaps are detected, and it

---

[1] Short for contiguous sequence, originally used by Staden (1980)

```
(BestFit) SEGMENTS from: Td  March 16, 1989  13:44

(Nucleotide) WORDSEARCH of: $3:[Rice.Hul2.Consensus]E160uaah.Con
                                 check: 7135  from: 1  to: 331
TO: GelData:[Consensus]*.CON  Sequences: 6  Total-length: 14,844
                                              March 16, 1989  13:44
Word-size: 6  Words: 17541  Diagonals: 460  Total-diagonals: 8,348
Integral-width: 3 Alphabet: 4  List-size: 10  CPU minutes: 0.31

E160uaah.Con              check: 7135  from: 1      to: 331
$3:[Rice.Hul2.Consensus]E162uaah.Con;1 check: 3893  from: 3813  to: 3844

Gaps: 0  Quality: 29.4  Ratio: 0.948  Score: 30  Width: 3  Limits: +/-4
                          .                     .
    1 GCAGTGAGCCGAGATTGCGCCACTGCACTCC 31
      ||||||||||||||||||| |||||||||||
 3814 GCAGTGAGCCGAGATTGCACCACTGCACTCC 3844
```

Figure 7: Vector screening after sequence entry using the GCG program WordSearch program. The program found parts of M13mp19 vector sequence in a group of six partially assembled contigs as seen in the sequence alignment at the bottom. Bases 1 to 31 are vector sequence which almost completely match (1 mismatch) contig E162uaah sequence (bases 3814 to 3844). This contig sequence (3814-3844) should be deleted from the file.

is useful to understand how this procedure works in order to resolve problems.

Each group of overlapped fragments is stored as a "contig," which contains the names, directions, and start positions of each individual sequence fragment, and a consensus sequence for the entire group (or cluster) of sequences.

The overlap detection programs compare these consensus sequences to one another and collect all cases where two consensus sequences overlap. Next, additional steps try to resolve problems where a consensus sequence appears to overlap in more than one way.

In the GCG package, overlap detection uses the word-searching algorithm of Wilbur and Lipman (1983) to locate short exact matches (words) between two consensus sequences. The user selects a "word size" (for example, 5 bases) when starting the program, which then finds all exact matches of that size between each pair of consensus sequences. To allow for gaps to be inserted to complete the alignment, the method begins with the scores produced by the best alignment of two sequences, then adds the scores produced by sliding each sequence one base along until no improvement is found. The default values for the program allow only three extra gaps in one sequence to complete the alignment, which may be too few when the project nears completion and many fragments have "extra" bases which are not yet removed. Scores can also be reduced by the method's inability to compare ambiguity codes at uncertain positions. On the other hand, simple sequence patterns such as "CACACACA" will score once for the original alignment, and again each time one sequence is shifted right by two bases. This effect can give high scores (even above 100%) when there is no true overlap, so that reported overlaps must always be checked for consistency before being accepted.

Other packages use different approaches to overlap detection. The Staden package (Staden, 1980; Staden, 1990b) simply searches for a minimum number of consecutive matching bases and does not compare existing contigs once they are in the project database making it difficult to find further overlaps. The Intelligenetics GEL program (Grymes et al., 1986) finds the longest exact match and tries to extend this by allowing a limited number of short gaps. The match must begin in the first few bases (usually the first 10 to 15), so the method is sensitive to the presence of short vector sequences at the ends of fragments. Both programs are able to automatically insert gaps to complete any overlap that they can detect.

Any of the overlap detection methods can give problems, especially if short overlaps are accepted without some additional evidence, for example, by reading manually a little further in one fragment to check that the sequencing results are consistent with the sequence suggested by the overlap, even if the manually read sequence is not reliable enough to include.

Confirming Overlaps

Incorrect overlaps cause such large problems in the assembly of later contigs that, whenever possible, overlaps should be accepted only if clearly correct. In the GCG package, the overlap detection program can be run repeatedly, beginning with extremely stringent conditions to reduce the risk of errors. For example, let's say a series starts with a batch of 50 shotgun fragment sequences to be overlapped, and perhaps 10 contigs already in the database. A stringent first run would specify an overlap length of at least 100 bases, with "words" of seven consecutive unambiguous bases counting and a requirement for 95% of a perfect match score. Having completed these obvious overlaps, which would greatly reduce the number of contigs to be compared, a second run could be performed reducing the overlap length to 50 bases. The next stage would allow shorter "words" and reduce the stringency to increase chances of detecting overlaps where the contig consensus has many extra bases as a result of gaps inserted to complete previous overlaps. This could be followed by another run which allows up to 7 gaps in the overlap (that is, 7 more gaps in one consensus sequence than in the other to complete the overlap) to check for long overlaps that were excluded by the gap restriction.

Finally, one could perform a run which allows a minimum overlap size of 30 bases and reduces the number of gaps again because 3 gaps in 30 bases is still quite high. At the end of this series, all true overlaps would probably be found, and some of those found probably will be rejected in the last two runs. Any unwanted overlaps are easily rejected by using a text editor to remove them from the GelOverlap program output before continuing with the assembly. The conditions could be further relaxed to check for further overlaps, but if more shotgun sequencing is planned, there is little need at this stage.

The GelAssemble editor uses the overlap file to load contigs (or single fragments) in the correct alignment for inspection and formation or rejection of an extended contig. Conflicts between the new consensus sequence and all fragments are clearly highlighted (Figure 8) on the terminal screen. The overlap is checked by inserting gaps in the new fragment(s) or the original contig as necessary. It is inadvisable to delete or change any bases at this stage, since this is a distortion of the primary data. Gap insertion in more than one fragment is ensured by the concept of anchoring, where any change made to one fragment is also made to all fragments that are anchored to it. Typically, all fragments in one original contig are anchored together before editing. When a contig is being edited, and a new single fragment is loaded,

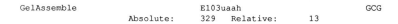

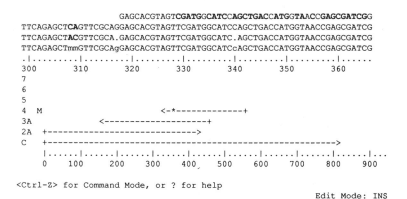

Figure 8: Overlap assembly in GCG. This display shows four sequences that cross the same region. The upper sequence, however, disagrees with the others beginning at position 329 (residues which differ from the consensus are shown in bold face). Addition of a gap character at position 329 of the top sequence and subsequent rightward shifting of the sequence will restore the alignment of the four sequences. This will cause the upper sequence to then return to normal type.

The lower part of the display shows the location of the mismatch (indicated by *) within the sequence of the fragments as a whole. In the panel, the sequenced regions are indicated as a series of dashes (-). Pluses (+) mark the starting direction of the fragment sequencing with right (<) or left (>) arrows marking the ends.

the fragment is anchored but the fragments in the original contig are not. To insert gaps in all the original fragments, this anchoring must be reversed before editing. For example, when editing a contig of 15 fragments (numbered 2 to 16) and loading a new fragment (number 17), the commands "17 17 NOANCHOR" and "2 16 NOANCHOR" will set the correct anchoring. Most overlaps are of high quality (assuming the sequencing error rate was truly 1-2%), so that the gapping process mainly involves rapidly scanning through the sequence. The quickest way to do this is with a key sequence like "55 right-arrow" to move 55 bases to the right. With practice the cursor is rapidly positioned at gap locations so that the manual addition of gaps is not a time-consuming stage of assembly. Once the end of the overlap is reached, a satisfactory overlap is accepted with the MELD command, which combines the two contigs into a single new contig and updates the project database. Overlaps can be rejected by simply using QUIT to leave the editor without updating the database. Naturally, it is wise to MELD every time an overlap is accepted in case the next one is dubious, and must be rejected.

```
? Option number=4
 Default Contig identfier=MU5.SDN
 ? Contig identfier=
 Edit contig

 Edit options are:
 ? = Help
 ! = Quit
 3 = Insert
 4 = Delete
 5 = Change
 ? Option number=5
 ? Gel number (1-11) (0) =2
 This gels relative position =   228 and length =   -42
 ? Position to edit (228-269) (0) =230
 ? New characters=GA

 Edit options are:
 ? = Help
 ! = Quit
 3 = Insert
 4 = Delete
 5 = Change
 ? Option number=!
```

Figure 9: Contig editing in Staden's SAP program. By answering a series of questions, the two bases in one fragment at positions 230-231 of the contig can be corrected.

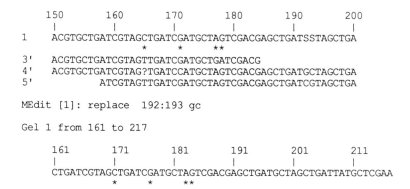

Figure 10: Contig editing in the Intelligenetics GEL program. The command "replace 192:193 gc" corrects the consensus sequence at those positions.

The GelAssemble editor is a great asset in the GCG package because most time is spent in assembly. The Staden package (Figure 9) lacks this interactive editing facility, while the GEL program (Figure 10) has a difficult and error-prone set of commands.

Shotgun Projects

A large shotgun DNA sequencing project (Messing et al., 1981; Deininger, 1983; Anderson, 1981), such as that of the human HPRT locus, can generate hundreds of sequence fragments with many possible incorrect overlaps. In such projects, it is essential to keep the overlap criteria as stringent as possible. An incorrect overlap can remain undetected for some time and be quite difficult to detect and correct at a later stage.

In order to check the accuracy of overlapping in a large project, additional information such as a restriction map of the cloned region can be very useful. A search for restriction sites in the current contig sequences allows the contigs to be checked for inconsistencies at an early stage by comparing to a restriction map of the original clone.

Known short sequences, such as a cDNA sequence when sequencing genomic clones, provide a good check on the sequence data's quality and the accuracy of the contig sequences. This can sometimes lead to errors wherein a correct base in the new sequence is changed to agree with an error in the previously determined sequence.

Progressive Deletions

Sequencing by progressive deletions (Poncz et al., 1982) uses carefully timed exonuclease digestions to delete an increasing number of bases from the 5' end of a template. Each sequencing read starts at the new 5' end, about 100 bases (for example) further along the sequence from the previous read. In theory the order in which the sequences overlap is known. In practice there can be problems if the deletion reaction conditions are not carefully controlled and deletion endpoints are not in the expected positions. The results of overlap detection can provide an important control on the quality of the experimental technique by indicating the true endpoints of deletions.

Walking Primers

In most large-scale sequencing projects, primer-directed sequencing is used at some stage to complete the last few gaps between contigs. The computer can help with the task of selecting suitable primer sequences and keeping track of which primers are used for each sequencing run. Several approaches have been suggested (Barnes, 1987; Rychlik and Rhoads, 1989; Lowe et al., 1990).

The Last Few Gaps

After all the reasonable sequence fragment overlaps have been found and the fragments have been assembled into contigs, decisions must be made about how to best obtain the missing sequence between contigs; how to improve the quality of the sequence in regions with unresolved ambiguities; and how to confirm the sequence in regions that have only been sequenced a few times or in only one direction.

For a pure shotgun project, Lander and Waterman (1988) showed that it is possible to predict the number and size of unsequenced regions using a knowledge of the final expected sequence length and the minimum acceptable overlap size. This analysis, which can allow variability in the lengths of the known sequence fragments, provides an estimate of the probability of one or more large unsequenced regions remaining. Using the GCG Procedure Library, a program was written to apply this method to the HPRT database. The result, part of which is shown in Figure 11, produced good agreement with the actual progress of sequence assembly, and could in general be trusted when the database contains only shotgun fragments with no duplicates. When the largest unsequenced region is (probably) less than 100 bases, it can be economical to use walking primers to close gaps.

As a first approach to closing unsequenced regions, it is useful to examine the ends of all contigs in the database to check for possible vector sequence and incorrect overlaps. The GCG fragment assembly programs compare each contig to all contigs in the project using the WordSearch program (which is like overlap searching, but will report the highest similarities found without regard to whether it forms a good overlap). The highest score will be, of course, for a contig matching itself. The next few scores should be checked in case they show high similarity to part of another contig. If this is not an expected repeat (for example, an Alu repeat for a human

	HUL3	HUL14	HUL2
(a) Current status of projects			
Total length (kb)	15500	18200	18800
Number of fragments	166	137	160
Average fragment length	276	224	267
Total fragment length	45786	30647	42656
Redundancy	2.95	1.68	2.26
Number of contigs	18	33	18
(b) Predicted status of projects			
Expected contigs	14	35	23
Probability of 100 base gap	0.97	1.00	1.00
Probability of 200 base gap	0.66	1.00	0.96
Probability of 300 base gap	0.30	0.94	0.74
(c) Predicted status of projects with 50 more random fragments			
Expected contigs	9	29	17
Probability of 100 base gap	0.72	1.00	0.98
Probability of 200 base gap	0.26	0.92	0.70
Probability of 300 base gap	0.07	0.59	0.32

Figure 11: Lander and Waterman (1988) predictions for three shotgun projects. a. the current status of each project. b. the probability that there are gaps of the indicated size between contigs given the current status of the projects. c. the probability that there will be gaps of the indicated sizes after sequencing an additional 50 random fragments. For example, there will be only a 7% chance that the remaining gap in HUL3 is longer than 300 bases after sequencing as additional 50 fragments. At this time, it may be useful to try to close the gap by the walking primer approach.

genomic sequence), the target contig should be checked for a possible incorrect overlap at the end of this region.

Once the overlaps have been checked, inspection of the contigs may show that some ends are built from short sequence reads with the 3' end at the start/end of the contig. In such cases, repeating this sequencing run could give a longer read and provide a considerable amount of missing sequence. Similar analysis can be used to find candidates for resequencing to provide sequence of the second strand and to resequence regions with unresolved ambiguities.

Figure 12 shows the stages by which one of the HPRT lambda clones was sequenced. The first 95% of the sequence was obtained by standard shotgun methods, giving a redundancy of four- to five- fold. Most of the unsequenced regions were then simply closed by resequencing fragments at the ends of the contigs. To close the remaining unsequenced regions, clones at the ends of contigs were sequenced in the reverse direction to identify those that covered the regions, and walking primers were used to sequence across the unsequenced regions, and to resolve other ambiguous regions (Edwards et al., 1990).

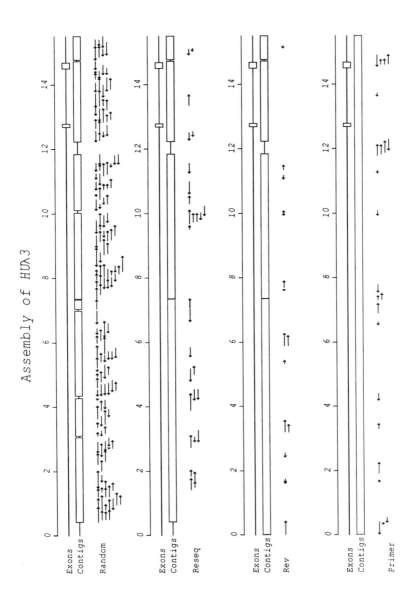

Figure 12: HPRT sequencing strategy illustrated by the origins of fragments for a single lambda clone. Top row: 95 percent of the sequence was obtained initially by random (shogun) sequencing. Second row: At this stage, the fragments at the ends of contigs were resequenced to close many of the gaps. Third row: Reverse primer was used to sequence M13 clones from the opposite end. Bottom row: Finally, those clones that were found to span gaps were sequenced using walking primers.

Error Detection and Correction

The hardest part of any sequence assembly is the resolution of sequencing ambiguities. The quality of the editor is critical to this stage of the project, as this is where most time will be spent. The GCG package has an editor called GelAssemble which makes error detection and correction tasks fairly simple, and compensates for the lack of automated addition of gaps to overlaps in this package. The editor (Figure 13) shows the sequence fragments in the top part of the screen, and a diagram of a wider region of the assembled sequence in the bottom part. The consensus sequence is shown immediately below the fragment sequences. Any conflict between a base in a fragment and the consensus is clearly highlighted. To correct conflicts, you simply insert gaps to align the fragment and the consensus and then change individual bases by overtyping (or inserting and deleting), based on a reinspection of the original gels or the raw data from a fluorescent sequencer.

Incorrect Overlaps

The most serious error in sequence assembly is accepting an incorrect overlap, as it is usually some time before the problem is detected. Figure 14 shows an overlap from the HPRT sequence assembly with 30 out of 31 identical bases, which was later found to be wrong. A new fragment of over 500 bases overlapped the end of one contig, but the GelOverlap program could not find an overlap with any other contig. No unsequenced region was expected to be so large. This newly sequenced fragment was compared to all

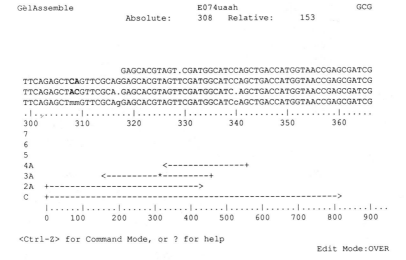

Figure 13: Contig editing in the GCG program GelAssemble. To correct fragment 3, put the cursor on the first highlighted base and simply overtype with AC.

```
(BestFit) SEGMENTS from: Td  March 16, 1989  13:44

(Nucleotide) WORDSEARCH of: $3:[Rice.Hul2.Consensus]E160uaah.Con
                                  check: 7135  from: 1  to: 331
 TO: GelData:[Consensus]*.CON  Sequences: 6  Total-length: 14,844
                                            March 16, 1989  13:44
 Word-size: 6  Words: 17541  Diagonals: 460  Total-diagonals: 8,348
 Integral-width: 3  Alphabet: 4  List-size: 10  CPU minutes: 0.31

E160uaah.Con              check: 7135  from: 1      to: 331
$3:[Rice.Hul2.Consensus]E162uaah.Con;1 check: 3893  from: 3813   to: 3844

 Gaps: 0  Quality: 29.4  Ratio: 0.948  Score: 30  Width: 3  Limits: +/-4
         .                .             .
    1 GCAGTGAGCCGAGATTGCGCCACTGCACTCC 31
      ||||||||||||||||||| ||||||||||||
 3814 GCAGTGAGCCGAGATTGCACCACTGCACTCC 3844
```

Figure 14: An incorrect overlap from the HPRT locus. Despite the 30 out of 31 exact match, this overlap was later shown to be false.

contigs in the database using the WordSearch program, and was found to match perfectly within this contig. The incorrect overlap was found at the end of this match. The incorrect overlap was separated into two contigs, and the new fragment then matched one of the contigs. In addition, the ends of the old contig that had included the incorrect overlap were themselves found to match. This had not been found before as GelOverlap does not allow circular contigs. The remaining contig end was also found to overlap another contig and, as a result, all of the remaining unsequenced regions in the 18kb lambda clone were completed. This situation would have been difficult to resolve without the use of WordSearch, normally a database searching program, to compare the contigs.

Progress Reports

Once the sequence data is stored in the computer, informative reports on the quality of the assembled sequence are essential to correcting conflicts between sequence fragments, locating regions where too little data exists, and closing the remaining unsequenced regions between contigs. Two forms of report are useful, a project status report and a detailed report for each contig. The options available in the GCG package (Figure 15) give too little detail for a large scale sequencing project, so two additional programs were developed using the GCG Procedure Library and reading directly from the project database.

The GelStatus program[2] (Figure 16) shows the current size of each contig, the number of bases sequenced in both directions, and the number of bases sequenced only once. In addition, it reports the number of conflicts between the consensus sequence and individual fragments. For each fragment it reports the direction, size, and number of conflicts. A conflict is defined as any base position with an ambiguity code or gap, or where the consensus and fragment sequences have a different base.

---

[2] The GelStatus and GelPicture programs are available as part of the GCGEMBL package from the EMBL File Server (Fuchs et al., 1990; see Appendix VII).

```
GELASSEMBLE PrettyOut of Contig: E022ubah from Project: Hul2
     October 26, 1989  12:06

    From: 2501  To: 3000

E057uaah   > TAGA.G                                                     251
E005uaah   > TAGAAGGAAGTGATAAGAGAGAAAGCCGGATAGGAGGGCCTTTGTGCCAGTTAGGATGTT 154
E007uaah   > TAGAAGGAAGTGATAAGAGAAGAAGCCGGATAGGAGGGCCTTTGTGCCAGTTAGGATGTT 154
E083ubah   >                                   GGCCTTTGTGCCAGTTAGGATGTT  24

             .........+.........+.........+.........+.........+.........+

E005uaah   > CTAGACTTCCAGCCAGGTTGCCCAGCTCAAACTGGCTTAAACAATGAGGGGGTTTATTGG 214
E007uaah   > CTAGACTTCCAGCCAGGTTGCCCAGCTCAAACTGSCTTAAACAATGAGGGGGTTTATTGG 214
E083ubah   > CTAGACTTCCAGCCAGGTTGCCCAGCTCAAACTGGCTTAAACAATGAGGGGGTTTATTGG  84
E213uaaj   <                                 TGGCTTAAACAATGAGGGGGTTTATTGG  28
E086vbbz   <                                       TGAGGGGGTTTATTGG  16

             .........+.........+.........+.........+.........+.........+

E005uaah   > CTATGTAATT.GGGAAGTGCAGAGGTAGCTCAGGCCAGATCAGTTTGATCCACTGCTCCA 273
E007uaah   > CTATGTAATTTGGGAAGTGCAGAGGTAGCTCAGGCCAGATCAGTTTGATCCACTGCTCCA 274
E083ubah   > CTATGTAATT.GGGAAGTGCAGAGGTAGCTCAGGCCAGATCAGTTTGATCCACTGCTCCA 143
E213uaaj   < CTATGTAATT.GGGAAGTGCAGAGGTAGCTCAGGCCAGATCAGTTTGATCCACTGCTCCA  87
E086vbbz   < CTATGTAATT.GGGAAGTGCAGAGGTAGCTCAGGCCAGATCAGTTTGATCCACTGCTCCA  75

             .........+.........+.........+.........+....*....+.........+
```

Figure 15: GCG GelAssemble contig report. This display shows bases 2501 to 3000 of the contig E022ubah. Each sequence fragment is shown on a separate line with its name and the direction in which it was sequenced (as indicated by < or >) to the left. The position of the rightmost base of each fragment is given on the right. Disagreements between the fragments at positions 2505, 2521-2522, 2595 and 2631 are highlighted, and a decision is required about what sequence character to include in the consensus sequence.

The GelPicture contig report (Figure 17) shows the full sequence of every fragment in a contig. The consensus line shows only sequence where there is a conflict. The remainder of the consensus line shows a double line (=) to indicate both directions are sequenced, or a single line (-), otherwise

```
Gelstatus of project Hul2,      October 26, 1990  12:31

                                    No.  Pct                    Working  No.  Pct
Contig    Length  Both  Many  Once  Err  Err  Fragment    Dir   Length   Err  Err
--------- ------  ----  ----  ----  ---  ---  ----------  ---   ------   ---  ---

                                              E036uaah     +        72    0  0.0
                                              --------------      ------   ---  ---
E036uaah      72     0     0    72    0  0.0  ( 1 fragments)        72    0  0.0

                                              E038uaah     +       184    1  0.5
                                              E038uabh     +       247    4  1.6
                                              --------------      ------   ---  ---
E038uaah     249     0   182    67    5  2.0  ( 2 fragments)       431    5  1.2

                                              E073ubah     -       108    5  4.6
                                              E077uaah     -       247    2  0.8
                                              E193uaah     +       132    0  0.0
                                              E029uaah     -       258    2  0.8
                                              E188uaah     -       272    3  1.1
                                              E006uaah     +       123    7  5.7
                                              E150uaah     -       232    6  2.6
                                              E085ubbh     -       365    7  1.9
                                              E169uaah     +       270    1  0.4
                                              E058uaah     +       269    5  1.9
                                              E058vlah     +       461    4  0.9
                                              E022vlbh     -       190    3  1.6
                                              E022vlah     -       306    4  1.3
                                              E160raah     +       120    2  1.7
                                              --------------      ------   ---  ---
E073ubah    1953  1590   323   140   37  1.9  (14 fragments)      3353   51  1.5
```

Figure 16: A GelStatus project status report.

```
Pretty of contig GelData:[Consensus]E022ubah.Con,
October 26, 1989  12:00

(60)  E057uaah + TAGA.G                                                       251
(57)  E005uaah + TAGAAGGAAGTGATAAGAGAGAAAGCCGGATAGGAGGGCCTTTGTGCCAG          144
(56)  E007uaah + TAGAAGGAAGTGATAAGAGAAGAAGCCGGATAGGAGGGCCTTTGTGCCAG          144
(55)  E083ubah +                                   GGCCTTTGTGCCAG           14
( 1)  Consensus   ----A----+---------+RR-------+---------+---------+        2550


(57)  E005uaah + TTAGGATGTTCTAGACTTCCAGCCAGGTTGCCCAGCTCAAACTGGCTTAA         194
(56)  E007uaah + TTAGGATGTTCTAGACTTCCAGCCAGGTTGCCCAGCTCAAACTGSCTTAA         194
(55)  E083ubah + TTAGGATGTTCTAGACTTCCAGCCAGGTTGCCCAGCTCAAACTGGCTTAA          64
(54)  E213uaaj -                                          TGGCTTAA           8
( 1)  Consensus   ---------+---------+---------+---------+--==G====+        2600


(57)  E005uaah + ACAATGAGGGGGTTTATTGGCTATGTAATT.GGGAAGTGCAGAGGTAGCT         243
(56)  E007uaah + ACAATGAGGGGGTTTATTGGCTATGTAATTTGGGAAGTGCAGAGGTAGCT         244
(55)  E083ubah + ACAATGAGGGGGTTTATTGGCTATGTAATT.GGGAAGTGCAGAGGTAGCT         113
(54)  E213uaaj - ACAATGAGGGGGTTTATTGGCTATGTAATT.GGGAAGTGCAGAGGTAGCT          57
(53)  E086vbbz -      TGAGGGGGTTTATTGGCTATGTAATT.GGGAAGTGCAGAGGTAGCT          45
( 1)  Consensus   =========+=========+=========+T========+=========+        2650
```

Figure 17: A GelPicture contig status report. Similar to the GelAssemble contig status report shown in Figure 15 except that the sequencing direction is indicated by + or -, and an automatically generated consensus is shown on the lowest line. In regions where the sequences of the fragments agree, a - or = is shown to indicate that one or both strands have been sequenced. In positions of disagreements, the program inserts the least ambiguous sequence character that agrees with the observed sequence.

fragment numbers are the same as those in the GelAssemble editor.

After overlapping a group of new fragments, these reports can be generated and used as a guide for the reinspection of the original data to resolve ambiguities and conflicts. The corrections are marked on the GelPicture report, which is used as a guide when making the corrections to the database using the GelAssemble editor.

Additional useful reports include restriction maps of each large contig so that they can be positioned on the restriction map of the original clone. This is one way to detect incorrect overlaps and to check the accuracy of the final consensus sequence.

Finally, when all the conflicts are resolved and the final consensus sequence is produced, the project database can be used to prepare figure(s) for publication. Figure 18 was produced by another new program using the GCG Procedure Library. Such figures can be sent by E-mail (see Appendix VII) and printed in high quality at any laboratory in a large scale project, with a considerable saving in manpower and FAX costs.

Open Reading Frames and Other Traps

The question of when to start the analysis of the developing consensus sequence is a difficult one. Cases are known where a preliminary search of EMBL/GenBank databases, using a few sequence fragments revealed that a cDNA had already been sequenced in another laboratory. On the other hand, the temptation to check for an open reading frame to allow the protein

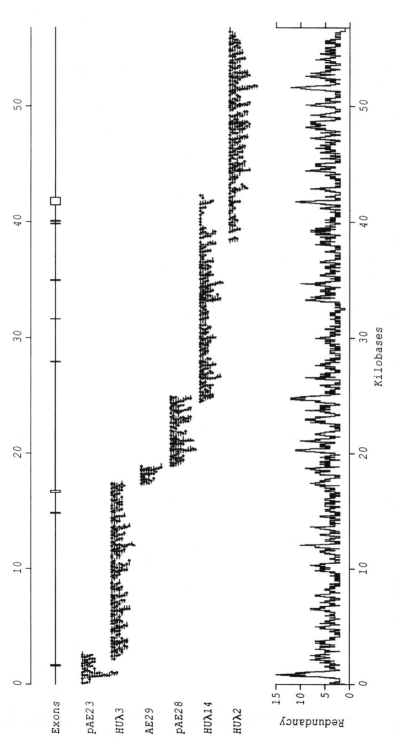

Figure 18: Summary of the HPRT locus prepared by the analysis of the six project databases (Edwards et al., 1990). Arrows represent each of the subclones used in the project and the direction in which they were sequenced. In addition, the inferred location of exons is shown on the second line from the top, and the number of times each base was independently sequenced (redundancy) shown in the bottom panel.

sequence to be analyzed, and to stop when the open reading frame is complete, is dangerous. Figure 19 shows the sequence of the *E. coli dsdC* gene, a regulatory protein with a proposed helix-turn-helix DNA-binding motif (see Chapter 2). The proposed motif is derived from a region with 89% identity to the M13 vector, and is generally not detected by programs that search for such motifs.

```
                 ArgThrCysProGluArgSerGluArgAsn
dsdC     952     CGGACTTGCCCTGAACGGAGTGAGCGCAAC     981
                 |    || |   | |||||||||||||
m13mp19  6072    CCCGACTGGAAAGCGGGCAGTGAGCGCAAC     6101

                 ******************************
                 AlaIleLysCysGluLeuAlaHisSerLeu
dsdC     982     GCAATTAAATGTGAGTTAGCTCACTCATTA     1011
                 ||||||  |||||||||||||||||||||||
m13mp19  6102    GCAATT.AATGTGAGTTAGCTCACTCATTA     6131

                 *****************************
                 GlyXxxProAspPheHisThrLeuCysPhe
dsdC     1012    GGC...CCAGACTTCCATACTTTATGCTTC     1041
                 |||    |||| |||  |  ||||||||||||
m13mp19  6132    GGCACCCCAGGCTTT ACACTTTATGCTTC     6161

                 ********
                 ArgLeuLeuCysValCysTrpAsnCysGlu
dsdC     1042    CGGCTGCTATGTGTGTGTTGGAATTGTGAG     1071
                 |||||  ||||| |     ||||||||||||
m13mp19  6162    CGGCTCGTATGT..TGTGTGGAATTGTGAG     6191

                 ArgIleThrIleSerHisArgLysArgLeu
dsdC     1072    CGGATAACAATTTCACACAGGAAACGACTG     1101
                 |||||||||||||||||||||||   ||
m13mp19  6192    CGGATAACAATTTCACACAGGAAACAGCT.     6221

                 ValThrMetThrTyrAlaLysLeuGlyHis
dsdDC    1102    GTGACCATGACTTACGCCAAGCTTGGGCAT     1131
                 ||||||||| |||||||||||||  ||||
m13mp19  6222    ATGACCATGA.TTACGCCAAGCTT..GCAT     6251

                 AlaCysArgSerThrLeuGluAspProPro
dsdC     1132    GCCTGCAGGTCGACTCTAGAGGATCCCCCC     1161
                 |||||||||||||||||||||||||  ||||
m13mp19  6252    GCCTGCAGGTCGACTCTAGAGGAT..CCCC     6281

                 SerAsnSerAlaArgAsnGlyTrpAsnLeu
dsdC     1162    AGCAACAGCGCCAGAAACGGGTGGAATTTG     1191
                 |  || | ||  |||      |||    | |
m13mp19  6282    GGGTACCGAGCTCGAATTCACTGGCCGTCG     6311
```

Figure 19: Possible vector sequence in the *E. coli dsdC* sequence (EMBL/GenBank accession number M31095). The asterisks show the proposed helix-turn-helix of the DNA-binding domain.

The Final Result

Once all the unsequenced regions are closed, the GC-rich regions are sequenced in both directions and all conflicts are satisfactorily resolved, sequence analysis can begin in earnest. It is becoming increasingly difficult to publish new sequences without reporting some interesting features, but the need to find interesting features must be balanced against the risk of error (see, for example, Figure 19).

Sequences can be submitted to EMBL or GenBank prior to publication, with the papers following later when the results of biological experiments can be related to new features in the sequence (see Appendix IX).

IDENTIFICATION OF SIMPLE SITES AND TRANSCRIPTIONAL SIGNALS

The analysis of a newly completed sequence is exciting. The great hope is to determine all biologically relevant information by running a few programs on the new sequence, and then to publish the results. In a very few cases, such as the cystic fibrosis transmembrane conductance regulator (Riordan et al., 1989), this can be spectacularly successful, resulting in a possible model for the structure of the protein before any protein product has been experimentally identified. In the great majority of cases, however, the analysis will yield very little unless approached very carefully. The methods have been recently reviewed by von Heijne (1987), Staden (1990a), and Stormo (1990) (see Chapter 2 and 4).

The analysis of nucleic acid sequences for transcriptioanl signals is full of traps for the unwary or the inexperienced. The sequences themselves are usually correct; the problems arise when deciding what patterns to search for. For example, eukaryotic transcription factor binding sequences could be biologically active when few of the bases actually match a published consensus sequence.

Sequence Patterns

The ability to search a nucleotide sequence for a pattern or motif is critically dependent on the quality of the sequence motif definition. In the worst case, when you know there is a sequence pattern but have no previously known examples, the task is impossible and you have to resort to physical methods such as footprinting analysis to locate the sequence. The situation is nearly as bad if there is one other example of a sequence which contains the target site. Again, it is not practical to find such a site by comparing the two sequences. A comparison of two nucleotide sequences will show the overall similarity between them, but will not be able to uniquely identify a common short (and possibly imperfect) transcription factor or enhancer binding site.

The ideal starting point is an alignment of several known examples of the target site. These can be used to build a target site definition that takes into account the possible base variation at each position. Such target definitions, and usually completely new programs to search for them, are published with increasing frequency in the literature. Usually, the original alignments can be used in other programs, in your favorite sequence analysis package, with reasonable results. There are also databases of consensus sequences for many of these target sites, which will be discussed below.

A group of aligned target sequences is used to produce three forms of probes. A simple consensus sequence, with the most common base at each position and ambiguity codes where there is a choice of two or three bases, can be useful if the site is well conserved, for example, splice site donor-acceptor sequences. The consensus sequence is simpler to search for, but is usually insufficient to unambiguously define a target site. A frequency table holds the number of occurrences of each base at each position and can be used to calculate a similarity score for each position in a new sequence. Improved scoring methods first convert the frequency table to a weight matrix, in which the numbers better reflect the significance of finding each base at a given position. Bucher (1990) reviews the methods available for converting a frequency table to a weight matrix.

Pattern Matching Programs

Most, if not all, sequence analysis packages have a program that allows you to search for an exact target sequence. If not available as an independent program, it is usually possible to enter short consensus conserved sequences (such as promoter consensus sequences) into the restriction enzyme database. There are major disadvantages in using the consensus sequence approach to searching for sequence patterns. First of all, a consensus sequence is often only a poor description of the pattern, and allowing sufficient ambiguity in the consensus to detect all known examples often results in a probe that has an unacceptably high level of false positives. Many consensus sequence searching programs, especially restriction enzyme searching programs, do not allow mismatches to the probe sequence and usually do no allow insertions or deletions. Their inability to take insertions and deletions into account makes it difficult to detect patterns, such as bacterial promoter sequences, that are composed of more than one conserved region separated by variable distances.

A more flexible, and nearly universally available, method of searching for patterns is dot matrix analysis (see Chapter 3). The probe pattern is entered as if it is a sequence, and then compared to the target sequence. Dot matrix methods allow defined amounts of mismatching to be tolerated and permit insertions and deletions. The result of such an analysis is a pattern of diagonal lines at the positions corresponding to the location of the pattern in the target sequence. A broken diagonal line with a vertical or horizontal offset then indicates in insertion or deletion in the pattern.

The most flexible general purpose method of searching for sequence patterns employs a frequency matrix or weight matrix as a probe (reviewed by Stormo, 1988). A frequency matrix is simply a tabulation of the frequency of occurrence of each of the nucleotides at each position in the pattern, and is transformed into a weight matrix by converting the values to a measure of the significance of finding the possible bases at each position (Bucher, 1990). In the examples shown in this chapter, we have calculated the values in the weight matrices as the natural logarithm of the ratio of the observed frequency of a base at a given position to the expected frequency at that position. The expected frequency is the frequency of the base in the region of the signal. These matrices are thus log-odds matrices (see Chapter 3, Scoring Systems, for further discussion and Appendix IV). The result of this normalization is that, for instance, the occurrence of a C residue in a very G rich sequence is more significant than that of a G. This makes intuitive sense.

To calculate the score for comparison of a sequence to a frequency or weight matrix, the values at each position in the matrix for each base in the sequence are added. When the values in the weight matrix represent the logarithm of the probability of finding each base at each position in the signal, this sum represents the probability of finding a corresponding signal by chance. In the case of log-odds type weight matrices, the sum of the scores is the logarithm of how many times more probable it is that the sequence represents the signal rather than random DNA. For instance if the sum of the scores at each position is 1.61 (ln 5), the sequence is 5 times more likely to represent the signal than a non-signal (random) sequence. A consensus sequence is easily represented as a weight matrix by simply giving equal scores to each allowed nucleotide at each position, but a weight matrix cannot be represented as a consensus sequence without sacrificing some information. The matrix approach is therefore more general and is recommended.

Most frequency tables are assembled from a number of visually aligned sequences. Methods for the automatic generation of frequency or weight matrices (Stormo and Hartzell, 1989; Bucher 1990; Stormo et al., 1990) are coming into more frequent use as the increasing amount of sequence makes manual alignment of motifs increasingly difficult. The matrix approach makes the implicit assumption that the occurrence of the bases at each position are independent; the base used at position 1, for instance, will have no effect on the base allowed at other positions. This is certainly not always the case. An obvious example of a situation where the base frequencies are correlated is when the pattern represents a stem-and-loop structure. Matrix methods do not usually allow for insertions or deletions within the pattern. Exceptions to this rule are profile analysis (Gribskov, 1990; see Chapter 2) which combines a weight matrix type of pattern with dynamic programming techniques to allow insertions and deletions, and the method of Harr et al.

(1983) which applies a weighting scheme dependent on user-defined distances between conserved motifs.

Matrix methods are the preferred technique for locating most of the transcriptional and translational signals described in the following sections. Specialized programs that take advantage of information not reducible to the matrix representation are also available for some specific signals, such as rho-independent terminators, and are described in the appropriate sections below.

Restriction Enzymes

Restriction Enzyme Databases

Producing restriction maps from nucleotide sequences requires an up-to-date listing of restriction enzymes. Most sequence analysis packages include such a list, with details of enzyme names, target sites, isoschizomers[3] and commercial sources.

The restriction enzyme database usually is derived from the REBASE database (Roberts, 1985; Figure 20), available from the EMBL File Server (Fuchs et al., 1990; see Appendix VII), in the original and GCG formats, and from the database author, in other formats on request.

Searching for Fixed Patterns

Every sequence analysis program should be able to search for a short fixed pattern, by entering the pattern into the program's database of restriction

---

[3] Restriction enzymes with the same target sequence, but possibly different cut sites within the target. For example, SacI and SstI both have the target sequence G/AGCT'C.

```
    A.
<1>Ecl136II          <1>SacI              <1>SstI
<2>SacI              <2>                  <2>SacI
<3>GAG^CTC           <3>GAGCT^C           <3>GAGCT^C
<4>                  <4>                  <4>
<5>F                 <5>AEGIKLMNOPRSUVX   <5>BL
<6>237               <6>5                 <161,394>
References:
5.      Arrand, J.R., Myers, P.A., Roberts, R.J. unpublished
        observations.
161.    Goff, S.P., Rambach, A. (1978) Gene 13: 347-352
237.    Janulaitis, A.A., Steponaviciene, D., Butkus, V.,
        Maneliene, Z., Petrusyte, M. unpublished observations.
394.    Muller, F., Stoffel, S., Clarkson, S.G. unpublished
        observations.
    B.
Enzyme     Overhang   Comment  Isoschizomers   Commercial    source
;Ecl136II  3 GAG'CTC       0 !  SacI,SstI       >F
;SacI      5 G_AGCT'C     -4 !  SstI,Ecl136II   >AEGIKLMNOPRSUVX
SstI       5 G_AGCT'C     -4 !  SacI,Ecl136II   >BL
```

Figure 20: Entries from the REBASE restriction enzyme database for the target site GAGCTC in a. original format b. GCG package format.

enzyme sites. The result can be either a list of the sequence positions where the site was found (Figure 21), or a plot of the restriction sites (Figure 22). The more sophisticated programs allow the user to specify sites that occur once or twice, or sites of a given size (such as six-base targets for restriction sites).

Promoters and Enhancers

The problems of searching for promoters and related target sites remains difficult due to the poorly defined nature of most target sequences. In some cases where the sequences are well characterized and understood, mostly in prokaryotic systems, programs are able to search quite successfully for the desired features. For sequences of eukaryotic genes, location of functionally important sequences is much more difficult, and the results must be considered to be tentative.

```
! FIND on Epri:Hshprtb allowing 0 mismatches

! Using patterns from: Hprt-Enzyme.Dat  October 25, 1990  16:31 ..

  Hshprtb  ck: 676  len: 56,736 ! M26434   Human hypoxanthine phosphoribosyltransf
  erase (HPRT) gene, complete
"BamHI"          ..... GGATCC .....
          1,777: GCGCG GGATCC GCAGT
         21,729: GATGT GGATCC TCTAA
         21,970: TCAAG GGATCC TCTGC
         24,463: TTCTA GGATCC TAAAA
         28,204: ATTTG GGATCC TTCAA
         32,266: GTTTA GGATCC CTTGT
         54,274: AACCC GGATCC ATGCT
"EcoRI"          ..... GAATTC .....
             1:        GAATTC TCGTA
         10,609: GTTGT GAATTC ATACC
         10,820: TGCCA GAATTC CTGTT
         10,896: GGGCA GAATTC ACATG
         11,777: TAACT GAATTC CATAA
         20,140: CTAAA GAATTC TCTCT
         21,793: AGACA GAATTC ATTTT
         24,135: TAAAA GAATTC ATAAA
         34,297: CATCA GAATTC TGCCT
         42,102: TTTAT GAATTC AATTT
         42,385: TTTTG GAATTC TGTTC
         43,959: GTATT GAATTC TATAT
         47,296: TATGG GAATTC AAAGA
         48,321: AATCA GAATTC GATGA
         51,445: CCATG GAATTC TAAAG
         52,339: TGACA GAATTC ACTAT
         53,309: GGATC GAATTC ATTCA
"HindIII"        ..... AAGCTT .....
          4,636: AGAAA AAGCTT TTAGA
          8,404: ATTTT AAGCTT TTTTT
         11,092: TGAGT AAGCTT CAAGG
         11,956: CGCCA AAGCTT AAATC
         18,865: ATTCC AAGCTT TTTAG
         25,008: GGAGG AAGCTT TCCCC
         25,098: GTGGG AAGCTT GTTCC
         25,718: ATCTG AAGCTT GTTGC
         30,555: GGTGG AAGCTT TACTT
         45,907: TGGAC AAGCTT GCCTT
         46,677: ATAAG AAGCTT GTCCA
         46,824: TCCTG AAGCTT GGCAC
         47,351: AGGAG AAGCTT CAGGG
         50,770: GAGGC AAGCTT TTTTT

    Total finds:      38
    Total length:  56,736
  Total sequences:     1
      CPU time:    01.84
```

Figure 21: Searching for restriction enzyme target sites with the GCG Find program.

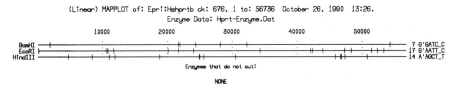

Figure 22: A restriction map produced by the GCG MapPlot program.

Bacterial Promoters

Bacterial promoter sites, specifically the *Escherichia coli* RNA polymerase promoter site, are now very well characterized. It has further been shown (for example, Stormo et al., 1986) that the scores calculated by programs that search using defined sequence motifs can be correlated to the biological activity of the promoters.

Figure 23 shows two frequency tables for the *E. coli* promoter site, one based on an alignment of 112 naturally occurring promoters (Hawley and McClure, 1983), and the second based on an analysis of a smaller number of active promoters selected by screening random oligonucleotide sequences for promoter activity (Oliphant and Struhl, 1988). These alignments remain in use, although many more *E. coli* sequences are now known (Kroeger et al., 1990).

Bacterial promoters may be found in several ways using these frequency

(a) Hawley & McClure

Base	-36	-35	-34	-33	-32	-31		-13	-12	-11	-10	-9	-8
A	1.8	5.4	1.8	64.3	23.2	44.6	...	1.8	94.6	25.9	58.9	50.9	0.9
C	6.3	5.4	9.8	16.1	53.6	7.1	...	8.9	1.8	14.3	12.5	19.6	2.7
G	9.8	5.4	78.6	2.7	9.8	15.2	...	9.8	0.9	16.1	15.2	12.5	0.0
T	82.1	83.9	9.8	17.0	13.4	33.0	...	79.5	2.7	43.8	13.4	17.0	96.4
	T	T	G	A	C	w		T	A	t	A	a	T

(b) Oliphant & Struhl

Base	-36	-35	-34	-33	-32	-31		-13	-12	-11	-10	-9	-8
A	0.0	5.2	1.7	56.9	19.0	27.6	...	1.9	90.4	25.0	40.4	23.1	3.8
C	0.0	6.9	5.2	25.9	55.2	19.0	...	28.8	3.8	26.9	15.4	46.2	1.9
G	1.7	6.9	72.4	3.4	3.4	13.8	...	5.8	1.9	21.2	13.5	11.5	3.8
T	98.3	81.0	20.7	13.8	22.4	39.7	...	63.5	3.8	26.9	30.8	19.2	90.4
	T	T	G	A	C	t		T	A	n	W	c	T

Figure 23: Two definitions of the *E. coli* promoter sequence a. using a set of aligned naturally occurring promoters b. by selecting active promoters in a set of random sequences.

tables (or the corresponding consensus sequences). The main problem is that the two conserved regions of the bacterial promoter, the -10 and -35 regions, are separated from each other by 15 to 21 bases (Hawley and McClure, 1983), making the detection of the entire promoter as a single pattern difficult. One option is to use several matrices in which the conserved regions are separated by varying lengths of bases with no preference for any base, i.e. one with the -10 and -35 regions separated by 18 bases, one with the conserved regions separated by 19 bases, etc. A second approach is to use one of the programs specifically designed to find promoters (Mulligan, 1986; Staden, 1984). Both matrix searching programs and programs designed specifically to find known promoter sequences find strong promoters fairly well, but they suffer from a high level of false positives. Often as many as 50% of the top scoring matches to the pattern do not correspond to known promoters. Some of these promoter-like sequences are probably weak or otherwise undetected promoters, but the bulk of them are probably not promoter sequences at all.

Eukaryotic Promoters

Eukaryotic promoters are less well characterized than their bacterial equivalents. The major elements are the CCAAT box, GC box, TATA box and cap site. These elements were recently reviewed by Bucher (1990). The analysis of these elements has become possible after the sequencing of a large number of eukaryotic promoters. These elements are collected in the Eukaryote Promoter Database (EPD, Bucher, 1988), which is distributed quarterly with the EMBL nucleotide sequence database and available by E-mail from EMBL (Fuchs et al., 1990; see Appendix VII). Figure 24 shows a group of entries from EPD, including the *Drosophila Notch* locus (see Chapter 4).

Bucher (1990) used EPD to select over 500 promoter sequences, aligned at their transcription start sites. Figures 25 through 28 show the new fre-

```
*--------------------------------------------------------------------------*
*    3.1.5.3.3. Neurogenic loci                                            *
*--------------------------------------------------------------------------*
XX
FP   Dm[notch]          :+S   INV:DMNOTCH1   1+      78; 15018.
XX
DO        Experimental evidence: 5
DO        Expression/Regulation: throughout development; dividing cells
RF        MCB6:3094      TiG4:95
//
FP   Dm[AS-C] tr-4      :+M   INV:DMACS2     1+      544; 16023.
XX
DO        Experimental evidence: 4,<8>
DO        Expression/Regulation: embryo; neuroblasts; spatially reg.
RF        Cell44:303     Cell50:415     Cell50:425
//
FP   Dm[AS-C] tr-5      :+S   INV:DMACS1     1+      871; 16024.
XX
DO        Experimental evidence: 4,<8>
DO        Expression/Regulation: embryo; neuroblasts; spatially reg.
RF        Cell44:303     Cell50:415     Cell50:425
//
```

Figure 24: Selected entries from the Eukaryote Promoter Database.

Base Frequency

	-2	-1	0	1	2	3	4	5
A	49	0	288	26	77	67	45	50
C	48	303	0	81	95	118	85	96
G	69	0	0	116	0	46	73	56
T	137	0	15	80	131	72	100	101

Weight Matrix

	-2	-1	0	1	2	3	4	5
A	-0.43	-5.01	1.34	-1.06	0.02	-0.12	-0.51	-0.41
C	-0.77	1.08	-5.33	-0.24	-0.08	0.13	-0.19	-0.07
G	0.43	-4.50	-4.50	0.95	-4.50	0.02	0.48	0.22
T	0.54	-5.07	-1.67	0.01	0.50	-0.10	0.23	0.24
Consensus	T	C	A	G	T	n	G	t
	G						t	g

Figure 25: Eukaryotic promoter cap region. Base frequencies from Bucher (1990). The weight matrix is a log-odds matrix corrected for the local composition of the motif as described in the text. The consensus sequence is shown in upper case when the conserved base is present at 1.5 or more times the expected frequency, and in lower case when present at more than 1.25 times the expected level.

quency tables and weight matrices for each motif. The method could also be applied to other promoter elements and sequence motifs where enough sequence data can be collected and aligned.

Promoters can be defined in general by the quality and position of these sequence elements. Staden (1988) developed a method for combining such motifs in a single search for potential transcription start sites.

Base Frequency

	-7	-6	-5	-4	-3	-2	-1	0	1	2	3	4
A	56	32	25	102	51	0	0	175	119	17	23	116
C	55	52	47	1	6	173	174	0	8	0	90	6
G	12	43	24	70	99	1	0	0	21	15	59	52
T	52	48	79	2	19	1	1	0	27	143	3	1

Weight Matrix

	-7	-6	-5	-4	-3	-2	-1	0	1	2	3	4
A	-0.06	-0.62	-0.87	1.71	-0.16	-4.78	-4.78	1.08	0.69	-1.26	-0.95	0.66
C	0.08	0.02	-0.08	-3.93	-2.14	1.22	1.23	-4.62	-1.85	-4.62	0.57	-2.14
G	-1.01	0.26	-0.32	0.75	1.10	-3.50	-4.19	-4.19	-0.45	-0.79	0.58	0.45
T	0.48	0.40	0.90	-2.78	-0.53	-3.47	-3.47	-4.16	-0.18	1.49	-2.37	-3.47
Consensus	T	t	T	A	G	C	C	A	A	T	G	A
		g			G						C	

Figure 26: Eukaryotic promoter CCAAT region. Base frequencies from Bucher (1990). See Figure 25 for a description of the weight matrix and consensus sequence.

Base Frequency

	-6	-5	-4	-3	-2	-1	0	1	2	3	4	5	6	7
A	102	97	50	67	0	2	54	46	1	79	23	0	20	40
C	40	31	6	1	0	0	137	1	3	0	17	166	86	24
G	50	112	154	206	274	272	0	224	222	171	192	35	52	109
T	82	34	64	0	0	0	50	3	48	24	42	73	116	101

Weight Matrix

	-6	-5	-4	-3	-2	-1	0	1	2	3	4	5	6	7
A	0.90	0.85	0.19	0.48	-4.42	-3.03	0.26	0.10	-3.73	0.64	-0.59	-4.42	-0.73	-0.04
C	0.03	-0.23	-1.87	-3.66	-4.35	-4.35	1.47	-3.66	-2.56	-4.35	-0.83	1.45	0.79	-0.48
G	-1.09	-0.28	0.04	0.33	0.62	0.61	-5.69	0.41	0.40	0.14	0.26	-1.44	-1.05	-0.31
T	0.59	-0.29	0.34	-4.51	-4.51	-4.51	0.09	-2.72	0.05	-0.64	-0.08	0.47	0.94	0.80
Consensus	A	A	T	A	G	G	C	G	g	A	g	C	T	T
	T			g			a					T	C	

Figure 27: Eukaryotic promoter GC region. Base frequencies from Bucher (1990). See Figure 25 for a description of the weight matrix and consensus sequence.

Enhancers and Transcription Factors

The sequence specificity of transcription factors and the sequence of enhancers in eukaryotes are less well defined, and such motifs can be distant from the transcription start. Where the presence of a site is to be inferred from sequence data, the safest approach is to simply search for any sequence that has high similarity to one or more published sites and test it for biological activity. Transcription factor site collections have been published in journals. The latest collection, by Ghosh (1990), is also available by E-mail (Fuchs et al., 1990; see also Appendix VII).

Base Frequency

	-3	-2	-1	0	1	2	3	4	5	6	7	8	9	10	11
A	61	16	352	3	354	268	360	222	155	56	83	82	82	68	77
C	145	46	0	10	0	0	3	2	44	135	147	127	118	107	101
G	152	18	2	2	5	0	20	44	157	150	128	128	128	139	140
T	31	309	35	374	30	121	6	121	33	48	31	52	61	75	71

Weight Matrix

	-3	-2	-1	0	1	2	3	4	5	6	7	8	9	10	11
A	-0.89	-2.23	-0.86	-3.91	0.86	0.59	0.88	0.40	0.04	-0.98	-0.59	-0.60	-0.60	-0.79	-0.66
C	0.79	-0.36	-4.88	-1.88	-4.88	-4.88	-3.09	-3.49	-0.40	0.72	0.81	0.66	0.59	0.49	0.43
G	0.63	-1.50	-3.70	-3.70	-2.78	-5.09	-1.40	-0.61	0.66	0.62	0.46	0.46	0.46	0.54	0.55
T	-1.10	1.20	-0.98	1.39	-1.13	0.26	-2.74	0.26	-1.04	-0.66	-1.10	-0.58	-0.42	-0.22	-0.27
Consensus	C	T	A	T	A	A	A	a	G	C	C	C	C	G	C
	G					t		t		G	G	G	G	C	G

Figure 28: Eukaryotic promoter TATA region. Base frequency for the TATA region according to Bucher (1990). See Figure 25 for a description of the weight matrix and consensus sequence.

Terminators and Attenuators

Gene expression is also regulated by control of transcription termination (Platt, 1986; Friedman et al., 1987). In *E. coli*, two forms of terminator are known. The type I constitutive[4] terminator or rho-independent terminator can be identified by its base composition and stem-loop structure with reasonable success (Brendel et al., 1986). The type II or rho-dependent terminator is less well defined, but often used in regulation.

The basic structure of a rho-independent terminator signal is that of a stem-loop in the mRNA followed by a series of U bases. The stem of the hairpin is rich in GC base pairs, and is usually followed by at least six uridines. The length of the stem varies form 7 to 20 base pairs long. Both of these features are necessary for the formation of an active terminator. Brendel and coworkers (Brendel and Trifinov, 1984; Brendel et al., 1986) have developed an algorithm for the detection of these terminators, and it is very efficient at identifying these signals. A recent study (Carafa et al., 1990) has refined the parameters important for the structure of the rho-independent terminator by statistical analysis of 148 known examples. Using a combination of the calculated free-energy of the stem and the size of the loop as parameters, they are able to correctly locate about 95% of the rho-independent terminators.

Eukaryotic terminators do exist, but are very difficult to predict. McLauchlan et al. (1985) describe the consensus sequence YGTGTTYY as a eukaryotic termination sequence (Figure 29). This sequence is usually located about 30 bases downstream of the terminal polyadenylation signal. McLauchlan et al. (1985) report that this sequence is found in about two-thirds of all eukaryotic gene sequences. One difficulty in the identification of eukaryotic terminators is that they often appear beyond the ployA addition site, and are thus not present in cDNA sequences. With increasing genomic sequence data, eukaryotic termination signals may become more accurately defined.

CODING REGION IDENTIFICATION

The coding region is defined as the region that is translated by ribosomes into a polypeptide. The coding region is delimited by sequences that function in the initiation and termination of transcription and translation. In prokaryotes, the coding region is a single open reading frame (ORF), or continuous stretch of sequence that contains no termination codons. Eukaryotic genes, however, are commonly organized as exons and introns and hence may comprise several disjoint ORFs.

The initiation codon, usually an AUG, signals the start of translation while a termination codon in the same reading frame marks the end of the

---

[4] Active as a terminator in the absence of any protein factors

Base Frequency

	1	2	3	4	5	6	7	8
A	9	6	2	2	3	0	8	9
C	12	1	0	0	2	20	15	15
G	13	57	6	66	10	7	8	13
T	36	6	62	2	55	43	39	33

Weight Matrix

	1	2	3	4	5	6	7	8
A	0.61	0.21	-1.18	-1.18	-0.49	-2.28	0.50	0.98
C	0.39	-2.09	-2.79	-2.79	-1.40	0.90	0.61	0.61
G	-0.55	0.93	-1.32	1.08	-0.81	-1.17	-1.03	-0.55
T	0.04	-1.75	0.59	-2.85	0.47	0.22	0.12	-0.04
Consensus	A	G	T	G	T	C	C	A
	c					t	A	C

Figure 29: Possible eukaryotic termination signal. Base frequencies for 70 sequences were determined by McLauchlan et al. (1985). The weight matrix is a log-odds matrix corrected for the local composition of the motif as described in the text. The consensus sequence is shown in upper case when the conserved base is present at 1.5 or more times the expected frequency, and in lower case when present at more than 1.25 times the expected level.

translated region. Any sequence between an initiation and termination codon is thus an ORF, and potentially encodes a protein. As a result of the use of a triplet code for translation, any particular DNA sequence has six potential reading frames that can encode proteins, three on one strand of the DNA, proceeding in the 5' to 3' direction, and another three, also proceeding in the 5' to 3' direction, on the complementary strand. Thus, there are six possible reading frames in which to look for the open reading frames that encode the protein of interest. A DNA sequence will therefore contain many small ORFs that do not encode protein.

One method of finding a coding region is to locate all ORFs in the sequence, and then examine each one for the signals and sequence patterns typical of actual coding sequences. The ORFs can be easily located by plotting the location of each stop codon and each start codon in the six reading frames of the sequence. A simple way of doing this is to draw six lines on a sheet of paper to represent the three forward and three reverse reading frames of the sequence. Then draw a perpendicular line for each stop codon in each of the six frames. The start codons can be represented as small circles on each of the six lines. By connecting the circles and perpendicular lines every possible open reading frame can be located. Since the organization of eukaryotic genes into exons and introns may separate some or all of the ORFs from initiation codons, it is advisable to consider an ORF to be the entire region between termination codons in these systems. Computer programs that perform this analysis are available in most sequence analysis packages, and produce results that resemble Figure 30. Since most ORFs are not part

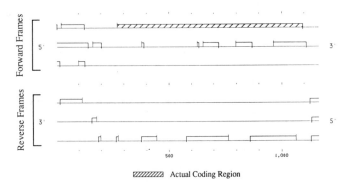

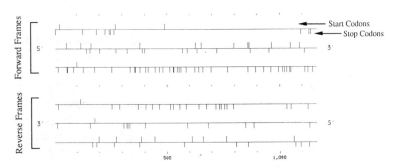

Figure 30: ORF analysis. A representation of the open reading frames (ORFs) in the sequence of the Manganese stabilizing protein (MSP) of Synechocystis 6803 is presented (Philbrick and Zilinskas, 1988). Both representations where constructed using the program FRAMES of the GCG package (Genetics Computer Group, Inc., Madison, WI). The top representation shows each of the ORFs in the three forward frames, or 5' to 3' direction, and those in the three frames on the reverse strand or 3' to 5' direction. The actual coding region for the MSP gene is indicated. The lower panel shows the positions of each of the start and stop codons in each of the six reading frames. This is a very useful representation, particularly when used to indicate the positions of alternate initiation codons.

of the coding sequence, it is desirable to confine subsequent analyses to those open reading frames that are biologically significant, or long enough to be considered as possible protein coding region.

The main problem in identifying coding regions is to discriminate between coding and non-coding ORFs, and in the case of eukaryotic genes, to identify the exons of the gene and assemble them into a continuous coding sequence. Present methods for the prediction of coding regions fall into two broad categories; those that search for the signal sequences that delimit the coding sequences (search by signal), and those that assess sequences statistically to determine whether they appear to be more similar to coding or non-coding sequences (search by content).

The identification of the signals that delimit coding regions helps to confirm or reject the hypothesis that an ORF is an actual protein coding region. In the analysis of prokaryotic DNA sequences, these features include signals for the initiation of transcription and translation, the ribosome binding site (RBS), and transcriptional and translational termination signals. The analysis of eukaryotic genomic DNA sequences is a bit more complex because the features that must be recognized are less well understood, and because the interrupted nature of eukaryotic genes may place the signals very far from the coding regions. These features include signals for the initiation of translation, the intron/exon boundaries (splice sites), termination of translation, and polyadenylation sites. It is the identification of the introns and exons which presents the most difficulties because introns interrupt coding sequences and make the identification of coding regions more difficult. The use of cDNA sequences can considerably reduce this problem as it is only necessary to identify the correct initiation and termination codons since the mRNA has had all the introns removed during processing.

Protein coding sequences have characteristic sequence patterns that can be used to distinguish them from non-coding regions. These patterns are a result of the constraints placed on a coding region by its function of encoding a protein, and by the translation machinery used to express the gene. Patterns useful in distinguishing coding from non-coding regions include periodic patterns of base frequency, positional preferences of the bases within codons, and codon usage.

Identification of mRNA Signals

Ribosome Binding Sites

Structural gene expression requires the binding of ribosomes to mRNA and the initiation of translation. In prokaryotes, Shine and Dalgarno (1975) showed that the choice of the start codon is related to complementarity between the mRNA 5' of the start codon, and the 3' end of the 16S ribosomal RNA. Figure 31 shows the originally proposed ribosome binding sequences (RBS) for several bacterial species. Most reported RBSs are derived by simple inspection of the sequence before each potential start codon in each ORF, looking for complementarity to the central 5 to 7 bases of the RBS, while allowing for several mismatches. A simple method for locating an RBS is to search for sequences complementary to the 16S rRNA using a simple pattern searcher such as a restriction enzyme mapping program (see Pattern Matching Programs). While this approach will correctly locate some RBSs,

```
Species                        16SrRNA and mRNA

Escherichia                    AUUCCUCCACY  5'
     coli                      --AGGAGGU--  3'

Pseudomonas                    AUUCCUCUCY   5'
     aeruginosa                --AGGAG---   3'

Bacillus                       AUCUUUCCUY   5'
     stearothermophilus        -----AGGA-   3'

Caulobacter                    UCUUUCCUY    5'
     crescentus                ----AGGA-    3'
```

Figure 31: Shine-Dalgarno sequences. The sequence immediately 5' of a start codon should be partly complementary to the 3' end of the 16S rRNA from the same species. Examples rRNA and mRNA sequences from several species are shown.

it also has a high rate of false positives (Stormo, 1987). A more powerful way to locate a bacterial RBS is to use a weight matrix searching technique (Stormo et al., 1982), although this method will also incorrectly assign many non-RBS sequences as RBS sequences. It is interesting to note that the most powerful weight matrix for detecting RBSs (Figure 32) extends 60 bases before the initiation codon to 40 bases after initiation codon, far beyond the region thought to base pair with the 16S RNA (Stormo et al., 1982).

In eukaryotes, the RBS does not follow the bacterial model (Kozak, 1983). The 5' end of the mRNA is identified by a cap structure of modified guanosine, which ribosomes appear to recognize and then to initiate, in the great majority of case, at the first AUG in the sequence. In a few cases, where the sequence composition immediately surrounding the first AUG is extremely unfavorable (in about 5% of the cases, often when the first AUG is surrounded by pyrimidine bases at positions -3 or +4), an alternative AUG may be used. In analyzing genomic sequences for initiation codons, the situation is complicated by the difficulties of both identifying the transcriptional start site, and the possible presence of splice sites that may cause the first AUG to occur outside of the first exon.

The Initiation Codon

Whether a sequence is of eukaryotic or prokaryotic origin, the protein coding region must start with an initiation codon. In eukaryotes, there is a preference for certain sequences in the neighborhood of the AUG initiation codon. This preference has been well described by Kozak, with some elucidation of the rules surrounding the recognition of the initiation codon by the eukaryotic ribosome (Sargan et al., 1982; Kozak, 1983,1984). Consensus sequences have been described for initiation codon contexts for various organisms

	-13	-12	-11	-10	-9	-8	-7	-6	-5	-4	-3	-2
A	8	2	8	0	-3	-5	4	-20	-11	5	6	-2
C	-7	-36	-44	-15	-50	-43	-35	-38	-29	-29	1	-9
G	15	21	42	35	22	16	-6	-5	-15	-25	-33	-28
T	-36	-8	-27	-53	-27	-26	-23	2	-7	-14	-40	-28
Consensus	G	G	G	G	G	G	a	t	n	a	a	n
	a	a	a								c	

	-1	0	1	2	3	4	5	6	7	8	9	10
A	-15	66	-69	-52	-5	-4	6	8	-24	-7	-10	-7
C	1	-87	-55	-64	-45	11	-22	-14	-20	-15	-15	-10
G	-53	-36	-50	107	-5	-37	-44	-27	-15	-23	-16	-29
T	0	-53	75	-62	-20	-40	-10	-35	-5	-12	-1	4
Consensus	c	A	T	G	n	C	a	a	n	n	n	t

	11	12	13	14	15	16	17	18	19	20	21
A	13	14	-9	-18	14	-12	-42	1	-5	-4	-32
C	-22	-5	2	6	6	-8	19	-7	9	-3	17
G	-47	-17	-29	-15	-23	-7	-1	-6	-17	-4	0
T	14	-23	7	-2	-26	1	4	-7	3	-4	0
Consensus	G	A	t	c	A	t	C	a	c	n	C
	A		c		c		t		t		

Figure 32: Prokaryotic ribosome binding site (RBS). Weight matrix refined by Stormo et al. (1982) using the perceptron method. A matrix covering the region from -60 to +40 (matrix W101) gave the best diferentiation of RBS signals from non-RBS signals. Only the highly conserved central portion is shown here. The consensus sequence shows bases with a score above 0 in lower case, and those with scores above 10 in upper case. The levels were chosen arbitrarily.

(Figure 33), with a marked preference found for the three positions preceding and the two positions following the initiation codon. Kozak has shown that, *in vitro*, the translational efficiency of an ORF is related to how well it adheres

Base Frequency

	-7	-6	-5	-4	-3	-2	-1	1	2	3
A	50	27	27	19	86	36	34	102	0	0
C	20	15	32	65	5	42	52	0	0	0
G	6	29	12	6	11	6	11	0	0	102
T	19	24	31	12	0	18	5	0	102	0

Weight Matrix

	-7	-6	-5	-4	-3	-2	-1	1	2	3
A	0.33	-0.29	-0.36	-0.71	0.80	-0.07	-0.13	0.97	-4.35	-4.35
C	-0.09	-0.37	0.31	1.02	-1.54	0.58	0.80	-3.85	-3.85	-3.85
G	-1.06	0.52	-0.44	-1.13	-0.52	-1.13	-0.52	-3.61	-3.61	1.70
T	-0.05	0.19	0.37	-0.58	-3.76	-0.17	-1.45	-3.76	1.56	-3.76
Consensus	A	G	t	C	A	C	C	A	T	G
			c							

Figure 33: Eukaryotic translation initiation context. Base frequencies for the region preceding the initiation codon are from Sargan et al. (1982). The weight matrix is a log-odds matrix corrected for the local composition of the motif as described in the text. The consensus sequence is shown in upper case when the conserved base is present at 1.5 or more times the expected frequency, and in lower case when present at more than 1.25 times the expected level.

to the preferred AUG context. The better the adherence to the consensus, the more efficiently translated the mRNA is in an *in vitro* system. Again these sites can be searched for as simple consensus patterns, or more powerfully using weight matrix approaches.

A variety of prokaryotic organisms, as well as organellar genomes, use alternate initiation codons. These codons, which include GUG, UUG, and AUA, function in the same manner as the AUG, but must be considered as possible alternate start codons [Kozak, 1983; Gren, 1984]. To identify coding sequences from these varied sources, it is necessary to know what to expect as a start codon. Figure 34 lists some of the various start codons that are utilized, and the organisms that use these variant initiation codons. It is important to note that the use of alternate initiation codons can influence the translational efficiency of the ORF (Peabody, 1989).

Alternate Initiation Codons

Codon	Organism	Codon	Organism	Codon	Organism
GUG	Acinetobacter calcoaceticus	UUG	Agrobacterium rhizogenes	AUA	Escherichia coli
	Alcaligenes eutrophus		Bacillus amyloliquefaciens		
	Anacystis nidulans		Bacillus brevis		
	Bacillus amyloliquefaciens		Bacillus cereus		
	Bacillus brevis		Bacillus licheniformis		
	Bacillus sphaericus		Bacillus megaterium		
	Bacillus stearothermophilus		Bacillus polymyxa		
	Bacillus subtilis		Bacillus sphaericus		
	Bradyrhizobium japonicum		Bacillus subtilis		
	Brevibacterium lactofermentum		Brevibacterium epidermidis		
	Desulfovibrio baculatus		Clostridium acetobutylicum		
	Escherichia coli		Escherichia coli		
	Halobacterium halobium		Klebsiella oxytoca		
	Methanobacterium thermoautotrophicum		Methanobacterium thermoautotrophicum		
	Micrococcus luteus		Mycoplasma hyorhinis		
	Mycobacterium leprae		Pseudomonas aeruginosa		
	Mycobacterium tuberculosis		Rhodospirillum rubrum		
	Paracoccus denitrificans		Salmonella typhimurium		
	Pseudomonas aeruginosa		Staphylococcus aureus		
	Pseudomonas putida		Staphylococcus simulans		
	Rhodobacter capsulatus		Staphylococcus staphylolyticus		
	Rhodobacter sphaeroides		Streptococcus pyogenes		
	Salmonella typhimurium		Streptomyces clavuligerus		
	Staphylococcus aureus		Streptomyces coelicolor		
	Streptomyces actuosus				
	Streptomyces coelicolor				
	Streptomyces fradiae				
	Streptomyces griseus				
	Streptomyces kasugaensis				
	Streptomyces lavendulae				
	Thermus flavus				
	Thermus thermophilus				
	Yersinia enterocolitica				

Figure 34: Alternate initiation codons were identified in gene sequences from the organism listed. This was accomplished by a survey of the GenBank database (Bilofsky et al., 1986), and represents a cross-section of the organisms that normally utilize these alternate start codons. It is very important to consider that an alternate initiation codon may be used when examining potential coding regions from these organisms.

The Stop Codon

The second hallmark of a protein coding region is the termination or stop codon. Three stop codons, UAA, UAG, and UGA, suffice for all protein coding regions. A preference for the use of UAG and UGA is observed in genes from organisms that have a high GC content. In polycistronic genes, a re-initiation event may occur immediately distal to the stop of the preceding coding region. When re-initiation is observed, the initiation codon is usually preceded by a termination codon within 10 bases, and the following initiation codon may actually overlap the termination codon. In fact, an efficient cDNA expression vector has been developed in *E. coli* based upon this observation, with an initiation sequence of TGATG.

Suppressor tRNAs

The amber (UAG), opal (UGA) and ochre (UAA) codons normally do not encode an amino acid, and as such are termination signals. A very few coding sequences contain these termination codons at positions where specific translational mistakes are to occur as a part of the regulation of gene expression, or where the organism uses an alternate genetic code. Several species of ciliated protozoans, some Mycoplasma and various mitochondrial genomes have been observed to make use of stop codons to encode specific amino acids (Fox, 1985). In addition, suppressor tRNAs have been found in many eukaryotes, and have been hypothesized to actively participate in gene regulation (Kozak, 1986). These suppressors have proper anticodons to base pair to the stop codon, but instead of terminating, encode an amino acid residue. This substitution often occurs at a very low level with most polypeptides terminating at the proper stop codon. This low level of translational read-through can produce large effects, particularly when the extended polypeptide has a specific biological function. Any analysis of gene sequences should consider that suppressor tRNAs may be a part of the regulation of these genes.

RNA Splice Sites

Coding regions in eukaryotic DNA sequences are usually broken into pieces. The exons, or coding portions of the gene, are interspersed with introns or intervening sequences. The introns are spliced out of the primary RNA transcript during mRNA maturation before the processed message is translated into the cognate protein. Splicing appears to be dependent upon the recognition of specific signal sequences by the cell's splicing machinery. Conserved sequences have been observed at both the splice donor and acceptor sites, and appear to be necessary for proper splicing (reviewed by

Senapathy et al., 1990). Additional sequences within the introns also appear to be important for proper splicing. These splicing signal sequences can be used to identify splice sites in genomic DNA, and thus to define the extent of the introns as well as the exons.

Splice junctions are characterized by the conserved sequence (A/C)AG|GUAAGU surrounding the exon/intron boundary (also referred to as the 5' splice site, or splice donor site; Senapathy et al., 1990). The "|" designates the position of the endonucleolytic cleavage in the pre-mRNA. The intron/exon boundary, or 3' splice site (acceptor site), is also character-ized by a specific conserved sequence. The four nucleotides surrounding this ·site, which is preceded by a pyrimidine rich region, define the acceptor site. This sequence is of the form $(C/U)_2UU(C/U)_6NCAG(G/A)$. This site is more simply described as a pyrimidine rich region followed by the highly con-served sequence CAGR. Senapathy et al. (1990) have determined base frequency distributions for the donor and acceptor splice sites for each of the seven general categories, primate, rodent, other mammals, other vertebrates, invertebrates, plants, and viruses, of GenBank as listed. Base frequency and weight matrices compiled from all 3700 sequences are shown in Figures 35 and 36. Interestingly, in only 2% of analyzed cases was an AG sequence found within ten bases of the 3' splice site AG dinucleotide.

A signal for lariat formation, or the branch point signal may occur within the intron. This signal is usually 10 to 50 bases upstream of the acceptor site. Branch points often contain a conserved sequence CTRAY (Figure 37), but the conservation is quite weak. Senapathy et al. (1990) estimate that more than 60% of branch sites use a different recognition sequence. Introns also

Base Frequency

	-14	-13	-12	-11	-10	-9	-8	-7	-6	-5	-4	-3	-2	-1	1
A	11	11	10	8	11	10	11	11	7	8	25	3	100	0	27
C	29	33	30	30	32	34	37	38	39	36	26	75	0	0	14
G	14	12	10	10	9	11	10	9	7	6	26	1	0	100	49
T	46	44	50	52	48	45	42	43	47	51	23	21	0	0	10

Weight Matrix

	-14	-13	-12	-11	-10	-9	-8	-7	-6	-5	-4	-3	-2	-1	1
A	-0.43	-0.43	-0.52	-0.74	-0.43	-0.52	-0.43	-0.43	-0.88	-0.74	0.39	-1.73	1.78	-7.12	0.47
C	-0.04	0.09	-0.01	-0.01	0.06	0.12	0.20	0.23	0.26	0.18	-0.15	0.91	-7.71	-7.71	-0.77
G	-0.26	-0.42	-0.60	-0.60	-0.71	-0.51	-0.60	-0.71	-0.96	-1.11	0.35	-2.90	-7.20	1.70	0.99
T	0.28	0.24	0.36	0.40	0.32	0.26	0.19	0.21	0.30	0.38	-0.41	-0.50	-7.85	-7.85	-1.25
Consensus	t	t	t	t	t	t	n	c	t	t	a	C	A	G	G
								t	c		c				A

Figure 35: Splice donor (5') site. Base frequencies are given as the percentage of bases occurring at each position. The splice donor site was compiled based on about 3700 sequences from plants, vertebrates, invertebrates, and viruses (Senapathy et al., 1990). About two thirds of the sequences were mammalian. The weight matrix is a log-odds matrix corrected for the local composition of the motif as described in the text. The consensus sequence is shown in upper case when the conserved base is present at 1.5 or more times the expected frequency, and in lower case when present at more than 1.25 times the expected level.

Base Frequency

	-3	-2	-1	1	2	3	4	5	6
A	32	60	9	0	0	59	71	7	16
C	37	13	5	0	0	3	9	6	16
G	18	12	79	100	0	35	11	82	18
T	13	15	7	0	100	3	9	6	50

Weight Matrix

	-3	-2	-1	1	2	3	4	5	6
A	0.13	0.76	-1.14	-7.65	-7.65	0.74	0.92	-1.39	-0.57
C	1.32	0.27	-0.68	-6.60	-6.60	-1.19	-0.09	-0.50	0.48
G	-0.78	-1.19	0.70	0.93	-7.98	-0.12	-1.28	0.73	-0.78
T	-0.55	-0.41	-1.17	-7.43	1.49	-2.02	-0.92	-1.32	0.80
Consensus	C	A	G	G	T	A	A	G	T
		c							C

Figure 36: Splice acceptor (3') site. Base frequencies are given as the percentage of bases occurring at each position. The splice acceptor site was compiled based on about 3700 sequences from plants, vertebrates, invertebrates, and viruses (Senapathy et al., 1990). About two thirds of the sequences were mammalian. See Figure 35 for a description of the weight matrix and consensus sequence.

have compositional properties that distinguish them from exons. Introns have been observed to have an increased A+T composition compared to exons, and do not show any periodic bias in base composition (see Base Composition Bias, below).

Base Frequency

	-3	-2	-1	0	1
A	1	0	39	99	11
C	76	8	15	1	45
G	2	0	42	0	6
T	21	91	4	0	38

Weight Matrix

	-3	-2	-1	0	1
A	-3.41	-4.79	0.26	1.19	-1.01
C	0.97	-1.28	-0.66	-3.36	0.44
G	-1.61	-3.69	1.43	-3.69	-0.51
T	-0.39	1.08	-2.05	-4.82	0.21
Consensus	C	T	G	A	C
				a	t

Figure 37: Splicing branch point (lariat) site. Base frequencies are given as the percentage of bases occurring at each position. The splice acceptor site was compiled based on about 200 sequences from plants, mammals, chicken, and *Drosiphila* (Senapathy et al., 1990). See Figure 35 for a description of the weight matrix and consensus sequence.

The detection of splice sites and the prediction of exons is a very difficult proposition. The best methods use either a weight matrix (see Weight Matrices) or perceptron methodology. Currently none of the popular packages support the identification of splice site sequences. However, one can use the information from consensus sequences to search for possible sites, or construct a weight matrix from a set of known splice sites and use this to search for splice sites in unknown sequences (Stormo, 1990). Other methods that can be used to determine splice sites include syntactic analysis and k-tuple frequency analysis. Syntactic analysis is the search for a specific "grammar" that describes a sequence pattern. The connective patterns that exist between the various nucleotides at each position in the recognition sequence can be defined using this grammar. The basis for this method is that the importance of a nucleotide in any specific position may be altered by the nucleotide in the next position. If each position is independent of all the others, at least as far as its importance for recognition is concerned, then this method is equivalent to a weight matrix approach. This method has been used with some success in the prediction of 5' splice sites and may be of increasing importance for splice site prediction as well as other sequence pattern analysis.

K-tuple frequency analysis has many uses, among them the prediction of RNA splice sites. Basically, a k-tuple analysis breaks up the sequence to be assessed into words of length k. The number of possible k-tuples that can be formed from nucleotide sequences are k^4, while for proteins it is k^{20}. The analysis is based upon having a catalog of k-tuples that represents the pattern of interest. This catalog is then compared to the test sequence, and the number of k-tuples that match the catalog at each position are recorded. A score for the match is then calculated based upon the level of matching found. Bougueleret et al. (1988) have used k-tuple analysis to find potential splice signals in genomic DNA sequences. The authors found that a word length of six nucleotides was optimal for the determination of splice signals.

Polyadenylation Signals

The polyadenylation (polyA) signal, which is involved in the maturation and processing of eukaryotic pre-mRNAs, has the consensus sequence AAUAAA (Proudfoot and Brownlee, 1976). It has been hypothesized that the polyA addition signal sequence interacts with a nuclear factor, and forms a complex that is involved in both the cleavage of the transcript and the addition of the polyA tail (Zarkower and Wickens, 1987). A base frequency table and weight matrix, based on the 94 sequences listed by McLauchlan et al. (1985) are shown in Figure 38. This sequence is usually located 5-30 bases upstream of the polyA addition site. Many eukaryotic messages contain multiple polyadenylation signals, and these signals often result in mRNAs of distinct differing lengths, presumably arising from the same primary transcript.

Base Frequency

	1	2	3	4	5	6	7	8	9	10	11	12
A	24	19	24	94	90	0	94	94	94	34	26	22
C	19	25	28	0	0	0	0	0	0	21	22	35
G	10	17	15	0	2	0	0	0	0	26	22	12
T	41	33	27	0	2	94	0	0	0	13	24	25

Weight Matrix

	1	2	3	4	5	6	7	8	9	10	11	12
A	-0.76	-0.99	-0.76	0.60	0.56	-3.93	0.60	0.60	0.60	-0.41	-0.68	-0.85
C	0.42	0.69	0.81	-3.71	-3.71	-3.71	-3.71	-3.71	-3.71	0.52	0.56	1.03
G	0.14	0.67	0.55	-2.85	-1.46	-2.85	-2.85	-2.85	-2.85	1.10	0.93	0.33
T	0.65	0.43	0.23	-3.75	-2.37	1.48	-3.75	-3.75	-3.75	-0.50	0.11	0.15
Consensus	T	C	C	A	A	T	A	A	A	G	G	C
	C	G	G							C	C	g
		T	t									

Figure 38: Polyadenylation signal. Frequency and weight matrices for 94 sequences listed by McLauchlan et al. (1985). The weight matrix is a log-odds matrix corrected for the local composition of the motif as described in the text. The consensus sequence is shown in upper case when the conserved base is present at 1.5 or more times the expected frequency, and in lower case when present at more than 1.25 times the expected level.

Coding Region Sequence Patterns

Patterns that allow discrimination between coding and non-coding sequences arise primarily from the three base periodicity enforced on coding regions by the genetic code, the unequal use of synonymous codons, and the amino acid sequences of the encoded proteins. Surprisingly, the unequal usage of the amino acid residues in proteins is sufficient to cause a distinct bias in the frequencies of the bases at the three positions in the codon (Staden, 1984; McCaldon and Argos, 1988; Staden, 1990). This bias is increased by the preferential usage of certain of the synonymous codons (codon preference). It has also been suggested that the periodic bias in base composition arises from remnants of a primitive genetic code with codons of the form RNY (Shepard, 1981), but this, of course, is difficult to test. Non-coding regions such as introns do not display a strong periodic compositional bias.

The simplest method of using the base composition bias to search for coding regions is to look for regions that show a distinct bias. These are likely to represent coding regions. While this approach is useful for predicting whether a stretch of sequence is coding or non-coding, it does not provide any information about the reading frame. A more sophisticated approach is to use the base composition bias to determine the reading frame as well. This approach is based upon the observation that coding sequences will have preferences for specific bases in each of the three positions in the codon. This method is exceptionally powerful when the sequence in question is either very AT or GC rich, as third position bias will be very strong. Methods employing this approach will be able to predict whether a sequence is coding or non-coding, and will additionally be able to predict the reading frame. A third approach uses the codon preference of the organism to predict coding regions and the reading frame. This method is simply a comparison of the codons of all possible reading frames with a preferred codon usage for the organism. One drawback of this method is that you must have information about the codon preference of the organism involved. Furthermore, since codon preference is correlated with the levels of the corresponding isoaccepting tRNAs, it can not be assumed to be the same for all tissues or developmental states.

Base Composition Bias

The use of a specific subset of synonymous codons to encode proteins results in a preference for specific bases in each position in the codons. This effect is compounded when combined with the unequal use of amino acids in proteins, and produces a pronounced periodic base composition bias (positional base preference) in coding sequences. This positional preference in base composition can be used to identify regions of DNA that have coding potential. For example, an organism that has a very high G+C content in its DNA must have a high positional composition bias in its coding sequence if it is to use the universal genetic code and maintain its G+C content. The first two codon positions of the universal genetic code are close to 50% G+C content. The corresponding coding region will therefore be about 50% G+C in these two positions, if we are to assume a non-skewed amino acid content. If we are to maintain the high G+C content of this DNA segment, G or C must be used in position three of almost all codons. Thus, in high G+C DNA, we will find that the first two positions of codons are about 50% G+C, while the third position is almost entirely G+C. In this example, if the first two positions are 50% G+C and the third position is 100% G+C, the base composition of this segment will be 67% G+C. In organisms that have a GC content of 70% or more, such as many of the *Actinomycetes*, it is possible to find entire genes which have only one or two third position As or Ts.

Organisms with a more even base composition still show a positional base bias, although it is less pronounced. Positional base preference results not only from third position bias due to G+C content, but also a result of the unequal use of amino acids in protein sequences (Staden, 1984). The positional base bias in coding sequences has been very well described by Staden and many others (Shulman et al., 1981; Rodier et al., 1982; Bibb et al., 1984; Ohno, 1988).

TestCode Analysis

Fickett was one of the first investigators to design a statistically based method for determining coding versus non-coding sequence and to rigorously test it. His analysis, termed TestCode analysis (or Fickett's statistic), is based upon periodic base composition bias of coding regions (Fickett, 1982). TestCode analysis breaks the sequence up into three non-overlapping sets of bases. The first set comprises bases 1, 4, 7 ..., the second bases 2, 5, 8 ..., and the third 3, 6, 9 etc. The method then looks for unequal base composition in the three sets to determine whether the region is coding or non-coding. Because the method is only looking for asymmetry, the reading frame and the strand are both irrelevant. A statistic indicating the asymmetry of base composition is calculated within a window which is moved along the sequence, producing a plot of the asymmetry (coding potential) at each point in the sequence. Although there is considerable overlap in the range of scores produced by coding and non-coding regions, it is often possible to distinguish coding regions by this method alone (see Staden, 1990 for score distributions).

The TestCode method does not determine the reading frame, or even the coding strand, but has the advantage of requiring no information except the sequence to be analyzed. Nor does it precisely define the extent of the coding region. This information must be determined by looking for the signal sequences that define the coding region, i.e., the initiation codon, termination codon and intron/exon boundaries. This method works best for prokaryotic sequences or cDNA sequences. Coding regions in genomic sequences, particularly those with a large number of introns and small exons will not be correctly identified by this algorithm because the program requires rather large window size (100-200 bases) for its calculation. An example of a TestCode analysis is given in Chapter 4, using the *Drosophila Notch* locus.

Codon Bias

The isoaccepting tRNAs corresponding to the various synonymous codons are present in the cell at widely varying levels. The levels of the tRNAs vary both with the organism and, in metazoans, with tissue and developmental stage. The usage of the synonymous codons in genes has been observed to correlate with the levels of the corresponding isoaccepting tRNAs (Ikemura, 1981, 1982, 1985), with the most highly expressed genes using only the codons corresponding to the most abundant isoaccepting tRNAs. This effect is called codon preference and should be distinguished from codon usage which is simply the observed frequency of codons in all genes in an organism. Codon preference is thought to be arise from a requirement for translational efficiency in the most highly expressed genes (Grantham, et al., 1980; Grosjean and Fiers, 1982). Codon preference has been well described in *E. coli*; a look at the table of codons used in highly expressed genes demonstrates this preference (Figure 39). For example, of the six leucine codons, 83% of are encoded by the CUG codon and none by CUA. ORFs that exhibit a similar codon preference can be judged to be more likely to be actual coding regions than ORFs that do not exhibit the codon preference typical of the organism. This is the principle behind the codon preference method of defining protein coding regions (Staden and MacLachlan, 1982; Gribskov et al., 1984). These

Amino Acid	Codon	#/1000	Fraction	Amino Acid	Codon	#/1000	Fraction
Gly	GGG	1.89	0.02	Pro	CCG	27.58	0.77
Gly	GGA	0.44	0.00	Pro	CCA	5.23	0.15
Gly	GGU	52.99	0.59	Pro	CCU	2.76	0.08
Gly	GGC	34.55	0.38	Pro	CCC	0.15	0.00
Glu	GAG	15.68	0.22	Trp	UGG	7.98	1.00
Glu	GAA	57.20	0.78	End	UGA	0.00	0.00
Asp	GAU	21.63	0.33	Cys	UGU	3.19	0.49
Asp	GAC	43.26	0.67	Cys	UGC	3.34	0.51
Val	GUG	13.50	0.16	End	UAG	0.00	0.00
Val	GUA	21.20	0.26	End	UAA	0.00	0.00
Val	GUU	41.96	0.51	Tyr	UAU	7.40	0.25
Val	GUC	5.52	0.07	Tyr	UCA	22.79	0.75
Ala	GCG	23.37	0.26	Leu	UUG	2.61	0.03
Ala	GCA	25.12	0.28	Leu	UUA	1.74	0.02
Ala	GCU	30.78	0.35	Phe	UUU	7.40	0.24
Ala	GCC	9.00	0.10	Phe	UUC	24.10	0.76
Arg	AGG	0.15	0.00	Ser	UCG	2.03	0.00
Arg	AGA	0.00	0.00	Ser	UCA	1.02	0.02
Ser	AGU	1.31	0.03	Ser	UCU	17.42	0.34
Ser	AGC	10.31	0.20	Ser	UCC	19.02	0.37
Lys	AAG	16.11	0.26	Arg	CGG	0.15	0.00
Lys	AAA	46.46	0.74	Arg	CGA	0.29	0.01
Asn	AAU	2.76	0.06	Arg	CGU	42.10	0.74
Asn	AAC	39.78	0.94	Arg	CGC	13.94	0.25
Met	AUG	24.68	1.00	Gln	CAG	33.83	0.86
Ile	AUA	0.15	0.00	Gln	CAA	5.37	0.14
Ile	AUU	10.16	0.17	His	CAU	2.61	0.17
Ile	AUC	50.09	0.83	His	CAC	12.34	0.83
Thr	ACG	3.63	0.07	Leu	CUG	69.69	0.83
Thr	ACA	2.03	0.04	Leu	CUA	0.29	0.00
Thr	ACU	18.87	0.35	Leu	CUU	3.63	0.04
Thr	ACC	29.91	0.55	Leu	CUC	29.91	0.55

Figure 39: This table of highly expressed genes from *E. coli* is distributed with the GCG package (Genetics Computer Group, Inc., Madison, WI). The table illustrates the non-uniform use of codons for these genes, and suggests that there may be adverse affects of using the under-represented codons within a coding sequence. In addition, such tables can be used to identify additional genes in the organism, or to verify the assignment of an ORF as a true coding region.

methods generally evaluate the coding potential of each reading frame by comparing the codon usage within a moving window to the preferred codon usage. The results are usually displayed as three graphs showing the coding potential at every position in the three reading frames, often combined with a display of ORFs and rare codons (Figure 40). Codon bias methods that predict the reading frames are often useful in detecting sequencing errors that cause a frameshift. A frameshift is possible when the codon usage bias

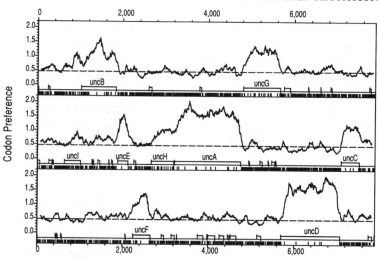

Figure 40: Codon Preference analysis of the *E. coli unc* operon. Each of the three frames shows the codon preference statistic (Gribskov et al., 1984) for one of the reading frames. The statistic is (f/F) / (r/R), where f is the frequency of the codon in highly expressed genes, F is the corresponding frequency of the entire synonymous family in highly expressed genes, and r and R are the calculated frequencies of codons and their synonymous family in a random sequence of the same composition. High values of the codon preference statistic indicate a codon usage similar to that of highly expressed genes. In this plot the codon preference statistic is averaged over a window of 50 codons. The ORFs in each frame are shown as boxes, and below the ORF plot the positions of codons that code for less than 5 % of their synonymous family in highly expressed genes are shown by vertical bars.

indicates that the reading frame switches from one frame to another in a very short span (see Chapter 4, Figure 4 for an artificial example).

Codon usage can easily be tabulated once you have defined the coding region. Programs to calculate this are ubiquitous to the various sequence analysis packages. Codon preference tables are usually the codon usage of genes known to be highly expressed, or of groups of genes with similar codon usage as determined by a cluster analysis (Sharp et al., 1986). Extrapolation of the use of codon preference to locate coding regions in eukaryotic systems has some obvious pitfalls. Different tissues and different developmental stages of the organism may use different pools of tRNAs, resulting in developmental stage or tissue specific codon preference. Furthermore, the method works best with genes with a strong codon preference, and therefore works better with highly expressed genes. Using the overall codon usage as the target codon preference may be completely useless if the organism uses distinct and different tRNA pools in translation at different developmental stages, or in different cell types. However, if you do not know the codon preference of the system you are using, there are a couple of approaches you can take. The most straightforward is to use the codon usage of a highly expressed gene for the preferred usage. Examples of highly expressed genes that can usually be used are ribosomal proteins, histones, actins, and tubulins, but any gene known to be expressed at high levels should work. A second approach is to use the overall codon usage of the organism, but remove all codons whose usage as a fraction of the synonymous codons in the family is less than 0.5 divided by the number of synonymous codons in the family. This method will probably not give as good results as using the actual preferred codon usage, but it is worth trying if there is no better alternative. It is important to consider this when using codon preference to determine coding regions, or to assess the translational efficiency of a coding region.

Correspondence Analysis

Correspondence analysis is based upon the observation that all of the coding sequences of a given DNA fragment are likely to exhibit a similar codon preference (Fichant and Gautier, 1987). This method does not require the knowledge of codon usage for the organism or a knowledge of any specific signals. The method can use a somewhat smaller window than TestCode, and as such, may be used to find small exons in genomic sequences. The first step in this method analyzes the codon usage in a window of 30 codons in each of the three reading frames. A measure of the degree to which the codon usage of the three frames agree is calculated using correspondence analysis and plotted. The thirty codon window is then moved along the sequence until the entire sequence has been addressed and a measure of the codon usage bias for each window of sequence has been determined. The sum of these calculations is then presented graphically by a plot combined with a plot of the positions of initiation and termination codons. This method requires no external reference system and uses the observation that all coding sequences of any one gene will exhibit a similar codon usage. Spurious results can be a problem if the region in question is either less than 50% coding sequence or if there is a strong triplet repeat structure within the sequence. However, in most cases this method is equivalent or better than the TestCode analysis described above. When this method is combined with a search for the signals that define coding regions, it becomes a very accurate method of coding sequence prediction.

Codon Usage and Gene Expression Prediction

Many investigators have hypothesized a link between codon usage and the level of expression of a given gene (e.g., Grosjean and Fiers, 1982). If a gene uses a large number of rare codons, it has been hypothesized that the expression of this gene product will be lower than if it were to use codons corresponding to the more abundant isoaccepting tRNAs. Several methods using codon preference to predict the level of gene expression have been presented (Gribskov et al., 1984; Sharp and Li 1987). It must be kept in mind, however, that such methods can only predict the maximum possible expression level and do not take the possible regulation of the expression level into account.

Assembly of Continuous Coding Sequences

Most sequence analysis packages have some set of programs or subprograms for the definition of coding sequences. These subprograms range in complexity from the ability to simply define open reading frames, to the ability to define a given eukaryotic gene sequence's distinct exon/intron boundaries as well as promoters and other sequence features. Particularly interesting are the programs that determine statistical measures of coding sequence probability, and in particular one program which uses both signal sequences and statistical methods to predict possible coding regions with their respective protein sequences. The use of any of these programs to define coding regions should be undertaken with the understanding of the strong points and weak points of each individual method.

Gene modeler, or gm, is a very good program that has been developed by Fields and Soderlund (1990). gm is an integrated system that identifies specific signal sequences using a weight matrix approach and combines this information with statistical measures of coding sequence probability to arrive at a set of predicted coding regions. This program requires that the user provide the weight matrices for each type of signal sequences, as well as information on the base composition and other statistical parameters for the organism of interest. The program iteratively examines each of the potential signal sequences that define the coding regions and evaluates the region statistically to determine its probability of being a coding region. It then constructs a set of potential gene structures that fit the given criteria. The decision as to which of the candidate genes is actually "real" is left up to the user to determine by experimentation or perhaps intuition.

RNA STRUCTURE

The function of an RNA, whether mRNA, rRNA, tRNA or snRNA is intimately related to its folded structure. The folded structure of the molecule, while dependent upon its primary sequence, cannot accurately be determined solely from its primary sequence (see Turner, et al., 1988 for a review). The only completely accurate method of determining the folded structure of an RNA molecule is by X-ray crystallography. However, very accurate predictions of the secondary structure of RNA molecules can be made from primary sequence information, if additional experimental data are available.

The three-dimensional structure of tRNA[Phe] has been experimentally determined by X-ray crystallographic methods (Kim et al., 1974; Robertus et al., 1974), and other tRNA molecules conserve the same cloverleaf structure found in this structure. Thus, the secondary and tertiary structure of tRNAs is well understood, and newly sequenced molecules can be modeled by comparison with these known structures. Ribosomal RNA structures, while not determined in three dimensions, have been well studied in two dimensions with well established and accepted secondary structures. Again, the folded structure of rRNAs are primarily determined by comparison with accepted folded structures. The secondary and tertiary structure of self-splicing introns, or catalytic RNAs, have been of recent interest. These molecules fold into catalytic complexes with a variety of metal ions such as Mg(II), Mn(II), Ca(II) and others. The folding of these catalytic complexes is highly dependent upon the binding of the metal ion, and thus rather difficult to model from primary sequence data (Celander and Cech, 1991). The major area of interest in RNA folding, for the average molecular biologist, is in the folding of mRNA molecules. It has been hypothesized that the three-dimensional structure of an mRNA influences its overall stability, efficiency of translation and processing. It is the folding of these molecules that will be discussed in this section.

RNA molecules fold by intramolecular base pairing and are stabilized by the hydrogen bonds that result from this base pairing. Additionally, the stacking of base pairs in a helix also stabilizes the molecule and decreases the free energy of the folded structure, and the presence of loops destabilizes the structure. Base pairs that can form in RNA are G-C, A-U and G-U. Three hydrogen bonds can form between G-C base pairs, two between A-U base pairs, and one between G-U base pairs. The most common method used to generate RNA secondary structures involves the recursive calculation of the structures that have the lowest free energy of all possible structures, or have the highest number of possible base pairing and stacking interactions. The energy values used in these calculations are derived from *in vitro* studies on the stability of small oligonucleotides (e.g., Freier et al., 1986).

Many computational algorithms have been developed in an attempt to predict RNA secondary structures. The main goal of all of these algorithms is the definition of the base pairing relationships that exist within the molecules. This information can then be used to assess the relationship between structure and function. It must be remembered that computational methods that attempt to predict base pairing relationships, and ultimately secondary and tertiary structures, cannot accurately take into account the large number of variables involved in the actual folding of the molecule *in vivo*. That is, RNA is not a pure molecule in solution in the cell. It may be complexed with a variety of proteins and ions that can stabilize or destabilize both secondary and tertiary structures. RNA is also a dynamic structure, and the static picture indicated by the lowest energy structure may be highly unrepresentative of the range of structures seen in solution. All of the following information should be considered in that light.

Messenger RNAs do not form a consensus structure as do the rRNAs and tRNAs. That is not to say that mRNAs do not have consensus structures within their overall structure. A consensus structure that seems to appear at the 5' end of many eukaryotic mRNAs has been hypothesized to affect

Le and Maizel, 1989, for example). If the random sequences have free energies within 10% of the energy of the predicted structure of the sequence of interest, the predicted structure is probably not significant. However, if the free energy of the random sequences are 50% greater than that of the original sequence, then the folded structure may indeed be significant. The use of experimental evidence to support a folded structure is obviously desirable. When nuclease protection or base modification experiments support a folded structure, it can be deemed significant. A major shortcoming of optimally folded structures is that they may not represent the actual base pairing relationships found in the RNA molecule. There may be many folded structures that have a very similar free energy but that have a completely different predicted structure. To calculate a folded structure that is closer to the actual folded structure of the RNA it may be necessary to predict not only the best folded structure, but a number of structures that are of sufficiently low free energy as to be possible folded structures of the molecule in question.

Suboptimal Folding

Suboptimal folding is the process of determining a set of possible folded structures that have very similar free energy minima, but may be of greatly differing structure. Several methods of determining suboptimal foldings have been developed recently. The most popular of these appears to be that of Zuker (1989b), but there are others (Yamamoto and Yoshikura, 1985; Williams and Tinoco, 1986). This approach, which is an extension of the optimal folding method, makes good use of experimental information on the single-stranded and double-stranded regions of the molecule. It is possible to code information, such as nuclease sensitivity and chemical modification data, into the sequence to assist in the accurate prediction of secondary structures. This information is very important in the determination of the actual secondary structure as it exists *in vivo*. The result of a suboptimal folding run is a series of structures that have similar free energy minima. The common features in these various structures represent the more significant local structures, while regions that are not in common may or may not be important *in vivo*.

Pseudoknots

An interesting and new method of structure prediction relies upon the simulation of the folding process (Abrahams et al., 1990). This method assumes that RNA folding proceeds from "nucleation centers" which are focal points for local RNA folding. These foci can form pseudoknots, which are structures that result from the base pairing of sequences in a loop (adjacent to a stem) with sequences external to this loop. Various forms of pseudoknots have been found experimentally and others have been hypothesized (see

Pseudoknots in RNA Secondary Structure
Predictions

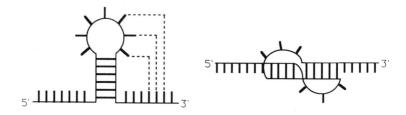

Type H Pseudoknot

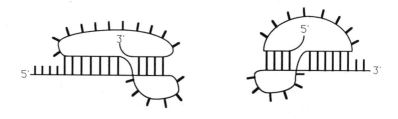

Additional Pseudoknot forms

Figure 42: Representations of the H-type pseudoknot are presented, with additional possible forms identified by Abrahams et al. (1990). The H-pseudoknot forms from the interaction of the bases in the loop with additionally unpaired nucleotides proximal to the stem structure. The pseudoknot forms by stacking of the two helical segments of the molecule. Additional pseudoknots which may form in RNA are shown, but there not yet any biological evidence for their existence.

Figure 42). Programs to predict pseudoknot formation are rare, but the programs by Abrahams et al. (1990) are a good place to start.

Interactive Folding

An interesting method for RNA folding has been developed recently which takes an interactive approach to structure determination. Such approaches provide an environment in which the experimentalist can participate in the folding of the RNA molecule. Cedergren et al. (1988) have developed this concept into an RNA folding editor. This program, called RNASE for RNA

Structure Editor, is one of the first of its kind. Programs like RNASE that allow one to interact with the program in an intuitive and informative way may provide results which are more significant than those simply determined by a computer algorithm. The user may be able to provide structural information and intuition which the computer can not derive on its own. This approach is also very adaptable to new situations in which the user can provide known information on the actual structure that would be difficult to include in a computer program. Another system that is based upon this type of user interaction is RNAFOLD (Martinez, 1988). This set of programs facilitates the identification of both local and global secondary structures using dynamic programming and Monte Carlo methodologies (see Chapter 3).

Representation of Folded Structures

Predicted RNA structures can be displayed in many ways. The traditional representation shows the stem-and-loop structures (Figure 43) with the backbone of the molecule represented by a solid line that is drawn around the predicted stems and loops. While this representation of RNA folding is very pleasing and intuitive, it is very difficult to compare structures depicted in this way. Small rotations of parts of the structure, or changes in the angles of substructures, may make similar structures very difficult to detect. Some examples of other representations are shown in Figure 43 (see also Chapter 3).

Common secondary structure motifs can be difficult to identify using graphical representations. The placement of stems and loops are often arbitrarily made by the graphics package present on the particular computer system. One method of detecting common motifs in RNA secondary structures is based upon a comparison of tree structures [Margalit et al., 1989; Shapiro and Zhang, 1990]. A tree representation of the various folded structures is constructed with the eventual identification of common structural motifs. With this system it is even possible to search for a specific structural motif in a newly determined folded structure. Additionally, the system has been used by Shapiro and Zhang (1990) to produce results which can be used to construct a taxonomic tree of related structures. The use of tree comparisons to analyze the computed structures of related RNAs appears to be the best method of assessing the reproducibility of the folding, as well as the possible biological significance of the final structure.

One important aspect of RNA secondary structure analysis is the use of these methods to design synthetic genes and PCR primers. Folding programs have been used to design regions for PCR primer hybridization with a high rate of success (Pallansch et al., 1990). The construction of synthetic genes may also require that the secondary structure surrounding the initiation of translation conform to a consensus structure (Konings et al., 1987). If this is the case, then the accurate prediction of RNA secondary structure is a prerequisite for the construction of synthetic genes as well.

RNA Secondary Structure
Representations

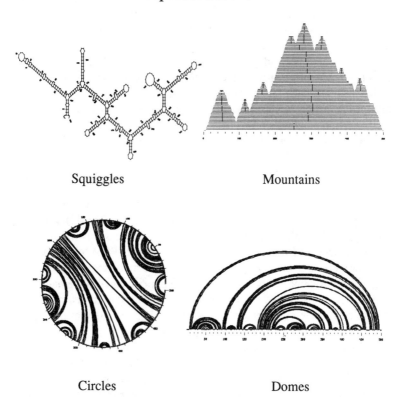

Squiggles   Mountains

Circles   Domes

Figure 43: Various representations of optimal folds of the first 500 bases of the Synechocystis 6803 gene sequence are presented. The folding data is identical for each of the representations, and was generated using the FOLD program of the GCG Package (Zuker, 1981; Genetics Computer Group, Inc., Madison, WI). The top left representation was drawn by the Squiggles program, is a very intuitive representation of the basepairing interactions in the molecule. The Circles and Domes representations facilitate the identification of non base-paired regions, and the Mountains representation makes the identification of base-paired regions less difficult. Each of the representations is useful in visualization of different aspects of the data, and may be interchangeably used to illustrate various aspects of an RNA structure.

DNA STRUCTURE

DNA conformation can be viewed from the perspectives of primary structure (sequence), secondary structure , and tertiary structure. Secondary structures, such as the stem -and-loop, have been suggested to be important in the recognition of specific sites on the DNA molecule. To form a stem-loop, there must be an inverted repeat present in the DNA with some non-base paired sequences between the repeats. Such structures have been shown to be important for transposition, and may have other associated functions in sequence recognition. It is more likely that the tertiary structure of DNA primarily determines the binding of various protein factors.

Identification of Stem and Loop Regions

Stem-and-loops may form in double-stranded DNA that can dissociate and form intramolecular base pairs resulting a cruciform structure. Such structures have been implicated in numerous types of signalling events, from transcription initiation to the recognition of origins of replication. Prediction of stem-loop regions can be accomplished by many methods, including dotplots (see Chapter 3, and for an example, Chapter 4). Cruciform structures, or stem-loops, have been shown to be kinetically forbidden in normal negatively supercoiled DNA and thus may not have any biological effect (Courey and Wang, 1983).

DNA Conformation

DNA exists in one of three conformations known as the A, B, or Z forms (see Saenger, 1984 for a comprehensive description of nucleic acid geometry). The biological activity of a particular fragment of DNA may be related to its conformation, as this influences the binding of various DNA binding proteins. B-DNA is the canonical form of DNA usually present in solution. It is a right-handed helix with a wide major groove and narrow minor groove. A-DNA is found primarily in dehydrated DNA, and in base-paired sections of RNA and is also a right-handed helix, but in comparison to B-DNA has a deeper, narrow, minor groove and a broader, shallow, major groove. In the left-handed Z- DNA the minor groove is so narrow as to be almost closed, and the major groove is broad and flat. The conformation that a DNA fragment assumes can be fairly readily determined from the primary sequence of that fragment using a set of rules defined using synthetic oligonucleotides (Peticolas et al., 1988). Simply stated, the rules are: repeats of AA or TT tend to hold a DNA in the B conformation, repeated CG sequences tend to induce B to Z transitions, and GG or CC repeats tend to induce a B to A transition. The transition from the B to Z or from the B to A conformations has been hypothesized to be biologically significant, particularly for the binding of specific DNA binding proteins. The conformation of a DNA molecule also affects the flexibility of that molecule. This flexibility has been suggested to be a major factor in DNAse I cleavage of DNA (Hogan et al., 1989). This has increased importance when considered with the fact that DNAse I hypersensitivity is highly correlated with active transcription (Weisbrod, 1982).

Until recently, sequence specific recognition of nucleic acids by proteins was considered to depend on the formation of hydrogen bonds between the protein and the nucleic acid. In the last decade considerable evidence has accumulated to suggest that intrinsic local conformational variation of the nucleic acid (e.g., bends, curves, or kinks) is important in some kinds of recognition (reviewed by Travers, 1989). Some structural properties of nucleic acid structure that may be important in recognition are the propellor twist (the dihedral angle between the planes of the two bases in a base pair), the width of the major and minor grooves, and bending of the helix axis (see Dickerson et al., 1989, for a comprehensive description of the conformational parameters of nucleic acids). Although the basis of local conformational variation of DNA has not been fully determined, a set of rules useful for predicting the structural variation are in wide use (Calladine, 1982; Dickerson, 1983). In particular the Calladine-Dickerson rules suggest that homopolymeric A or T regions will have a high propellor twist and therefore cause a significant curvature of the helix axis. Predictions of DNA curvature have been successfully used to predict the positions of nucleosomes on DNA (Drew and Calladine, 1986; Kefalas et al., 1988). DNA curvature has also been suggested to be important in promoter recognition, and in the binding of a variety of enzymes and transcription factors to DNA (see Travers, 1989).

SUMMARY: HOW TO APPROACH THE ANALYSIS OF A NEW DNA SEQUENCE

This is our recommendation for DNA analysis (in this order). This plan assumes that genomic sequence is being analyzed. Some steps (such as the first one) can be skipped if a cDNA sequence is being analyzed.

1) Assemble the sequence. It is probably a good idea to use your assembled sequence as a probe in a fast database search (Chapter 3), using a program such as FASTA, in case someone has already sequenced the same region. In general, you will be more likely to find non-identical homologous sequences if you search using a protein sequence as a probe (see below).

2) Check the sequence. Two straightforward means of checking the accuracy of the sequence are to compare the predicted and actual restriction digest patterns, and to use a codon bias analysis to check for possible frameshift errors. In practice the comparison of restriction maps is usually performed concurrently with the sequencing, but a careful look at the map predicted by the final assembled sequence is a good idea.

3) Perform a codon bias analysis to try to locate coding regions. If the codon preference of your system is unknown, methods such as TestCode or correspondence analysis, that do not require this information can be used. If the codon preference is known, you should at least try a codon preference method to see if it gives a clearer result.

4) Use weight matrix or consensus sequence methods to located signals such as promoters, translation initiation regions, RNA processing sites, and terminators in the region of likely coding frames.

5) Try to assemble the coding sequence into a continuous segment. This can be done manually, or with the assistance of a program such as gm (gene modeler). The resulting inferred protein sequence should be analyzed as in Chapter 2 and used as the probe in a rapid database search to try to determine if there are homologous proteins (see Chaptre 3). If a similar sequence is found compare it carefully to your sequence paying particular attention to the possibility of errors in your sequence that result in a truncated product, incorrect choice of intron-exon boundaries, or closely spaced frameshifts that insert non-coding sequence. One way of doing this is to compare the sequence of all six translated reading frames to the homologous sequence by dotplot or hashing (rapid search) methods. If you cannot assemble a continuous sequence, use the most likely coding frames as probes in fast database searches; maybe one will match and allow you to find the rest of the exons based on homology.

6) **Search interesting regions for stem-and-loop structures possibly important in regulation of expression.** In particular, examine the 5' and 3' noncoding regions, and possible introns as well. The analysis can be done visually using dot-matrix methods (see Chapter 3), or using programs designed to find stem-and-loop structures. If you use RNA folding programs, keep in mind that they are very CPU intensive, and can be quite expensive if you are paying for computer time.

2   Protein

Roland Lüthy and David Eisenberg

Today it is generally accepted that the amino acid sequence of a protein determines its three-dimensional structure as well as its function. This means that the amino acid sequence contains much of what we would like to know about a protein, if only we could extract it. The challenge of extracting this information has stimulated many approaches to this "protein folding problem." This chapter describes some of the most commonly used techniques for extracting some of the information contained in a protein sequence. Most methods discussed here are based on assumptions and approximations that are not always valid. Therefore, the results have to be analyzed carefully and accepted only with caution.

PHYSICAL PROPERTIES

Molecular Weight and Amino Acid Composition

Given a protein sequence, the amino acid composition can be determined by counting the number of residues of each type. Then a molecular weight can be calculated by summing the molecular weights of the individual amino acid residues, taking into account the loss of one H_2O molecule per peptide bond. Table 1 lists the molecular weights of the twenty amino acids and water. This approach assumes that the protein has not been covalently modified. Because of extensive glycosylation of some proteins, this approach can significantly underestimate the actual molecular weight.

61

Residue	IUPAC Letter Code		Molecular Weight at pH7	Side chain pKa	ε_M at 280 nm
	1 letter	3 letter			
Alanine	A	ALA	89.09		
Cystiene	C	CYS	121.16	10.28	120[a]
Aspartate	D	ASP	132.10	3.65	
Glutamate	E	GLU	146.13	4.25	
Phenylalanine	F	PHE	165.19		
Glycine	G	GLY	75.07		
Histidine	H	HIS	155.16	6.00	
Isoleucine	I	ILE	131.17		
Lysine	K	LYS	147.19	10.53	
Leucine	L	LEU	131.17		
Methionine	M	MET	149.21		
Asparagine	N	ASN	132.12		
Proline	P	PRO	115.13		
Glutamine	Q	GLN	146.15		
Arginine	R	ARG	175.20	12.48	
Serine	S	SER	105.09		
Threonine	T	THR	119.02		
Valine	V	VAL	117.15		
Tryptophan	W	TRP	204.22		5690
Tyrosine	Y	TYR	181.19	10.07	1280
Water			18.01		
alpha-amino group			8.56		
alpha-carboxyl group			3.56		

Isoelectric Point and Extinction Coefficient

With the pK_a values of Table 1, it is possible to calculate the theoretical charge of a protein at a given pH by summing the charges of the amino acid side chains and of the amino terminus and carboxyl terminus. By performing this calculation over a pH range, one obtains a theoretical titration curve and an isoelectric point (the pH at which the protein has a net charge of zero). This method assumes that all normally titratable groups are accessible to water, and that all side chains have the intrinsic pK_a values listed in Table 1. This

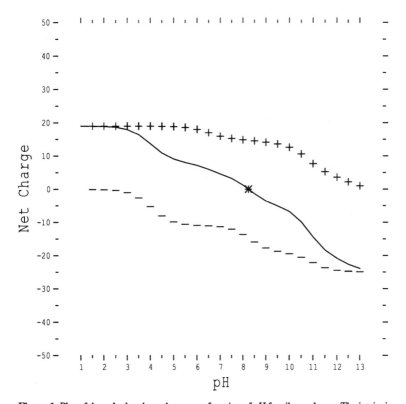

Figure 1: Plot of the calculated net charge as a function of pH for ribonuclease. The intrinsic pK values in Table 1 were used to calculate the total number of positive charges, shown by ++++, and the total number of negative charges, shown by - - -. The line is the net charge, the sum of total negative and total positive charges. The calculated isoelectric point, indicated by *, is 8.2. The observed isoelectric point is 9.6 (Lehninger, 1977).

Table 1: (See page 62) Amino acid properties and IUPAC codes. In addition, the one letter code B (Asx) is used to mean either aspartate or asparagine, and Z (Glx) to mean either glutamate or glutamine. X is generally used to indicate any amino acid residue. "a" absorbance is for cystine, and is due to the disulfide.

assumption is not completely correct, and consequently, the theoretical isoelectric point may differ from the experimentally determined value. Figure 1 shows the calculated titration curve for pancreatic ribonuclease: the calculated isoelectric point is 8.2, whereas the measured value is 9.6 (Lehninger, 1977).

The calculation of extinction coefficients (Gill and von Hippel, 1989) is performed in much the same way as that of the isoelectric point. Individual residues are treated as if they are free amino acids, and the overall extinction coefficient is calculated as the sum of the extinction coefficients of the residues. The same basic assumption is made: Residues are assumed to be in typical environments and not to show unusual absorption due to their local environments. In the case of the extinction coefficient, however, this assumption seems to be generally acceptable; calculated extinction coefficients are typically within a few percent of the experimentally determined value, and errors of more than 15% are rare (Gill and von Hippel, 1989).

STRUCTURAL PROPERTIES

Secondary Structure Prediction

Several methods have been developed to predict the positions of α-helices, β-strands and turns from the amino acid sequence (Chou and Fasman, 1978; Garnier et al., 1978; Lim, 1978; Taylor and Thornton, 1984; Zvelebil, et al., 1987; Qian and Sejnowski, 1988; Kneller et al., 1990). Some methods are based on physical properties of amino acids (Lim, 1974), others on statistics of amino acid distributions in secondary structures as determined by X-ray crystallography (Chou and Fasman, 1978; Garnier et al., 1978). Still others are based on sequence patterns typical of the various types of secondary structure segments (Cohen et al., 1986). Some newer prediction methods use neural nets (Qian and Sejnowski, 1988; Holley and Karplus, 1989) and other artificial intelligence approaches (Kneller et al., 1990).

Unfortunately, the predictions made by any of these methods are only correct for approximately 55-65% of all residues. While this level of success shows that some of the principles of secondary structure formation are understood, it is usually not high enough to serve as a guide to further conjecture about the three-dimensional structure of the protein. The accuracy of the prediction can be enhanced by using an alignment of several homologous sequences and combinations of different methods (Zvelebil et al., 1987; Crawford et al., 1987). In some special cases, when the protein is known to contain exclusively α-helices or β-strands, the prediction is more accurate for these secondary structure elements (Taylor and Thornton, 1984). However, in general one must be cautious in interpreting the results of any secondary structure prediction program.

Nevertheless, predictions may sometimes be used in recognizing structural

```
      1                                                                   70
Seq1  VKETAAAKFERQHMDSSTSAASSSNYCNQMMKSRNLTKDRCKPVNTFVHESLADVQAVCSQKNVACKNGQ
Seq2  VSESSAKKFERQHMDSRGSPSTNPNYCNEMMKSRNMTQGRCKPVNTFVHEPLADVQAVCFQKNVLCKNGQ
Seq3  VAESSAMKFQRQHMDPEGSPSNSSNYCNVMMIRRNMTQGRCKPVNTFVHESLADVQAVCFQKNVLCKNGQ
Seq4  .KETPAEKFQRQHMDTEHSTASSSNYCNLMMKARDMTSGRCKPLNTFIHEPKSVVDAVCHQENVTCKNGR


CF_1  .HHHHHHHHHHHHHHTTTT..TTTTTTTHHHHHH...TTTT..BBBBBB.....BBBBBHHHHHH.TTTB
CF_2  ..TTHHHHHHHHHHHTTT.TTTTTTTT.HHHHHHHHHHTTT..BBBBBHHHHHHBBBBBBBBBBBBTTTB
CF_3  .HHHHHHHHHHHHHHTTT.TTTTTTTT.HHHHHHHHHHTTT..BBBBBB.....BBBBBBBBBBBTTTB
CF_4  ..HHHHHHHHHHHHHHHHHHHHHTTTTT.HHHHHHHHHTTTT..BBBBB..TTTBBBBBBB......TTTT


GOR1  .HHHHHHHHHHHH.......TTTTTTTBBBBBTTTTTTTTT.TT..HHHHHHHHHHHHHHTTTTTTTTTT
GOR2  .HHHHHHHHHHHTTTTTT.....TTTHHHHHHHHTTTTTT.TTBBBB..HHHHHHHHHHHTTTTTTTTT
GOR3  .HHHHHHHHHH.........TTTTTTTBBBBBBTTTTTTTT....HHHHHHHHHHHHHHTTTTTTTTTT
GOR4  ....HHHHHHHH.......TTTTTTTTTHHHHHHHHHHTTTTT...BBBB..TTTHHHHHHHHHHTTTTTTTTT


DSSP  ....HHHHHHHH..TT......TTHHHHHHHHTTTT......BBBBB...HHHHHHHHH.BBB..TT..
```

```
      71                                                       125
Seq1  TNCYQSYSTMSITDCRETGSSKYPNCAYKTTQANKHIIVACEGNPYVPVHFDASV
Seq2  TNCYQSNSNMHITDCRVTSNSDYPNCSYRTSQEEKSIVVACEGNPYVPVHFDASV
Seq3  TNCYQSYSRMRITDCRVTSSSKFPNCSYRMSQAQKSIIVACEGDPYVPVHFDASV
Seq4  TNCYKSNSRLSITNCRQTGASKYPNCQYETSNLNKQIIVACEGQ.YVPVHFDAYV


CF_1  BBBBBTTT.....TT..TTTTTTTTBBBBBBBBBBBBBBBBBTT..BBBBBB....
CF_2  BBBBBTTTTBBBBBBBBBBTTTTTTTTTT..HHHHHBBBBBTT..BBBBBB....
CF_3  BBBBBTTTBBBBBBBBBBBTTTT.TTTTTHHHHHHHBBBBBTT..BBBBBB....
CF_4  TTTTTTTTTBBBBBBBB.TTTTTTTTT....TT...BBBBBBTT..BBBBBBBBBB


GOR1  TTTTTTTTTBBBBBBTTTTTTT.TTT.HHHHHHHBBBBBBTT.TTBBBBBBB..
GOR2  TTTTTTTTTTTTBBBBBBTTTTT.TTTTT....TT.BBBBBBTT.TTBBBBBBB..
GOR3  TTTTTTTTTTTBBBBBBBTTTTT.TTTTTTTTTTTTTBBBBBBTT.TTBBBBBBB..
GOR4  TTTTTTTTTTTTTTTTTTTTTT.TTBBBBTTTTTTBBBBBBTT..TBBBBBBBBB


DSSP  ..BBB....BBBBBBBB.TT.BTTB..BBBBBBBB.BBBBBBTTTTBBBBBBBB.
```

Figure 2: Chou-Fasman and Garnier-Osguthorpe-Robson secondary structure prediction for four ribonuclease sequences. These two secondary structure prediction methods were applied to four ribonuclease sequences. The pairwise alignments have about 70% identical residues among each other; overall, 70 of the 124 residues are conserved in all four sequences. The sequences used were: Seq 1 = bovine pancreatic ribonuclease; Seq 2 = nutria pancreatic ribonuclease; Seq 3 = guinea pig pancreatic ribonuclease; Seq 4 = kangaroo pancreatic ribonuclease. CF 1 to 4 are the Chou-Fasman predictions, GOR 1 to 4 the Garnier-Osguthorpe-Robson predictions. H = helix, B = strands, T = turn, . = other. The last line, labeled DSSP, shows the actual secondary structure extracted from the Brookhaven coordinate database entry for bovine pancreatic ribonuclease (PDB-code 5RSA, Wlodawer et al., 1982) using the program DSSP (Kabsch and Sander, 1983).

elements if one uses an alignment of several homologous sequences and more than one prediction method and combines the predictions (Zvelebil et al., 1987; Crawford, et al., 1987). Figure 2 shows an example of secondary structure prediction for four homologous pancreatic ribonuclease sequences using the methods of Chou and Fasman (Chou and Fasman, 1978) and Garnier, Osguthorpe, and Robson (Garnier et al., 1978). The sequences used were the bovine, nutria, guinea pig and kangaroo pancreatic ribonuclease.

Each of the six sequence pairs share approximately 70% identical residues; overall, 70 of the 124 residues are identical in all four sequences. In Figure 2 the lines starting with CF are the Chou-Fasman predictions; lines labelled GOR are the Garnier-Osguthorpe-Robson predictions. The actual secondary structure of bovine pancreatic ribonuclease (PDB-code 5RSA, Wlodawer et al., 1982), as extracted by the program DSSP (Kabsch and Sander, 1983), is given in the line labelled DSSP. There are two regions that are correctly predicted by both methods and for all sequences: the first α-helix and the last two β-strands with the turn in-between. For the rest of the sequence, there is little agreement between the different predictions.

The Chou-Fasman method is based on observed propensities of amino acid residues to take up α, β or turn conformations. The preferences of the twenty amino acids are expressed in three sets of parameters: the first set gives the preference of each residue to occur in an α-helix, the second set gives the preference for β-strands, and the third set gives the preference for each residue to be in a turn. Helix and strand structures are predicted by first searching for nucleating regions, and then extending the nucleated structure until a region unlikely (probability less than 1.0) to fold into the structure is found. For α-helices, the nucleating condition requires that four out of six residues have a high α-helical propensity (i.e., greater than 1.03). For β-strands the nucleating condition requires that three out of five residues have a high β-strand propensity (i.e., greater than 1.00). After nucleation, the predicted α-helical and β-strand structures are extended until a tetrapeptide with average α-helical or β-strand propensity less than 1.00 is encountered. Any segment that is at least six residues long, has an average α-helical propensity above 1.03, and has an average α-helical propensity greater than the average β-strand propensity is predicted to be an α-helix. Any segment with an average β-strand propensity over 1.05 and an average β-strand propensity greater than α-helical propensity is predicted to be β-strand.

An ambiguity in the Chou and Fasman procedure arises when a segment has high propensities for both α-helix and β-strand, or in other words, the structural predictions overlap. The general rule is that whichever structural propensity is higher, α-helical or β-strand, is the structure that should be predicted. However, various extenuating circumstances should be considered. For instance, a short segment with a high propensity for one structure is not generally allowed to disrupt a longer segment with a high propensity for another when the short segment is contained entirely within the longer one. Moreover, the environment of the overlapping region must be considered. If the overlapping region is adjacent to a turn followed by a predicted β-strand, the prediction of β-strand is favored for the overlapping region (in order to form a β-strand sheet).

In the Chou and Fasman method, turns are considered to be tetrapeptides in which the direction of the polypeptide chain reverses by about 180°. Prediction of turn regions is slightly more complicated than that of α-helical or β-strand structures because residues have a distinct preference for particular positions within the turn. For this reason, the turn propensities are tabulated for each of the four positions within a turn. The average turn propensity is the average of these position-specific propensities for a specific tetrapeptide, and the turn probability is the product of the four values. A turn is predicted where the average turn propensity is greater than the average α-helical or β-strand propensities, and the turn probability is greater than 7.5×10^{-3}.

The Garnier-Osguthorpe-Robson (GOR) method uses position-specific probabilities reminiscent of those used in the Chou and Fasman turn prediction. For each of four predicted secondary structures, α-helix, β-strand, turn, and coil, the probability of observing the structure is calculated based on the residues observed in the eight positions immediately before and after the position being predicted. The position of a residue within this 17 residue window (-8 to +8) is extremely important. For instance, the presence of a phenylalanine residue at position -5 is conducive to turn structure and opposes β-strand structure, whereas a phenylalanine at position 0 has precisely the opposite effect. These position-specific scores are referred to as directional information values, and the tendency of a residue to fold into a given structure is simply the sum of the 17 directional information values for the residues around the position. Whichever structure has the highest tendency is the structure predicted at each position. Additional factors, known as decision constants, are added to bias the prediction when some information about the actual structure is available, for instance, from circular dichroism measurements. Although the results of a GOR prediction do not suffer from the ambiguity inherent in the Chou and Fasman method, the results should still be carefully inspected and "impossible" structures such as α-helices shorter than four residues or β–strands less than two residues eliminated.

Hydrophobicity Patterns

An important property of amino acid side chains is their hydrophobicity (hydropathicity) or hydrophilicity (hydrophobic = fears water; hydropathic = hates water; hydrophilic = likes water). Table 2 shows the three different scales of hydrophobicities used for the examples in Figures 3 and 4. Many other such hydrophobicity scales have been proposed (Rose et al., 1985; Cornette et al., 1987). In the hydrophobicity scales, positive numbers are assigned to the amino acids with apolar (hydrophobic) side chains and negative numbers to those with polar (hydrophilic) side chains. By convention, the signs are reversed for hydrophilicity scales. The values in the various scales differ because of the different experimental methods used to measure hydrophobicity. Perhaps the most direct method is that of Fauchere and Pliska (1983), who measured the free energy of transfer of side chain analogs from 1-octanol to water. In contrast, the hydrophilicity scale of Hopp and Woods is based on the measured free energy of transfer from water to ethanol of the amino acids (Levitt, 1976).

68   PROTEIN

Amino acid side-chain	Fauchere and Pliska ΔG^1	Kyte and Doolittle hydropathy index[2]	Hoop and Woods hydrophilicity[3]	Eisenberg et al. norm. consensus hydrophobicity[4]
R	-1.37	-4.50	3.00	-2.53
K	-1.35	-3.90	3.00	-1.50
D	-1.05	-3.50	3.00	-0.90
Q	-0.78	-3.50	0.20	-0.85
N	-0.85	-3.50	0.20	-0.78
E	-0.87	-3.50	3.00	-0.74
H	-0.40	-3.20	-0.50	-0.40
S	-0.18	-0.80	0.30	-0.18
T	-0.05	-0.70	-0.40	-0.05
P	0.12	-1.60	0.00	0.12
Y	0.26	-1.30	-2.30	0.26
C	0.29	2.50	-1.00	0.29
G	0.48	-0.40	0.00	0.48
A	0.62	1.80	-0.50	0.62
M	0.64	1.90	-1.30	0.64
W	0.81	-0.90	-3.40	0.81
L	1.06	3.80	-1.80	1.06
V	1.08	4.20	-1.50	1.08
F	1.19	2.80	-2.50	1.19
I	1.38	4.50	-1.80	1.38

Table 2: Hydrophobicity/hydrophilicity values of amino acids. Values calculated from [1] Fauchere and Pliska, 1983; [2] Kyte and Doolittle, 1982; [3] Hopp and Woods, 1981; and [4] Eisenberg et al., 1984a.

Residues forming the core of globular proteins have a moderately high hydrophobicity. In water-soluble proteins, the hydrophilic residues tend to be exposed on the surface of the protein. In membrane proteins the side chains in contact with lipid are hydrophobic and, on the average, even more hydrophobic than the interior residues of globular proteins (Rees et al., 1989).

Sometimes the pattern of hydrophobic/hydrophilic residues in a protein sequence can reveal aspects of protein structure. The following are examples of three frequently used methods and one newer method that exploit these patterns.

Membrane spanning segments (Argos et al., 1982; Kyte and Doolittle, 1982; Segrest and Feldman, 1974). The most common methods for locating transmembrane segments calculate the hydrophobicity of the residues as a function of their position in the sequence. To smooth the plot, the actual hydrophobicity $(H)_i$ assigned to each position is the average of the hydrophobicity of the residue at that position and those of the preceding and following

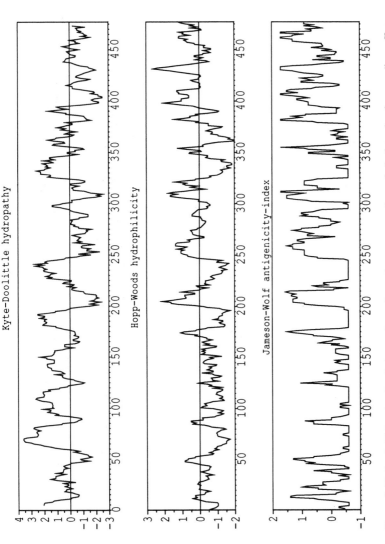

Figure 3: Hydrophobicity plots for the human beta adrenergic receptor. a. shows the hydropathy plot according to Kyte-Doolittle (1982) using the hydropathy index values from Table 2 and a window size of 19 residues. b. is the hydrophilicity of Hopp and Woods (1981). The hydrophilicity values used were those from Table 2 and the window size was 7 residues. c. plots the Jameson-Wolf antigenicity index (Jameson and Wolf, 1988).

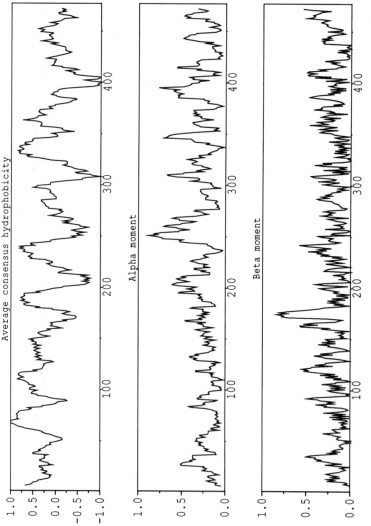

Figure 4: Hydrophobic moments for the human beta adrenergic receptor. The top panel shows the hydrophobicity plot using the normalized consensus hydrophobicity values from Table 2 and a window size of 11 residues. The middle panel plots the hydrophobic moment for alpha helices of length 11. The third panel is the hydrophobic moment for beta strands.

residues, as described by the following equation:

$$\langle H \rangle_i = \frac{\sum_{n=i-k}^{i+k} H_n}{2k+1} \qquad (1)$$

The size of the "window" $2k+1$ may be varied. To detect membrane spanning helices, the window is often taken to be 19 ($k=9$) or 21 ($k=10$) residues. The reason is that a helix consisting of 20 amino acids has approximately the length to span the apolar center of a membrane. This apolar center is approximately 30Å in a typical membrane (Engelman et al., 1986). An ideal helix with 20 amino acids would be about 31Å long (20 residues x 1.54 Å/residue). For membrane-spanning β-strands, the window length might be taken as 7 or 9. This value is based on the fact that a fully extended β-strand extends 3.5 Å/residue (8 residues x 3.5 Å/residue = 28 Å). These window sizes, where the window has the same size as the feature one hopes to detect, will produce a single "spike" for each potential transmembrane region. It may be easier to interpret plots where the window size is about half the size of the feature of interest, e.g., 10 or 4 for transmembrane helices or strands, respectively. Under these conditions, a possible transmembrane region will produce a peak that reaches a plateau half as wide as the feature before declining.

A hydrophobicity plot of the human beta adrenergic receptor is shown in the first panel of Figure 3a, using a window size of 19. On the basis of such an analysis, this protein is thought to have 7 membrane spanning helices (O'Dowd et al., 1989).

The problem with the prediction of transmembrane helices by such a moving-window hydrophobicity plot is that the core of globular, water-soluble proteins is also apolar. What is the difference between a sequence segment which is apolar because it traverses the hydrophobic core of a globular protein and a segment that forms a transmembrane helix? Eisenberg et al. (1984a) addressed this problem and suggested possible values of the mean hydrophobicity that can distinguish these two kinds of segments. In general, transmembrane helices are longer and more hydrophobic than interior helices of globular proteins (Eisenberg et al., 1984a; Rees et al., 1989).

Prediction of possible antigenic region (Hopp and Woods, 1981; Jameson and Wolf, 1988). X-ray crystallographic studies of the structures of complexes of antibodies with proteins show that antigenic surfaces are a contiguous three-dimensional patch on the protein surface formed by two or more sequence segments (Davies et al., 1988). Moreover, the antigenic regions seem to be well correlated with the surface accessibility of sequence H_n is the segments. Since hydrophilic residues tend to lie on the surface of proteins, one might expect a correlation between antigenicity and high values of amino acid side chain hydrophilicity. Thus one method to predict possible antigenic segments (Hopp and Woods, 1981) plots the hydrophilicity as a function of the sequence. The values are again averaged over a window, to provide a smoother plot. The regions with high hydrophilicity are inferred to be on the surface of the protein and therefore accessible to antibodies.

Figure 3b shows a hydrophilicity plot, with a window size of 7, of the human beta adrenergic receptor. The minima in the hydrophobicity plot (Figure 3a) correspond to the maxima in the hydrophilicity plot.

Another method of predicting antigenic determinants was proposed by Jameson and Wolf (1988). This method employs a linear combination of hydrophilicity, predicted side chain flexibility (Karplus and Schulz, 1985), surface probability (Emini et al., 1985), Chou-Fasman turn prediction and Garnier-Osguthorpe-Robson turn prediction. This linear combination is termed the antigenicity index. Figure 3a shows the antigenicity index plot of the human beta adrenergic receptor. The peaks in the antigenicity index plot correlate well to the peaks in the hydrophilicity plot (Figure 3b) and also to the valleys in the hydrophobicity plots (Figure 3a).

Amphiphilicity and hydrophobic moment (Eisenberg et al., 1982; Eisenberg et al., 1984a; Eisenberg et al., 1984b). The amino acid side chains of proteins are frequently arranged in a very asymmetric pattern, with the polar side chains extending out into the solvent, and the apolar side chains buried in the core of the protein. This asymmetry is called amphiphilicity or amphipathicity. Amphiphilicity has long been known to be an important factor in protein structure, and in α helices is readily depicted by graphical techniques such as the helical wheel (Schiffer and Edmundson, 1967) and the helical net method (Lim, 1978). A helical wheel plot shows the amino acid residues arranged as if one were looking down the helix (Figure 5). An amphiphilic helix will have most of the hydrophobic residues arranged on one side of the plot. The helical net plot shows the position of the amino acid residues as if the α-helix was a cylinder that was cut open and unfolded (Figure 6). In this case the hydrophobic residues of an amphiphilic helix form a vertical stripe in the plot.

The hydrophobic moment quantitatively describes asymmetry of residue hydrophobicities and is useful for detecting both amphiphilic α-helices and β-strands. For example, an α-helix having apolar side chains on one side and polar and charged side chains on the other side (see Figure 5) has a large hydrophobic moment. To calculate the hydrophobic moment at a sequence position, one again looks at a window around that position and assumes that the segment in the window has a regular secondary structure, folded as either an α-helix or β-strand. Another assumption is that the side chains protrude perpendicularly to the axis of the segment. The hydrophobic moment at position i is then calculated as

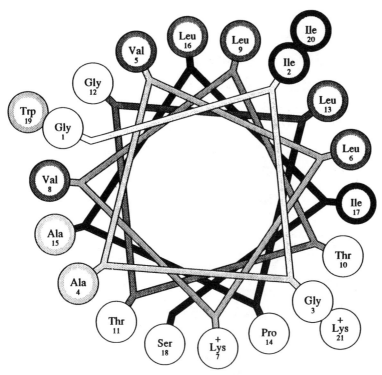

Figure 5: Helical wheel for melittin. The residues 1 to 21 of melittin are drawn as an idealized α-helix showing the amphipatic character of that helix. Hydrophobic residues are shaded according to their hydrophobicity. The average hydrophobicity of this peptide is 0.52 and the hydrophobic moment is 0.42. The figure was computed with a program provided by J. Segrest (Segrest et al., 1990).

$$\mu_{H_i} = \{[\sum_{n=i-k}^{i+k} H_n \sin(\delta n)]^2 + [\sum_{n=i-k}^{i+k} H_n \cos(\delta n)]^2\}^{1/2} \qquad (2)$$

hydrophobicity of residue n. The values of the hydrophobicities are normalized in such a way that the mean value of the 20 amino acids is 0 and the standard deviation is 1. ∂ is the angle between successive side chains viewed down the central axis of the assumed structure. For an α-helix, ∂ is 100°; for a β-strand, ∂ is about 160°.

Two physical interpretations can be given for Equation 2 (Eisenberg et al., 1984b). The first is that μ_H is the vector sum of the hydrophobicities of the sidechains of the protein segment, taking due regard of their directions. The second interpretation is that μ_H is the Fourier transform of the hydrophobicity function of the amino acid sequence. In this second interpretation, ∂ is regarded as a continuous variable, and $\mu_H(\partial)$ is regarded as the magnitude of the Fourier component of the hydrophobicity having frequency ∂. Thus $\mu_H(\partial)$ is large when the hydrophobicity is periodic at frequency ∂.

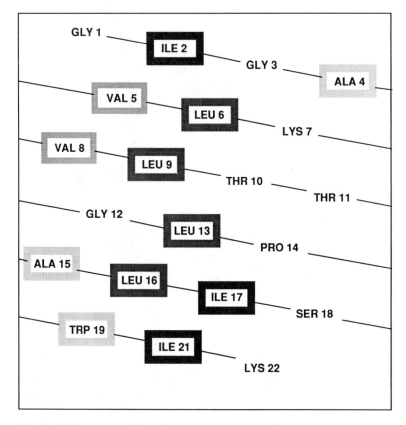

Figure 6: Helical net for melittin. The residues 1 to 21 of melittin are drawn in a helical net diagram. The helical net plot shows the position of the amino acid residues as if the α-helix were a cylinder that was cut open and unfolded. Hydrophobic residues are shaded according to their hydrophobicities.

The hydrophobic properties of an α-helix can be classified on a hydrophobic moment plot (Eisenberg et al., 1984a), an example of which is given in Figure 7. The horizontal coordinate represents the average hydrophobicity $(H)_i$ of the residues in the helix, using the normalized consensus scale from Table 2. The vertical coordinate registers the magnitude of the hydrophobic moment per residue. The curved boundary shows the largest moment per residue that any α-helix can have for a given average hydrophobicity. The curve intersects the horizontal axis at a value of 1.38, the average hydrophobicity of a hypothetical poly-isoleucine α-helix. Other points on the curve represent hypothetical helices consisting of isoleucine and arginine, isoleucine being on this scale the most hydrophobic residue and arginine the least hydrophobic residue. In general, hydrophobic helices plot toward the right; amphiphilic helices plot toward the top.

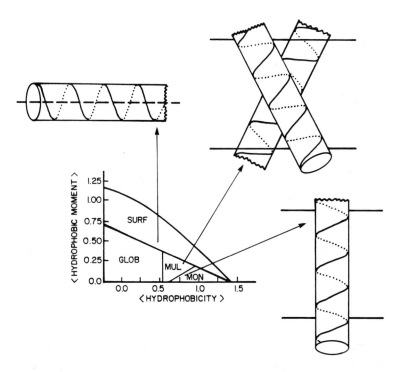

Figure 7: The hydrophobic moment plot. Each point on the plot represents the hydrophobic properties of an α-helix. The horizontal axis gives the average hydrophobicity of the helix, and the vertical axis gives the hydrophobic moment per residue. Helices that are characterized by the surface (SURF) region tend to be amphiphilic and to align themselves parallel to the boundary between a polar and an apolar phase. Helices that are highly hydrophobic, but have a small hydrophobic moment (MON region) tend to be immersed in an apolar phase (membrane interior) and are evenly hydrophobic around the helix. Helices that have somewhat larger hydrophobic moments may tend to form multimeric bundles with their hydrophilic faces together (MUL region). An 11-residue window is used to calculate average hydrophobicity (Equation 1) and hydrophobic moment (Equation 2) with the normalized consensus hydrophobicity scale in Table 2. (Reprinted from Eisenberg et al., 1989, *Prediction of Protein Structure and the Priciples of Protein Conformation*, Plenum Press, p. 640, Fig. 2)

Helices of different types tend to cluster in different regions of the hydrophobic moment plot. Helices from globular proteins tend to plot in the region of Figure 7 labeled GLOB, whereas probable transmembrane helices tend to plot in the two triangular regions at the lower right, labeled MUL for multimeric and MON for monomeric. The α-helix of the lytic protein melittin (Figure 5) and other membrane disrupting or membrane fusing peptides plot in the region labeled SURF.

Stroud et al. (Finer-Moore et al., 1989) carry the analysis one step further and plot the Fourier transform of the hydrophobicity as a function of

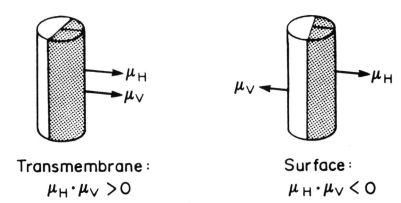

Transcription of figure labels:

Transmembrane :
$$\mu_H \cdot \mu_V > 0$$

Surface :
$$\mu_H \cdot \mu_V < 0$$

Figure 8: Cylindrical model for α-helices. The cylinders are split in half, perpendicular to the hydrophobic moment μ_H. One half is more hydrophobic than the other half. For transmembrane helices the variation moment μ_V points approximately in the same direction as the hydrophobic moment. For surface helices in globular proteins, the directions of the two moments are opposed.

sequence position. This corresponds to calculating the hydrophobic moment for all angles between 0° and 180°. Maxima around 100° indicate possible amphiphilic α-helices, and maxima around 160°, amphiphilic β-strands.

Mean hydrophobicity of helix faces (Rees et al., 1989b). If we model a helix as a cylinder (Figure 8), we can determine from the amino acid sequence which side of the cylinder is more hydrophobic by splitting the helix in two parts perpendicular to the hydrophobic moment. Then we can calculate the mean hydrophobicity of each half side of the helix. This was done systematically for helices from globular and membrane proteins by Rees et al. (1989b). For α-helices on the surface of globular proteins, the face towards the solvent is considerably more polar than the face toward the interior of the protein. However, for the α-helices in the transmembrane regions of membrane proteins, the reverse is true: the more hydrophobic face extends toward the lipid of the membrane. The same result can be expressed with the hydrophobic moments (Figure 8): the hydrophobic moments of helices in membrane proteins tend to point outwards; the hydrophobic moments of the helices on the surface of globular proteins tend to point inwards.

There is an interesting point concerning the mean hydrophobicity of the inside faces of surface helices of globular proteins and transmembrane helices: the mean hydrophobicities of the inside faces are approximately the same. This suggests that the interiors of globular and transmembrane proteins are similar in their hydrophobic character.

Detection of the Outside Face of Helices with the Variation Moment

In the preceding section, we noted that the side of a helix that is exposed to the solvent can be indicated by the hydrophobic moment. This direction can also be indicated by the variation moment (Rees et al., 1989a). The variation moment is based on the observation that the residues on protein surfaces are more mutable than those in the interior (Smith, 1967; Chothia and Lesk, 1986; Reidhaar-Olson and Sauer, 1988). The variation moment points toward the side of a helix that experiences more replacements of residues over the course of evolutionary time.

To determine the direction of the variation moment μ_V, one needs a set of aligned sequences of a family of proteins (see Figure 9). On a line below the alignment, one writes the number of non-identical residues found at each

```
MLAAYMFLLIMLGFPINFLTLYV    Rhodopsin - Bovine
LQAAFMGTVFLIGFPLNAMVLVA    Blue-sensitive opsin - Human
LTSVWMIFVVTASVFTNGLVLAA    Red-sensitive opsin - Human
LTSVWMIFVVIASVFTNGLVLAA    Green-sensitive opsin - Human
MLAAYMFLLIVLGFPINFLTLYV    Opsin         Mouse
ILTAYMIMIGMISWCGNGVVIYI    Rhodopsin     Fruit fly
ILGLFTLAIMIISCCGNGVVVYI    Opsin 2       Fruit fly
GMGIVMSLIVLAIVFGNVLVITA    Beta-2-       Human
GMAILMSVIVLAIVFGNVLVITA    adrenergic    Mouse
GMSLLMALVVLLIVAGNVLVIAA    receptor      Turkey
FIGITTGLLSLATVTGNLLVLIS    Muscarinic    M1 - Human
FIATVTGSLSLVTVVGNILVMLS    acetylcholine M4 - Rat
FIVLVAGSLSLVTIIGNILVMVS    receptor      M2 - Pig
WPALSIVVIIMTIGGNILVIMA     Serotonin receptor   Rat
LWTAAYLALVLVAVMGNATVIWI    Substance K receptor; Bovine
IVHWVIMSISPVGFVENGILLWF    Transforming protein (mas); Human


6876958736655596165 3495   Number of Amino acids
                           (Variability)
```

Figure 9: Alignment of helices to calculate variation moment. The segment corresponds to the first predicted transmembrane helix of the human beta adrenergic receptor. Segments from known homologous proteins have been aligned to this segment (O'Dowd et al., 1989). The variation moment for this alignment is 2.4 (Rees et al., 1989b).

position of the aligned sequences. This number is sometimes called the variability V. Then one looks for a helical periodicity in the values of V along the sequences. The relationship for doing this is recommended by (Rees et al., 1989b):

$$\mu_{V_i} = \{[\sum_{n=i-k}^{i+k} (V_n - <V>)\sin(\delta n)]^2 + [\sum_{n=i-k}^{i+k} (V_n - <V>)\cos(\delta n)]^2\}^{1/2} \quad (3)$$

In which V_n is the number of different residues occurring at position n; V_i is the average number of residues occurring in the entire sequence; and ∂ is $100°$ for α-helices and about $160°$ for β-strands.

For helices on the surface of globular proteins, the variation moment is expected to point outward. This is essentially opposite to the direction of the hydrophobic moment (Figure 8). For transmembrane helices, Rees et al. (1989b) found that the variation moment also points outwards, toward the lipid. Thus, for transmembrane helices, the variation moment and the hydrophobic moment tend to be in the same direction (Figure 8). The observation that the more variable surface is outwards in both globular and membrane helices is consistent with the idea that residues are more readily replaced if they do not participate in protein-protein interactions.

Detection of Motifs

It is sometimes possible to detect in a new protein sequence a *motif* which has been previously identified in other proteins. The presence of such motifs can indicate similar function or similar three-dimensional structure. These motifs can be defined in three ways: (1) by an amino acid pattern which recognizes proteins containing the motif; (2) by an alignment of several sequences containing the motif; or (3) by a single sequence. One can compare the new protein sequence to the motif to find out whether the sequence contains the motif or not. There are several computer programs available to perform the comparison.

A pattern is a way to describe which string of amino acid codes is sufficient to identify the motif. For example, a pattern can be defined in the form C-X_5-[L,I,M]-C where the IUPAC one letter codes are used to represent amino acids, X_5 means any residue is allowed 5 times; [L,I,M] means any of L, I or M, but no other. This method is used for PROSITE, a pattern database, which currently contains 338 patterns (Bairoch, 1989). These patterns recognize functional motifs. On the level of secondary structure, Cohen et al. (1986) defined patterns for turns, α-helices and β-strands and used them to predict secondary structures. There are programs available that match patterns against a protein sequence and decide whether it contains the motif represented by the pattern.

A major problem in this approach is the specificity of the pattern: if the pattern is too short or too vague, then many "false positives" will be found. For example, a pattern consisting of three amino acids is usually not specific enough because the probability of finding unrelated tripeptides is considerable. This can be verified by a simple experiment: Define a tripeptide as the pattern and find all proteins that contain this tripeptide. There will be many, and not all will have similar functions. The same is true for peptides of length four and five. On the other hand, if the motif is too specific, then it will miss many proteins that are closely related. For example, take a pattern consisting of 30 amino acids and search for all identical sequences. You will miss all sequences that have "only" 29 residues identical to the pattern. Before relying on a pattern, it has to be compared with the current protein database. The pattern should distinguish proteins that are known to contain the motif from those proteins that are known not to contain the motif.

When the motif is defined by an alignment of sequences, then the method of choice is the profile method (Gribskov et al., 1987; Gribskov et al., 1989). This method converts the alignment to a table, called a profile, and then uses the dynamic programming algorithm (Smith and Waterman, 1981; see Chapter 3, Dynamic Programming Methods) to find the best alignment of the profile and the sequence. Figure 10 shows the alignment procedure for a simplified profile. In the example below, we align the sequence "PROTEIN" to the profile computed from the motif "PROFILE." Notice that both the target sequence and the motif contain the nonstandard amino acid symbol O.

The table on the left of Figure 10 is the profile. The motif is written vertically down the left of the profile. Each line in the profile consists of a value that reflects the likelihood of every residue to occur at that position. In this simplified example, only the 9 amino acid symbols F, E, I, L, N, O, P, R and T are used. In any real example, the 20 amino acids would all be assigned likelihoods. The last two columns of the profile are the penalties for creating a gap or extending a gap at that position.

To align the profile of the motif "P R O F I L E" with a sequence ("P R O T E I N" in this example) a score matrix, S_{ij}, has to be calculated with its elements defined as follows:

$S_{0j} = S_{i0} = 0$; and for $i > 0$ and $j > 0$
S_{ij} is the largest of:

$S_{i-1,j-1}$ + Profile(i, Amino Acid(j));	(Diagonal step)
$S_{i-1,j}$ - Gap Penalty(i,j);	(Vertical step)
$S_{i,j-1}$ - Gap Penalty(i,j);	(Horizontal step)

Profile(i, Amino Acid(j)) is the score for the amino acid at position j of the sequence at row i of the profile. The gap penalty comes from the second to last column if a gap is opened at that position. A gap is opened if $S_{i-1,j}$ or

	F	E	I	L	N	O	P	R	T	Gap Len	
P	0	0	0	0	0	-1	5	-2	0	3	1
R	0	0	0	0	0	-2	5	5	0	3	1
O	0	0	0	0	5	-1	0	0	0	3	1
F	5	2	0	0	0	0	0	-3	0	3	1
I	0	-2	5	0	0	0	0	0	0	3	1
L	0	0	0	5	3	0	0	0	0	3	1
E	0	5	-2	0	0	0	0	0	0	3	1

$S_{i,j-1}$ was reached in a diagonal step. If $S_{i-1,j}$ or $S_{i,j-1}$ was already in a gap, then the penalty subtracted is from the last column of the profile, the penalty for extending a gap. Sequences are aligned with profiles using standard dynamic programming techniques (see Chapter 3).

Figure 10 shows the calculation of the first four elements of the score matrix. The first matrix element to be calculated is the one at the intersection of the P row and the P column. We call that element $S_{P,P}$. The score for the residue P in the P row of the profile is five. The value of the previous diagonal element is zero. Therefore the value for a diagonal step to element $S_{P,P}$ is $0 + 5 = 5$. This 5 is written at the upper left corner of the box at the intersection of the P row and the P column. Next we calculate the score for a vertical step. The value of the element above $S_{P,P}$ is zero and no gap has been opened, therefore the penalty for opening a gap has to be applied. The score for a vertical step to $S_{P,P}$ is $0 - 3 = -3$. This value is written at the upper right corner of the box representing matrix element $S_{P,P}$. In the same way, the score for a horizontal step is calculated to be -3 and written at the lower left corner of the box. Of the three possible values for $S_{P,P}$, the largest is the 5 for the diagonal step, and this value is assigned to be the final value of the matrix element $S_{P,P}$ (large number 5). Next we calculate the next element to the right, called $S_{P,R}$. The score for R in row P of the profile is -2. The value for the diagonal step is $0 + (-2) = -2$. The value for a vertical step is -3. The value for a horizontal step is $5 - 3 = 2$. The highest value for this element is the 2 obtained by the horizontal step, and so, $S_{P,R}$ is assigned a final value of 2. The next element is the one at the intersection of row R and column P, $S_{R,P}$. The score for P in row R of the profile is -2. The value for the diagonal step is $0 + (-2) = -2$. The value for a horizontal step is -3. The value for a vertical step is $5 - 3 = 2$. The highest value is assigned to element $S_{P,R}$ and is the value of 2 obtained by the vertical step. Now we calculate the element at the R,R intersection, $S_{R,R}$: The score in row R and column R of the scoring table is 5. The value of the element diagonally above is also 5. The score for a diagonal step is $5 + 5 = 10$. The score for a vertical step is $2 - 1 = 1$. The penalty is now 1 for extending a gap, because the element above was reached in a nondiagonal step. The score for a horizontal step is also $2 - 1 = 1$. The largest score for reaching element $S_{R,R}$ is 10. Thus 10 is the final value assigned to the $S_{R,R}$ element (large number 10).

The final score matrix is shown on the right in Figure 10 with three small

---

Figure 10 (see previous page): Simplified profile and the alignment procedure. The table on the left represents the profile. Each row in the profile gives the likelihood for each amino acid to occur at that position. The last two columns of the profile are the penalties for opening a gap or extending a gap at that position. The alignment matrix is shown on the right. The three smaller numbers are the temporary values from which the largest one is chosen and assigned to that element in the matrix. The traceback is indicated in by circles and arrows. The best alignment obtained for the simplified profile and the protein is:

```
PROTEIN
||| |
PRO-FIL
```

numbers and one large number in each element. The three smaller numbers are the temporary values for the diagonal, the vertical, and the horizontal steps from which the largest one is assigned to be the element at that position in the score matrix.

When all matrix elements are calculated, one obtains the best local alignment (see Chapter 3) by "tracing back" the path through the matrix. The starting point is the matrix element with the highest value. If this element was obtained by a diagonal step, then the next element considered is the one on the diagonal above and to the left. The two amino acid symbols are assigned the same position in the alignment. If the element was reached by a vertical step, this means a gap was introduced in the protein sequence. The amino acid symbol corresponding to that row of the profile is aligned with a '.' representing the gap. If the matrix element was reached from the left, with a horizontal step, it means a gap was introduced in the profile. Then the symbol for a gap is matched with the amino acid representing that position in the sequence. The traceback for the best alignment starting at $S_{L,N}$ is indicated in Figure 10 with circles and arrows. The best alignment obtained for this simplified profile and the protein is:

```
PROTEIN
| | |    |
PRO-FIL
```

Here the symbol "-" indicates a gap which is introduced by the alignment.

In order to test the effectiveness of any real profile, it must first be compared to each sequence in the protein database. It is completely effective only if it distinguishes the proteins containing the motif from all the other proteins. If the profile is able to separate the sequences containing the motif it represents from the unrelated proteins, then a minimal score for a significant alignment can be determined. Any sequence whose score for comparison to the profile is higher than the minimal score probably contains the motif defined by the original alignment. A library of tested profiles specific for sequence and structural motifs is available (Gribskov et al., 1989).

The following subsections give examples of motifs.

Post-translational Modification Sites

There many possibilities for post-translational modifications to proteins since there are plenty of reactive hydroxyl, amino, sulfhydryl, carboxyl, imidazole, guanidinium and tyrosyl groups present in amino acid side-chains (Yan et al., 1989). There are, however, some frequently observed modifications whose sequence specificity is known.

Glycosylation. Attachment of a sugar to asparagine or serine/threonine residues. It was observed that most glycosylated asparagines are in a tripeptide N-X-[S,T], where X can be any amino acid except proline (Marshall, 1972). But the pattern is not specific enough: not all such tripeptides are glycosylated and therefore the pattern only hints at potential N-glycosylation sites.

Disulfide bonds. Oxidation of two cysteines that make an intramolecular link between two parts of the same protein or an intermolecular link between two proteins.

Proteolytic cleavage. Some proteins are activated by proteolysis. There are many known proteases. Most of them have a preference for the amino acid immediately before or after the cleavage site. Some proteases cut at a specific peptide sequence. For example, chymotrypsin cleaves preferably after one of the big, hydrophobic residues: tyrosine, phenylalanine or tryptophan.

Phosphorylation. The activity of many proteins is modulated by phosphorylation/dephosphorylation cycles. In terms of specificity, there are two kinds of kinases: the tyrosine kinases, which phosphorylate tyrosines, and the serine/threonine kinases, which phosphorylate serine and threonine residues often found in surface turns.

Supersecondary structure: EF-hand, Helix-turn-helix, Dinucleotide Fold, Zinc Finger

Sequence segments have been identified in a variety of proteins that are believed to fulfill the same function and probably have the same three-dimensional structure. These motifs may occur in proteins that have no apparent similarity in the rest of their sequences. The following are four examples:

EF-hand (Kretsinger, 1987). This motif is found in calcium-binding proteins. It consists of a helix (E), a loop and a second helix (F). The calcium is bound by the loop region, and therefore there are negatively charged residues conserved in this region. Kretsinger (1987) describes a sequence alignment that can be used to construct a EF-hand profile (Gribskov et al., 1989).

Helix-turn-helix (Harrison and Aggarwal, 1990). This motif has been observed in many proteins that regulate the transcription of DNA. The motif is approximately 20 residues long and describes two α-helices with a turn in-between. Harrison and Aggarwal (1990) show an alignment of the amino acid sequences of 8 proteins with known three-dimensional structures containing this motif. When used with the profile method, this alignment distinguishes well between DNA-binding proteins and other proteins.

Zinc finger (Berg, 1990). This is another motif found in DNA-binding proteins. It can be described as an amino acid pattern of the form

$$C-X_{2,4}-C-X_{12}-H-X_{3,5}-H$$

The cysteines and histidines are conserved because they coordinate a zinc ion. The motif is usually repeated several times and it is useful to use a program that is capable of finding multiple occurrences of the pattern. The three-dimensional structure of a single zinc finger has been determined and it consists of two β-strands and an α-helix.

Dinucleotide binding fold (Birktoft and Banaszak, 1984). The known structures of NAD (nicotinamide-adenine dinucleotide) and FAD binding enzymes have been analyzed, and it was found that the dinucleotide was bound to a similar structural motif: a four stranded β-sheet and an α-helix. Two β-strands and the helix form the $\beta\alpha\beta$ motif that can be used to detect other dinucleotide binding proteins containing this motif. This can be done by using the profile method.

Folding Domain Motifs

The three-dimensional structures of several hundred proteins are known today. Comparisons of these structures have revealed several commonly occurring folding domains. These folding domains have similar three-dimensional structures, but in several cases the domains have no obvious amino acid sequence similarity. Examples of such domains are $\alpha\beta$-barrels, antiparallel β-barrels and four-helical bundles.

$\alpha\beta$ barrels. The $\alpha\beta$-barrel fold consists of eight consecutive α-helix/β-strand units. The eight β-strands form a cylindrical sheet that is surrounded by the helices. So far, there are 17 distinct proteins known to have this fold (Farber and Petsko, 1990). All of these proteins are enzymes that have the active site residues in the loops at the C-termini of the strands that form the barrel. It has not yet been possible to align the structures and no sequence pattern is known that recognizes all 17 proteins from their sequence.

Antiparallel β-barrels. There is a family of known proteins that bind small hydrophobic molecules (Cowan et al., 1990). These proteins have two four-stranded β-sheets facing each other. The hydrophobic molecules bind between the sheets. Examples are retinol binding protein and insecticyanin. Cowan et al. (1990) shows the alignment of 12 members of this family. This alignment can be used to detect other closely related members.

Four α-helical bundle. In this folding motif, four helices are packed together. The helices are antiparallel in the known examples (Presnell and Cohen, 1989). No amino acid sequence pattern is known that is able to detect the four helical bundle domain.

In short, it has not yet been possible to deduce general amino acid sequence patterns or to calculate profiles for three-dimensional domains. To date, effective patterns or profiles are able to detect other members only when they are clearly homologous. Construction of more general patterns or profiles is the topic of current research.

Sequence Families

Another way to analyze a protein sequence is to search the protein database for proteins having similar sequences. This is currently the best way to learn about the structure and function of a new sequence. A similar sequence may imply homology (common ancestry), and therefore may imply common function. And if the sequence is highly similar (for example, more than 50% identical residues) to a protein whose three-dimensional structure is known, then one can assume that both proteins have a similar three-dimensional structure, and one can try to build a model for the new sequence based on the coordinates of the known three-dimensional structure (Weber, 1990; Schiffer et al., 1990; Sali et al., 1990).

Once two sequences have been aligned, one would like to know whether the three-dimensional structures of the two proteins are similar. You can get an indication of this similarity by comparing the patterns of hydrophobicities along the two sequences. If the two proteins are folded in the same way, you would expect that the corresponding residues of the two proteins have the same attraction or repulsion for water. In practice, a convenient way to make the comparison is to calculate the correlation coefficient of the amino acid hydrophobicities between the two sequences (Sweet and Eisnberg, 1983):

$$r = \frac{\sum_{n}^{i=1} H_{i1}H_{i2}}{\sqrt{\sum_{n}^{i=1} H_{i1}^2 H_{i2}^2}} \qquad (4)$$

where the sums are over the residues in the paired sequences H_{i1} and H_{i2} are the hydrophobicities of the ith residue in sequences 1 and 2, respectively. The best values of H to use in this equation are given by Sweet and Eisenberg (1983).

The correlation coefficient has been suggested as a measure for the similarity of the two three-dimensional structures. For random sequences or unrelated three-dimensional structures, the hydrophobic correlation is close to zero. For proteins with similar three-dimensional structures, the hydrophobic correlation is greater than 0.3 (Sweet and Eisenberg, 1983).

A family of sequences may also be defined by an alignment. An example is the alignment for the protein kinases by Hanks et al.(1988). Using the profile method, it is possible to show whether or not a new sequence belongs to that family.

SUMMARY: WHAT CAN YOU LEARN FROM YOUR NEW PROTEIN SEQUENCE

We recommend the following sequence of analysis for characterization of a new protein sequence:

1. First compare the sequence to itself using dot matrix methods (see Chapter 3). This will reveal internal repeats in the sequence. If internal repeats exist, you should divide the sequence into pieces with each kind of repeat in its own segment.

2. Search the database for similar sequences. Start with FASTA (Pearson and Lipman, 1988). Examine the high scoring sequences, with a particular view to those which potentially would be biologically related. Likely candidates should be further analyzed to determine if the sequence similarity is statistically significant (see Chapter 3). If you do not find any significantly similar sequences, you might try PROFILESEARCH (Gribskov et al., 1989). This method can be more sensitive than FASTA, but is slower. PROFILESEARCH is more powerful when several similar sequences are combined into a profile than when the profile is made from a single sequence.

3. Compare your sequence to known motifs. Use PROFILESCAN for the motifs represented by profiles that have been tested against the protein database (for example, the profile library in Gribskov et al., 1989). Also compare the sequence to motifs that are defined by amino acid sequence patterns (for example, the PROSITE database (Bairoch, 1989)).

4. Search for hydrophobic stretches (possible transmembrane segments) with the Kyte-Doolittle method and amphiphilic α-helices or β-strands using the hydrophobic moment (Eisenberg et al., 1984a). Highly amphiphilic α-helices suggest segments that bind to the surface of a membrane.

5. If you found similar sequences in steps 1 or 2, you can also search for helices using the variation moment (see Mean Hydrophobicity of Helix Faces; Rees et al., 1989b).

6. If you found similar sequences in steps 1 or 2, you can estimate if they are folded in a similar way by calculating the hydrophobic correlation (Sweet and Eisenberg, 1983).

7. Secondary structure predictions: use several prediction methods, combine information from all available homologous sequences, and compare the results. Be cautious about your interpretation of the results, keeping in mind that they are typically only 55 - 65% accurate.

8. If you plan to elicit antibodies against segments of your protein, iden-

tify possible antigenic regions using hydrophilicity plots (Hopp and Woods, 1981) and antigenicity index plots (Jameson and Wolf, 1988).

9. Look for unusual features. For example, many of the DNA binding transcription factors have leucine zippers, regions rich in acidic residues, glutamine or proline.

10. If you plan to do protein chemistry on the protein, determine the potential sites of cleavage by various chemicals [(CNBr (M), NTCB (C), hot acidic conditions (DP), BPS-skatole (W)] and enzymes [(trypsin (K or R), etc.]

3 Similarity and Homology

David J. States and Mark S. Boguski*

Properly approached, molecular sequence data is a rich source of knowledge capable of teaching us much about the structure, function, and evolution of biological macromolecules. To effectively realize this potential, however, some understanding of the process of and theoretical basis for sequence comparison is needed as well as a variety of practical tools to access and manipulate the data. The volume of molecular sequence data has long since surpassed human information processing capacity for even simple tasks such as searching for related sequences, and with the ever increasing rate at which new sequences are being produced, the need for computer-assisted analysis becomes more and more acute. Automated tools can extend human capabilities by orders of magnitude in both speed and accuracy. The educated application of these automated tools is an essential part of modern molecular biology research.

This chapter considers the theory and practice of analyzing sequence similarity as it applies to database searching and sequence alignment. Five major areas will be examined. First, we describe the use of dot matrix plots to elucidate the structures and features relating a sequence pair. Secondly, we discuss optimal pairwise alignment of sequences using dynamic programming algorithms. Thirdly, we examine fast, approximate techniques for detecting local similarities. Fourthly, the uses of and techniques for multiple

---

*Dr. Michael Gribskov wrote portions of the sections on Dynamic Programming Methods and Scoring Systems. The contents of this chapter do not necessarily reflect the views or policies of the Department of Health and Human Services, nor does mention of trade names, commercial products, or organizations imply endorsement by the U.S. government.

sequence alignment are described. Finally, the statistical significance of sequence similarity is considered.

SIMILARITY VERSUS HOMOLOGY

In the analysis of molecular sequences, the terms similarity and homology are often used without a clear understanding of their distinct implications. Similarity is a descriptive term which only implies that two sequences, by some criterion, resemble each other and carries no suggestion as to their origins or ancestry. Homology refers specifically to similarity due to descent from a common ancestor (Patterson, 1988; Reeck et al., 1987). On the basis of similarity relationships among a group of sequences, it may be possible to infer homology, but outside of an explicit laboratory model system, descent from a common ancestor remains hypothetical.

There are philosophical issues in the inference of homology as well as practical ones. In classical morphology, conjunction (the occurrence of two traits in a single individual) is considered evidence that they are not homologous (Patterson, 1982). Because gene products are expressed at levels in excess of one copy per cell or organism, this rigid interpretation cannot be applied in molecular biology. A working definition of one copy of the gene per haploid genome has been suggested as an alternative (Patterson, 1988), although exceptions even to this exist (for example, repetitive genes such as the rRNA and histone genes)[1].

The hierarchical organization of macromolecules must also be considered. When we say that trypsin and chymotrypsin are evolutionarily derived from a common ancestor, we are not implying that where the constituent amino acid residues differ, the substituted residues are themselves evolutionarily related. Nor are we necessarily implying that particular structural features are evolutionarily related. Migration of an exon/intron junction may introduce unrelated sequences or completely delete sequences at a particular site (Craik et al., 1983). The preservation of function is also not an inviolate criterion. Haptoglobin is commonly described as a member of the serine protease superfamily even though it is not a functional protease, and angiotensinogen as a member of the serpin anti-protease superfamily even though its physiological function is unrelated and any anti-protease activity has apparently been lost. Nor is a simple majority rule sufficient. In proteins where the majority of the sequence has been replaced, the remaining elements

---

[1] It should be noted that while a variety of more precise and descriptive terms have been proposed to describe evolutionary and similarity relationships (orthology, paralogy [Fitch, 1970] , homoplasy [Simpson, 1961], homonomy, paraxenology, and plerology [Patterson, 1988]), these terms appear in only two molecular biology and biotechnology abstracts between 1986 and 1990, whereas the term homology (Hennig, 1966; Riedl, 1979) appears 11,360 times. For better or worse, the lexical preference of the molecular biological community is clear.

may be sufficient to establish what is generally regarded as homology (e.g., trypsin vs. chymotrypsin).

The dynamics of genome rearrangement further complicate the issue of what constitutes homology. Entire domains may be joined, swapped, and reordered. In some cases, it may be appropriate to speak of homology between entire proteins (trypsin vs. chymotrypsin) while in other cases, only one domain of several may be related (trypsin vs. prothrombin). In some sense, homology must refer to information content. In this view, a gene is a message, and homology is the inference that two messages were derived from a common origin. The point at which we say that the accumulated changes and rearrangements have destroyed the common core and that homology can no longer be detected may still be difficult to clearly define, but at least this view provides a rational basis for approaching the issue.

Information theory considers the properties of messages. Since macromolecular sequences are long series of letters, it is logical to apply information theory to them. The information content, or message length, of a sequence can be described as the number of bits needed to uniquely specify the message, where one bit distinguishes between two equally likely things. For instance, when the base frequencies are equal, it takes one bit to distinguish a purine from a pyrimidine, and two bits of information to uniquely specify a single base. The information content of a random message can be calculated from the symbols' frequencies as follows:

$$I = -\sum_{i=1}^{n} P_i \log_2 P_i \qquad (1)$$

where P_i is the probability of finding symbol i at any position. Using the overall amino acid frequencies from PIR database (release 26, see Appendices III and VIII), the information content of a random protein sequence is found to be 4.19 bits/residue. An average size protein domain, about 150 residues, would therefore correspond to a message length of approximately 630 bits. The probability that two random sequences would specify the same message is therefore 2^{-630} or about 10^{-190}. Even given generous estimates of all possible organisms and generations in biotic history, the odds of this occurring randomly are nil. This implies that convergent evolution at the molecular scale should be very rare (Patterson, 1988).

In contrast to protein sequences, many transcription factor binding sites are relatively short (eight or ten base pairs in length) and not uniquely specified (at least at the nucleotide sequence level). The corresponding message length is much smaller (16 to 20 bits or less) and the odds of two random sequences arriving at the same message is correspondingly higher (1 in 10^5). Given a population of a few thousand organisms and tens or hundreds of generations, one would anticipate that random, independently occurring mutations would arrive at the same message more than once. In this case, the observation of similar sequences in different genes cannot be accepted as sufficient evidence to infer homology.

DOT MATRIX METHODS

Nineteen ninety marked the 20th anniversary of the introduction of dot matrix[2] methods for molecular sequence analysis and, by all indications, this technique is in no danger of becoming obsolete. Dot matrix methods have enjoyed a wide variety of applications including analyses of gene structure and genome organization, identification of local sequence features, detection of internal sequence repeats, RNA folding, and molecular evolution. Examples of these applications will be detailed below. Dot matrix methods have previously been the subject of several reviews (Boguski et al., 1986c; Collins and Coulson, 1987; Davison, 1985; Doolittle, 1986; Lesk, 1988; Schulz and Schirmer, 1979; von Heijne, 1987).

Gibbs and McIntyre (1970) are usually credited with introducing dot matrix analysis for sequence comparison although, as for many other types of sequence analysis, if one excavates deeply enough, Walter Fitch's footprints are invariably found (Fitch, 1966; Fitch, 1969). Andrew McLachlan was also an early innovator in this area (McLachlan, 1971; McLachlan, 1972) and his technique will be discussed in detail below. Throughout the 1970s, sequence analysis was still a highly specialized research area with only a small number of practitioners. However, the rapid rise of DNA sequencing technology, with its attendant increase in the volume of data to be analyzed, ignited a renaissance of sequence analysis software development. Until this time, sequence analysis programs were almost exclusively denizens of mainframe computer systems. Maizel and Lenk (1981) implemented in BASIC a dot matrix program on a desktop system with only 64 kilobytes of core memory. Their enhancement of the technique allowed gene-sized segments of DNA (approximately 10,000 bases) to be analyzed and was extensively used in some of the initial characterizations of newly-available immunoglobulin gene sequences (Hieter et al., 1980; Maizel and Lenk, 1981). The Maizel-Lenk paper revived interest in the dot matrix method and is still the basis for popular implementations.[3] During this same period, Roger Staden (1982) wrote what was to become a very widely-used dot matrix program, DIAGON, for a DEC VAX 11/780. Staden's implementation not only provided the simple dot matrix approach but also incorporated McLachlan's window-based method with amino acid similarity scoring,

---

[2] The terms "dot matrix," "comparison matrix," "graphic matrix" and "diagonal comparison" have all been applied to this technique and will be used interchangeably in the present work. Dot matrices should not be confused with the matrices or arrays used to compute dynamic programming alignments.

[3] Such as the GCG program DOTPLOT (Genetics Computer Group, Inc., Madison, WI).

statistical filtering of the output, and a previously unavailable degree of interactivity using a graphics terminal (McLachlan, 1971; McLachlan, 1972; McLachlan, 1983; Staden, 1982). DIAGON and McLachlan's CMPSEQ were initially used to identify and characterize internal repeats in the myosin rod.

Pustell and Kafatos (1982, 1984) incorporated a number of improvements[4] to the basic method including more sophisticated filtering to improve the signal-to-noise ratio, the use of letters rather than dots to permit discrimination among matches of different stringency (scaling), and matrix compression and expansion to provide both global views of entire viral genomes as well as nucleotide-level resolution of local sequence features. These authors also seem to have been the first to apply hash table methods (see Hashing and Neighborhood Algorithms) to accelerate the computations. More recently, Argos (1987) introduced some important advances in the dot matrix method for protein sequence analysis. The use of multiple, varying-length "probes," residue physical characteristics for scoring, and new tests for the significance of sequence similarities has led to improvements in sensitivity and specificity for detecting weak sequence similarities (although at the expense of increased computation time). Reisner and Bucholtz (1988) have also employed the physical/chemical characteristics of amino acids for scoring matches and their paper provides a good example of the use of color scaling to indicate different degrees of sequence similarity.

Algorithms

The Simple Dot Plot

In its most elementary form, a dot matrix is easy to understand and can even be constructed by hand. To compare two sequences, A and B, sequence A is written out vertically with each letter (residue or base) representing a row, and sequence B is written out horizontally with each letter representing a column. Then, each letter (row) of sequence A is compared to each letter (column) of sequence B and a dot is placed at the intersection of each row and column where the letters are identical. One then visually inspects the matrix for meaningful patterns of dots that represent certain sequence features.

Figure 1a shows a self comparison (or *intra*sequence comparison) of the sequence of letters representing the title of this book. Note the *identity diagonal* representing a one-to-one alignment of the sequence with itself. (Self comparisons are always symmetrical and sometimes only the upper or lower triangle is displayed.) Two short palindromes, "ANA" and "SIS," are observed as linear patterns of three dots, each perpendicular to the identity

---

[4] Similar extensions involving filtering and scaling the output and examination at different levels of resolution have also been described by a number of authors. Personal computer implementations of the Pustell programs are commercially available from International Biotechnologies, Inc., New Haven, CT.

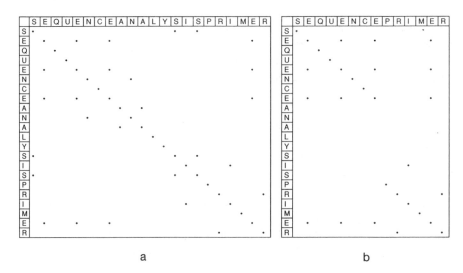

Figure 1: a. *Intra*sequence comparison of title "Sequence Analysis Primer." b. Comparison of "wild-type" title and deletion mutant, "Sequence Primer." Note the negative vertical displacement of the main diagonal. If the axes were reversed, this same deletion would be represented by a positive horizontal displacement.

diagonal. (Other palindromes are also present if one allows mismatches.) Palindromes and inverted repeats have no known functions in protein sequences but indicate regions of self-complementarity for DNA and RNA. Self comparison is also the method of choice for detecting and characterizing internal repeats in proteins and nucleic acids.

Figure 1b shows changes to the dot plot's appearance when one sequence has undergone an insertion or deletion with respect to another. Because the sequences are different, there is no identity diagonal. Instead, a diagonal(s) that dominates the plot is referred to as the *main diagonal*. We compare a "deleted" version of the title "SEQUENCE PRIMER" to the complete version and see that the main diagonal is vertically displaced at the point of deletion in the horizontally displayed sequence. Alternatively, this plot could be interpreted as showing an insertion in the vertically displayed sequence.[5] Such displacements are common features of real dot matrix analyses and are important indicators of gap placement in sequence alignments.

Figure 2a shows a more complicated example representing an *inter*sequence comparison. In this example, the title of this book is compared with the subtitle of Russell Doolittle's book (1986) on a related subject. The diagonals labeled 1, 2 and 3 represent alignments of obviously related sub-

---

[5] Because of this ambiguity, insertion/deletion events are often referred to as indels.

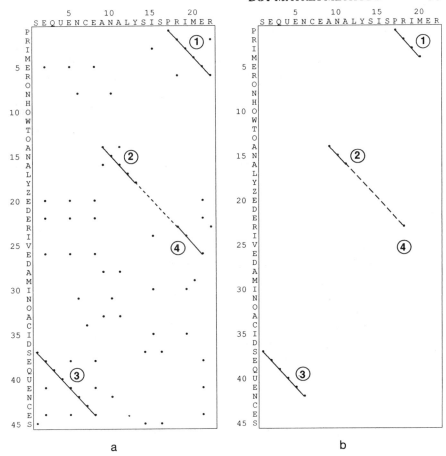

Figure 2: a. *Inter*sequence comparison (simple dot plot) of "Sequence Analysis Primer" and "Primer on How to Analyze Derived Amino Acid Sequences." Diagonals numbered 1 through 4 represent significant local similarities as described in the text. b. Same comparison as in panel A, but computed using a window of 5 letters and a "stringency" or threshold score of 60% identity.

sequences as shown below:

```
PRIMER          ANALYSIS        SEQUENCEA
||||||          |||||  .        ||||||||.
PRIMER          ANALYZED        SEQUENCES.
    1               2               3
```

The symbol 'l' is used to indicate identical sequence characters; the symbol '.', a conservative substitution.

A very important point to raise about this example is that, although the substring "ANALYxxx" (diagonal 2) is located at a similar location in both titles, the substrings "PRIMER" and "SEQUENCE" are transposed as indicated by the great shifts from the main diagonal (Figure 2a). If one likens words to sequence domains, this situation actually occurs quite frequently in real proteins and nucleic acids by a variety of genetic mechanisms. Dot matrix analysis is the only currently available tool that deals sensibly with this phenomenon. Global dynamic programming alignments (see Dynamic Programming Methods) of such rearranged sequences yield unpredictable, evolutionarily confusing results. For example, using the ALIGN program[6] we obtain:

```
SEQUENCE-----ANALYSISPRIMER-----------------
     |         |||||      || |
PRIMERONHOWTOANALYZEDERIVEDAMINOACIDSEQUENCES
```

The substring "SEQUENCE" in the top line is obviously misaligned with "PRIMER", and likewise "PRIMER" in the top line is misaligned with "DERIVED." Global alignment methods are generally incapable of dealing with intrasequence rearrangements, yet this phenomenon is quite common among mosaic and repetitive sequence proteins.

Another important point to make about the intersequence comparison in Figure 2a involves the diagonal labeled 4 which is contiguous or colinear with diagonal 2 and parallel to diagonal 1. This arrangement displays an ungapped alignment of the following subsequences:

```
ANALYSISPRIMER
|||||  . ||.|
ANALYZEDERIVED
```

The degree of "similarity" (57% identical) between these words is similar to that observed among real peptide subsequences. Furthermore, of the six non-identical "residues" shown here, one pair (S/D or Ser/Asp) represents a neutral substitution and another (M/V or Met/Val) represents a conservative replacement according to the PAM-250 scale, a commonly used scoring system (see Appendix IV and Scoring Systems). If these book titles were actual protein sequences, the occurrence of parallel diagonals 1 and 4 would be *prima facie* evidence of a diverged internal duplication, with "PRIMER" and "DERIVED" sharing a common ancestor. Although etymologically unlikely in this instance, such phenomena are quite common in real molecular sequences.

Thus far we have explained the meaningful dot patterns in Figure 2a. The remaining dots constitute the background noise of the analysis and are simply a reflection of the "amino acid" composition of the sequences. Note

[6] In addition to the Protein Sequence Database, NBRF/PIR distributes a collection of VAX/VMS sequence analysis software, including this implementation of the Needleman-Wunsch algorithm (Needleman and Wunsch, 1970). The alignment shown was computed scoring identities only and using a gap penalty of 1.

that the most frequent letter in the two titles is an "E" and regular patterns of dots[7] are present as a result. For nucleic acid sequences which are composed of only four letters, this composition-dependent background noise is an even more serious problem and various "filtering" techniques have been devised to improve the signal-to-noise ratio. These techniques are discussed next.

The Window Approach and Output Filtering

For a coding region, it is possible to increase the specificity of sequence comparison simply by first translating it into its corresponding amino acid sequence and then performing the analysis. This is the case for any sequence comparison method, not just the dot matrix approach. For non-coding sequences, and even for many proteins, other filtering techniques are necessary. The most widely-used procedure compares the sequences using overlapping, fixed-length "windows"[8] and requires that the comparison achieve some minimum threshold value or score, summed over the window, before qualifying as a match. Comparison scores may be calculated based on the degree of local sequence identity or, in the case of protein sequences, the chemical or mutational similarity of amino acid residues (see Scoring Systems). The minimum score indicative of a significant match may be found empirically or may be derived from some statistical model of sequence similarity. Filtering a dot plot is somewhat like washing a Southern blot and, in both cases, signals are present at a certain "stringency."

How does one decide what window size or span length to use? Most programs provide a default window that is adequate for preliminary analysis, but to stop here ignores the exploratory nature of comparison matrix analysis and neutralizes some of the advantages of the technique. For coding sequences in particular, there are some theoretical grounds on which to base a span length selection. For example, one could use the size of an average exon (Gilbert, 1987; Holland and Blake, 1987; Traut, 1986) or the size of an average secondary or supersecondary protein structural element (Schulz and Schirmer, 1979).[9] One can also rationally choose a window size based on the purpose of the analysis. For example, gene promoters, short stem-loop structures or enzyme active sites require a small window. For RNA/DNA secondary structure, one might want to choose the length of a stable duplex (allowing a certain degree of mismatch) under defined conditions (Quigley et al., 1984). A multiple of codon length (for instance, 9 nucleotides) is useful for distinguishing coding sequences from introns. For sequences that con-

---

[7] The "E" dots form vertical and horizontal patterns. For the dot matrix method, *diagonal* patterns are the important and meaningful features.

[8] The terms "window," "span," "segment" and "probe" have all been used in the literature to describe this concept.

[9] The average exon codes for a 17 to 47-residue polypeptide. The average lengths of α-helices and β-strands among crystallized proteins are 9-12 and 6 residues, respectively.

tain internal repeats, using a multiple of the repeat unit length is often desirable to suppress background noise, although for repeats that are polymorphic in length, using a window that is about half the size of the average repeat length is required for maximum sensitivity. In general, the larger window, the lower the background noise.

Let us return now to our title comparison example and recompute the matrix in Figure 2a using a window approach. We will use a window of 5 letters, and a stringency of 60%. Only identical characters will be counted as positive scores and, therefore, 3 out of 5 characters must match at this stringency. To begin the computation, characters 1-5 of the Doolittle title (hereafter title A) are compared with characters 1-5 of our title (title B) and the number of identities summed:

```
                1    5
A               PRIME        score 20% (1/5 matches)
                ----+
B               SEQUENCEANALYSISPRIMER
                1    5
```

Next, characters 1-5 of title A are compared with characters 2-6 of title B:

```
                1    5
A               PRIME  score 0%  (0/5 matches)
                -----
B               SEQUENCEANALYSISPRIMER
                2    6
```

This procedure is reiterated until the end of sequence B is reached:

```
                     1    5
A                    PRIME  score 100%  (5/5 matches)
                     +++++
B    SEQUENCEANALYSISPRIMER
                     17   21
```

```
                     1    5
A                    PRIME  score 0%(0/5 matches)
                     -----
B     SEQUENCEANALYSISPRIMER
                     18   22
```

This completes the processing for the *first row* of our matrix and results in only one span that meets or exceeds the threshold score of 60%. This span corresponds to a single dot[10] placed in row 1, column 17 with all other

[10] Some programs operate in manner that positions the dot at the *center* of the window, and in this case, our first dot would occur in row 3, column 19. Furthermore, rather than simply recording the presence (dot) or absence (blank) of a signal, one can scale the output using colors or different characters to indicate different degrees of similarity.

positions containing nulls. This "sliding window" computation is then repeated with characters 2-6 of sequence A, evaluating every overlapping span in row 2 and so on and so forth until the end of sequence A is reached.[11] The final result is the matrix displayed in Figure 2b. Note that the background pattern of dots has disappeared but the sensitivity of detecting positive signals is also somewhat attenuated. (In particular, diagonal 4 of Figure 2a is now represented by a single dot located at the intersection of row 23 and column 19.) However, by using a larger window, slightly lower stringency and/or a different scoring scheme, the sensitivity can be enhanced while maintaining the specificity.

A more sensitive way to measure the local similarity of protein sequences uses a scoring system that takes into account the physical, chemical, structural and/or evolutionary similarity of the amino acid residues (see Scoring Systems). A sliding window comparison is performed, exactly as before, but instead of summing the number of identities alone, the sum of similarity scores is calculated. We repeat, once again, the example of Figure 2, using a window of 5 residues and the PAM-250 matrix[12] (see Appendix IV) for scoring:

```
          1     5
A         P R I M E
          1-1-2+0+4 = score of +2
B         S E Q U E N C E A N A L Y S I S P R I M E R
          1     5
```

```
          1     5
A         P R I M E
          -1+0+0-2+1 = score of 0
B         S E Q U E N C E A N A L Y S I S P R I M E R
            2     6
```

Again, the procedure is reiterated until the end of sequence B is reached

```
                              1     5
A                             P R I M E
                              6+6+5+6+4 = score of +27
B S E Q U E N C E A N A L Y S I S P R I M E R
                              17    21
```

---

[11] This procedure will only take us to the end of sequence A or B minus 5 (length of sequence minus window size), and this is usually known as an "edge effect" or end artifact. Corrections can be made by progressively shrinking the window and scaling the stringency to extend the diagonals.

[12] Among the alphabetic characters, J, O and U are not used for amino acid abbreviations. In our English text examples, these symbols will be interpreted as "unknowns" with scores of zero.

	C	E	A	N	A	L	Y	S	I	S	P	R	I
T	-4	-8	-4	-8	-6	-7	-6	2	-1	-6	-3	-8	2
O	-7	-2	-8	-7	-10	-5	-9	-5	1	-1	-8	-5	-7
A	1	0	4	-2	-3	-3	-2	-2	-2	-1	0	-4	-3
N	-6	-2	-2	12	-3	-7	-1	-6	-3	-2	0	4	-8
A	-6	-8	-5	-3	22	-6	-8	-4	-11	-7	-3	-2	0
L	-9	-6	-8	-3	-3	20	-6	-10	-2	-8	-8	-2	-3
Y	-3	-9	-8	-7	-8	-3	16	-6	-8	-1	-11	-8	1
Z	-1	-1	-9	-10	-11	-10	-5	14	-5	-6	-4	-13	-6
E	-6	3	2	-6	-11	-9	-9	-3	7	-5	-5	-8	-6
D	-2	-2	3	-1	-6	-8	-9	-6	-2	3	-4	-4	-6
E	-1	-4	-3	5	-2	-7	-3	-10	-8	-4	8	-2	-6
R	-2	-7	-5	4	-1	-3	-4	-4	-8	-6	0	12	-4
I	0	-4	-9	-3	-3	-1	-7	-4	-1	-5	-8	0	16

Table 1: Portion of matrix of local alignment scores for the book title comparison in Figure 3. The scores represent the sum of PAM-250 values (see Appendix IV) for letter pairs summed over a window of five letters.

```
                                        1       5
A                                       P R I M E
                                        0-2+4-2-1=score of -1
B  S E Q U E N C E A N A L Y S I S P R I M E R
                                        18       22
```

This time, rather than storing either a "dot" or a space in each position of the matrix, the actual numerical score is stored in the position corresponding to the *center* of the window. A portion of this new matrix is shown in Table 1 and a three-dimensional graph of the entire matrix is shown in Figure 3a. It should now be clear that although most comparison matrices are collapsed to two dimensions for display, they actually possess a third dimension that consists of the magnitudes of the local alignment scores. The plotting threshold is usually based upon the observed distribution of raw scores in the whole matrix or Z scores[13] (standard normal deviate) derived from a Monte Carlo analysis (see Estimation of Statistical Significance). In this particular case, the "signals" are fairly obvious; although multiple, background peaks can be seen.

Estimation of Statistical Significance

The dot matrix method depends, in large part, on visual pattern recognition and it is common practice to empirically vary the stringency of an analysis until some signal appears to emerge from the noise. Nevertheless, one would like to have a criterion for determining if these signals could have arisen sim-

---

[13] Z score is also known as the z value, standard normal deviate, or standardized score.

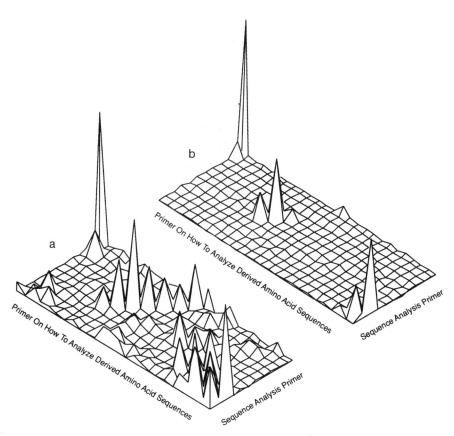

Figure 3: Three-dimensional versions of book title comparison matrix computed using a window of five letters and the PAM-250 values for scoring. Both panels represent the same analysis, but the results are displayed at different plotting thresholds. Panel a shows all positive-scoring segments (threshold score of zero) and panel b shows only those segments with raw scores greater than 13 which corresponds to a Z score of 3 (see Figures 4 and 5).

These images were created as follows. The matrix of values representing the local alignment scores (a portion of which is reproduced here as Table 1), were imported as text files into *NCSA Datascope* (version 1.1) running on a Macintosh computer. *Datascope* provides grayscale images resembling traditional dot matrix plots as well as direct access to all numerical values in the matrix using a mouse. The plotting threshold can be adjusted using the *Attributes* submenu of the *Numbers* menu (which also provides a free-text *Notebook* section for recording observations, etc.). Once data has been imported into *Datascope*, it can be saved as a binary (HDF) file for use by other NCSA tools.

The two "filtered" versions of the book title matrix in panels A and B were then opened in *NCSA Image* (version 2.1) which provides a comprehensive set of scientific visualization tools, including color raster, 3D, contour, shade and dither plots, as well as full interactive control over the color palette and a variety of other image analysis functions. 3D plots can be rotated with the mouse and viewed from any angle. A particularly useful function for dot matrix analysis is palette rotation for color raster images. This function allows one to continuously vary the plotting "stringency" to interactively study signals of various strengths or degrees of significance. All images can be "cut and pasted" to other Macintosh applications. NCSA tools are also available for Sun and Silicon Graphics workstations (National Center for Computer Supercomputer Applications, Urbana-Champaign, IL and Spyglass, Inc., Champaign, IL).

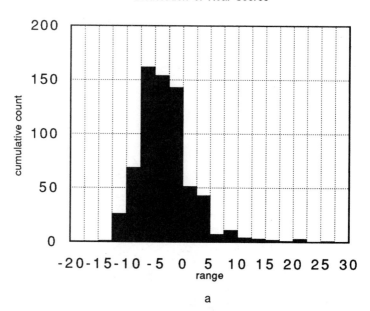

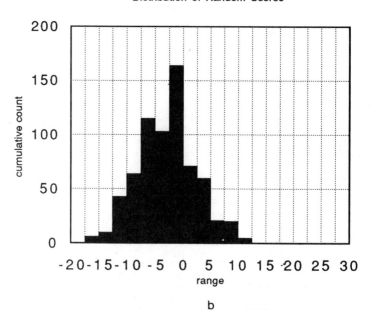

Figure 4: Distributions of scores for the book title comparison matrix in Figure 3.
a. Score distribution for real titles. The minimum and maximum scores are -13 and
27, respectively, with a mean score of -2.8 and a standard deviation of 4.95. b.
Score distribution for randomized titles. The titles were (continued next page)

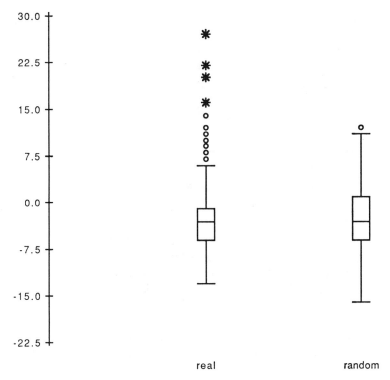

Figure 5: Box plots of same score distribution data as in Figure 4. The outlined central boxes depict the middle halves of the data between the 25th and 75th percentiles; the horizontal lines across the boxes marks the medians (-3 for both the real and shuffled sequence comparisons); the vertical lines extending from the tops and bottoms of the boxes show the extent of the main body of data; extreme values are individually plotted with circles; very extreme outliers are represented by circles. The plots were generated on a Macintosh using the Data Desk™ application (Odesta Corp., Northbrook, Illinois).

ply by chance. Estimations of statistical significance have most commonly been accomplished by Monte Carlo analysis[14]. First, a comparison of the two sequences is performed, and a distribution of local similarity scores and their mean are obtained (Figure 4a). Then, one or both of the sequences are "shuffled" (maintaining the same nucleotide or amino acid compositions) and the pairwise comparison is repeated to obtain a score distribution for the

[14] Also known as a "shuffling test," "jumbling test," "scrambling test" or "permutation reconstruction of the observed data." A widely-used implementation is the RDF or RDF2 program (Lipman, 1985; Pearson, 1990).

(**Fig. 4 cont.**) randomized using the GCG program "Shuffle" (Genetics Computer Group, Inc., Madison, WI) and then the comparison was recomputed using the same window (5 letters) and scoring matrix (PAM-250). The minimum and maximum scores are -16 and 12, respectively, with a mean of -2.6 and a standard deviation of 5.21. The plots were generated on a Macintosh using the Kaleidagraph™ application (Synergy Software, Reading, PA).

Local alignment	Raw score	z-value
seQUENCe seQUENCe	22	4.7
ANALYsis ANALYyze	22	4.7
PRIMEr PRIMEr	27	5.7
PRIMEr dERIVEd	16	3.6

Table 2: The aligned words in column 1 represent selected high-scoring local alignments from the book title comparison in Figure 2 (see also Table 1). The upper case letters of the aligned words represent the windows in which PAM-250 scores are summed to yield the raw scores in column 2. The Z scores in column 3 were calculated as described in the text.

randomized sequences[15] (Figure 4b). Based upon a comparison of these score distributions (most easily accomplished through the use of box plots (Figure 5), outlier scores are determined and likely represent significant and interesting local alignments. A plotting threshold can then be chosen to display these extreme values only and suppress the lower scoring segments.

A simple extension of this approach computes a new score, known as a *Z score*, that scales raw scores based upon their distance from the mean of the randomized sequence score distribution:

$$Z = (x - m) / \sigma \tag{2}$$

where x is the local alignment score, m is the mean of random scores and σ is the standard deviation of random scores (Dayhoff, 1978; Doolittle, 1981; Lipman and Pearson, 1985). By rearranging equation 2 and solving for x, we can determine what raw score to use as a threshold to detect signals greater than some Z score from the random mean. The mean score for the distribution in Figure 5b is -2.6 with a standard deviation of 5.2. Thus, a raw score that is 3 SD units[16] above the mean has a value of 13.0 and this is used as a threshold to filter the title comparison matrix (Figure 3b). The Z scores of the remaining peaks are shown in Table 2.

Although Monte Carlo analysis is the most popular approach to estimating the significance of sequence similarities, other methods based upon theoretical models of random sequences are used. For example, McLachlan (1971, 1972, 1983) devised the "double matching probability" function to calculate the frequencies of scores in infinite random sequences with the

[15] Normally, this procedure of shuffling the sequences and then comparing their randomized version is carried out 100 or more times to simulate rare events.

[16] The statistical properties of biological sequences are quite different from those of English words and phrases and extensive experience has indicated that Z score in the range of 3 to 6 may not be significant, whereas scores greater than 6 usually are (Doolittle, 1981; Lipman and Pearson, 1985; Pearson, 1990).

same amino acid compositions as the real sequences under study (see also McLachlan and Boswell, 1985). Reich and Meiske (1987) have also developed methods based upon a stochastic random sequence model to determine the significance of window scores in dot matrix analysis. Finally, Argos (1985) bases his significance tests on a collection of actual protein sequences rather than random sequences of specified composition.

Examples

Gene and Genome Structure and Evolution

A major advantage of using dot matrix methods to visualize sequence relationships is that it allows one to "see the forest for the trees" (Pustell and

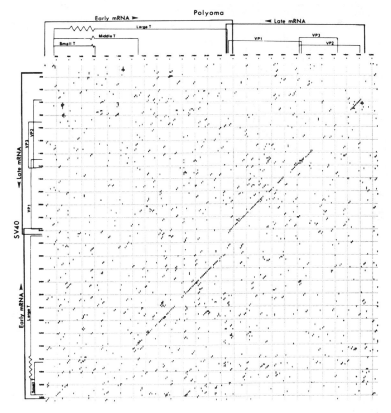

Figure 6: "Global" dot matrix comparison of the polyoma virus and SV40 genomes using a 41 nucleotide window and a minimum plotting threshold of 51% identity. Although not distinguishable in this image, the "dots" are actually different characters used to represent different degrees of sequence similarity (see Legend to Figure 16 for another example of this type of scaling). The compression factor is 20. (Reprinted with permission from Oxford University Press from "A High Speed, High Capacity Homology Matrix: Zooming through SV40 and Polyoma", Pustell and Kafatos, *Nucleic Acids Res.* Vol. 10, p. 4768, Fig. 1. Copyright 1982).

Kafatos, 1982). Consider the intersequence comparison of the SV40 and polyoma viral genomes reproduced in Figure 6. After only a brief visual inspection of the plot, one can readily apprehend that: 1) the viral DNAs are homologous; 2) sequence conservation is nonuniform; and 3) several large deletions and insertions have occurred. It would be difficult to appreciate this "global" picture of comparative genome structure by staring at dozens of pages of nucleotide sequence alignments. Once the big picture is apparent, one can then "zero in" and explore local features at higher resolutions. Figure 7 shows a matrix plot of a small region around the SV40 origin of DNA replication compared with its reverse complement (the sequence of the complementary strand). Lines perpendicular to the main diagonal identify potential secondary structures.

Figure 8 shows an intersequence comparison of two germ line immunoglobulin genes and demonstrates the dramatic effect of window-based filtering as well as the utility of dot matrix plots for visualizing degrees of sequence conservation among introns and exons (Maizel and Lenk, 1981). The original plots were color-coded to visualize local variations in base composition or to represent different degrees of similarity in the window-based version.

Hancock and Dover (1988) studied the molecular coevolution of large ribosomal RNAs using Staden's DIAGON program (Staden, 1982). Many eukaryotic 26S/28S ribosomal RNA genes consist of interspersed "core segments" and "expansion segments," the latter of which account for most of the length difference between eukaryotic and prokaryotic 23S ribosomal RNAs. These expansion segments have biased base compositions (either AT-rich or GC-rich, depending upon the species) and their sizes and locations are readily seen on self-comparison plots (Figure 9).

RNA and DNA Structure and Folding

The use of dot matrix analysis for detecting potential secondary structures in nucleic acids has been discussed in a previous section (see Chapter 1). A paper by Quigley et al. (1984) contains a number of informative examples and compares the predictions of dot matrix-based analyses to experimental data from enzymatic probes. Simple dot matrix comparisons in this context are based on hydrogen bonding properties of the bases. However, Shapiro et al. (1987) have extended the dot matrix approach to detect distortions in the local helical structure of DNA based upon the Calladine-Dickerson rules (Calladine, 1982; Dickerson, 1983).

Protein Sequence Organization and Comparison

We have already seen that there are a wider variety of matching/scoring criteria useful for protein sequence comparisons than there are for nucleic acids. In addition to the widely-used PAM-250 or MDM_{78} (mutation data

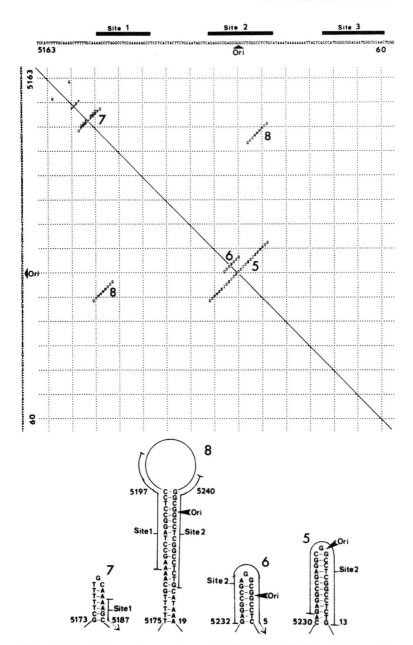

Figure 7: "Local" dot matrix comparison of the SV40 origin of DNA replication and its complement using a 21 nucleotide window and minimum plotting score of 68%. The compression factor is 1 (i.e., the plot is uncompressed, providing nucleotide-level resolution). Lines formed by letters perpendicular to the main diagonal represent reverse repeats and symmetries that correspond to self-complementary structures drawn in the lower panel. (Reprinted with permission of Oxford University Press from " A High Speed, High Capacity Homology Matrix: Zooming Through SV40 and Polyoma", Pustell and Kafatos, *Nucleic Acids Res.* 10, p. 4780, Fig. 6. Copyright 1982).

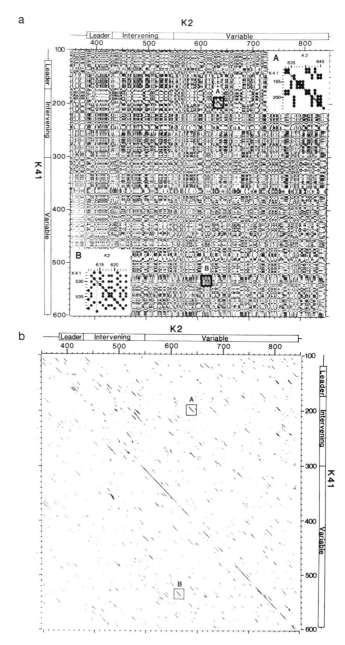

Figure 8: Intersequence (heterologous) graphic matrix comparison of two immunoglobulin kappa light chain genes (K2 and K41) from the mouse. The (a) panel represents a simple dot plot where each matching base is represented by a dot. In the original color version, each base was displayed in a different color so that the sequence could be read directly off the plot. The (b) panel is a window-based, filtered comparison of the same data using a window of 9 nucleo-(cont. next page)

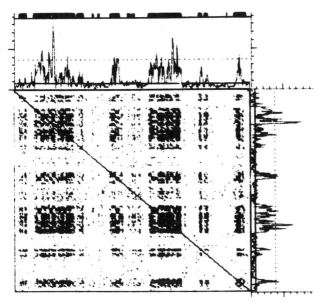

H.sapiens

Figure 9: Intrasequence (self) comparison of human 28S rRNA gene (GENBANK HUMRGM, accession no. M11167). The original analysis by Hancock and Dover was performed using the DIAGON program (Staden, 1982) with a window size of 35 nucleotides and a stringency of 54% (19/35 base pairs). Using these same parameters, we reproduced the analysis here with the "Pustell DNA Matrix" application from the MacVector™ sequence analysis package (International Biotechnologies, Inc., New Haven, CT).

matrix, 1978) (Schwartz and Dayhoff, 1979; see Scoring Systems), many investigators have used scoring systems based on the physical and chemical properties of the amino acids (for example, see Kubota et al., 1981). The reader is referred to Cornette et al. (1987) for a comparative analysis of 38 different hydrophobicity scales and their use in studying sequence-structure relationships in proteins (see Chapter 2). The following examples use the PAM-250 matrix, although we discuss the use of other PAM matrices in a subsequent section (see Appendix IV and Scoring Systems).

Analysis of Repetitive Sequence Proteins

Many protein sequences contain internal homology or repeats. In fact, recent surveys of the sequence databases have indicated that as many as 15 to 20% of all known proteins have some form of internally repetitive structure rang-

(Fig. 8 cont.) tides with a minimum score of 56% (i.e., 5 bases out of 9 must match). In the original version, different degrees of similarity were represented using different colors. [Reprinted from Maizel and Lenk, (1981), *Proc. Natl. Acad. Sci. USA*, Vol. 78, p. 7667, Fig. 2.]

ing from simple homopolymers and alternating copolymers, to multiple duplications of entire globular domains (Boguski, in preparation). Moreover, a separate survey of the MEDLINE bibliographic database has shown that, during the last 20 years, nearly 6,000 articles have been published in which the Boolean combination of "(repeat OR repetitive) AND (protein OR sequence)" can be found in the title or abstract (Boguski, in preparation). Clearly, internally repetitive protein sequences are widespread in nature and should be looked for during the characterization of any new sequence. A sensitive dot matrix analysis is one of the best ways to do this and we provide a number of detailed examples below. Nevertheless, there are many cases in the literature where important internal repeats have been overlooked, sometimes for years after the initial publication of the sequence.

Haptoglobin. This example shows that one of the earliest applications of dot matrices for sequence analysis was the detection and characterization of protein internal repeats. Haptoglobin[17], a plasma protein, binds avidly to hemoglobin and presumably "scavenges" free hemoglobin derived from lysed red cells . Haptoglobin is also an acute phase reactant with, as yet ill-defined, immunomodulatory functions (Oh et al., 1990) and is a member of the superfamily of complement component C3b/C4b-binding proteins (Kristensen et al., 1987). Haptoglobin is a tetramer consisting of two α and two β chains. The primary 346-residue translation product undergoes postranslational removal of its signal peptide and proteolytic processing into α and β subunits. The 245-residue β subunit resembles trypsin but is a nonfunctional member of the serine protease sequence family (Kurosky et al., 1980). In their paper which first described the dot matrix or "diagram" method, Gibbs and McIntyre (1970) compared the 2α-haptoglobin sequence with itself and showed that it was composed of two approximately 60-residue repetitive units (Figure 10) corresponding to residues 29-88 and 89-146 in the primary translation product and which are encoded by two exons of the haptoglobin gene (Maeda and Smithies, 1986). This same 60 amino acid repetitive sequence has so far been found in more than a dozen different proteins with the 60-residue unit being repeated up to 30 times in a single sequence (Kristensen et al., 1987). Haptoglobin is of considerable historical interest because it represents the first protein in which gene duplication, with subsequent non-reciprocal homologous recombination and exon shuffling, were shown to be mechanisms for protein evolution in multigene families (Maeda and Smithies, 1986).

Apolipoproteins and the LDL Receptor. The mammalian plasma lipoproteins are water-soluble, macromolecular complexes of lipids (triglycerides, phospholipids and cholesterol) and specific proteins referred to as apolipo-

---

[17] PIR code HPHU2; SWISS-PROT code HP@$HUMAN> See these database entries for references to older literature.

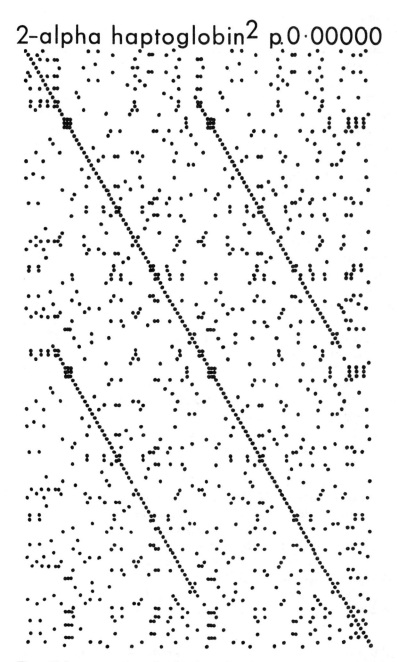

Figure 10: Intrasequence comparison (simple dot plot) of a subunit of haptoglobin showing internal duplication of a 60-amino acid sequence. [Reprinted from Gibbs and McIntyre (1970), *Eur. J. Biochem.*Vol. 16, p. 5, Fig. 5].

proteins. Lipoprotein particles are classified according to their density (e.g., high-density lipoprotein or HDL, low-density lipoprotein or LDL) which is a function of their relative content of protein and lipid. The plasma lipoproteins are involved in different phases of fat absorption, transport, and metabolism, and their apolipoprotein components have three major functions: 1) they maintain the micellar structure of lipoprotein particles; 2) they control the transport and redistribution of lipids among various tissues via their interaction with cell surface receptors; and 3) they function as cofactors for enzymes essential to lipid metabolism. Studies of genetic polymorphism in human apolipoprotein genes indicate that certain alleles are risk factors for atherosclerosis and coronary artery disease (Breslow, 1988; Humphries, 1988). There are eight major apolipoproteins in humans[18] and their structures have been extensively characterized using dot matrix methods (McLachlan, 1977; Boguski et al., 1984; Boguski et al., 1985; Boguski et al., 1986a; Boguski et al., 1986b; Boguski et al., 1986c; Yang et al., 1986; Cole et al., 1987; De Loof et al., 1987).

Figure 11 shows an *inter*sequence comparison of the primary translation products of human apoA-I and rat apoA-IV. The most striking feature of this plot is the presence of multiple internal repeats that comprise 65-80% of the total lengths of the sequences. In addition, however, there is a clearly discernible main diagonal (labeled "md" on the plot) indicating a colinear alignment of the proteins. Despite the fact that this diagonal "fades" at several locations, there are no vertical or horizontal displacements present[19], (excluding the signal peptide) indicating the absence of any insertion or deletion mutations. This type of evidence was used to establish that the mammalian apolipoproteins are all derived from a common ancestor and are largely composed of repeating sequences, 11 or 22 amino acids in length, that form amphipathic α-helical structures responsible for the lipid-binding properties of this protein family (Li et al., 1988; Segrest et al., 1990).

ApoE is closely-related to apolipoproteins A-I and A-IV (Boguski et al., 1985; Boguski et al., 1986c) but has evolved specialized functions and different patterns of gene expression (Mahley, 1988). Of particular interest is its role as a ligand for the LDL receptor and its participation in cholesterol transport. Four *intra*sequence comparisons for human apoE are shown in Figure 12. Note the effect of varying the window size (span length) and threshold levels. Although the repeat system is continuous throughout most of the protein, there is a central blank zone indicating considerable sequence divergence among the repeats that constitute this region. This zone is precisely the location of the LDL receptor-binding domain which is indicated by a box on the main diagonal (Figure 12) and demonstrates that repeated

---

[18] These are: apoA-I, apoA-II, apoA-IV, apoB, apoC-I, apoC-II, apoC-III and apoE. These can be retrieved from the PIR database by the superfamily name "apolipoprotein A-I."

[19] The easiest way to inspect a diagonal for small displacements is to look at it from one corner, holding the plot at a 10 degree angle from the line of vision.

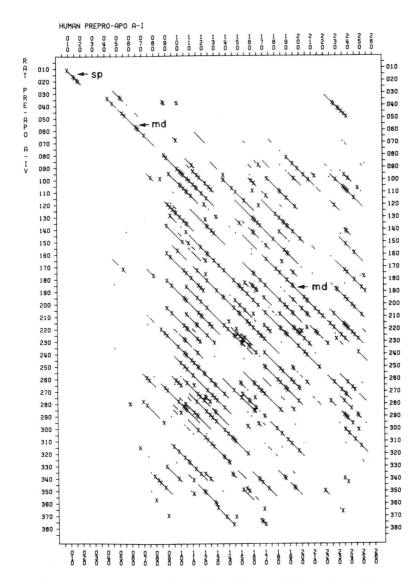

Figure 11: Intersequence comparison of the primary translation products of human apolipoprotein A-I and rat apolipoprotein A-IV using the CMPSEQ program (McLachlan, 1971; McLachlan, 1972). A span (or window) of 29 residues was used with the PAM-250 matrix for scoring. Dots and X's represent the centers of spans that achieved scores greater than 3 standard deviations above the mean, with X additionally representing a sequence identity. The arrows labeled "sp" and "md" indicate the signal peptide and main diagonal, respectively. Note the presence of multiple diagonals offset from and parallel to the main diagonal representing numerous internal repeats. Although the main diagonal "fades" at several locations, the signal resumes in register (i.e., without horizontal or vertical displacements) indicating sequence divergence but not insertion or deletion mutations. The NBRF/PIR retrieval codes for apoA-I and A-IV are LPHUA1 and LPRTA4, respectively. [Reprinted from Boguski et al. (1986b), *Methods Enzymol.*, Vol. 128, p.760, Fig. 2].

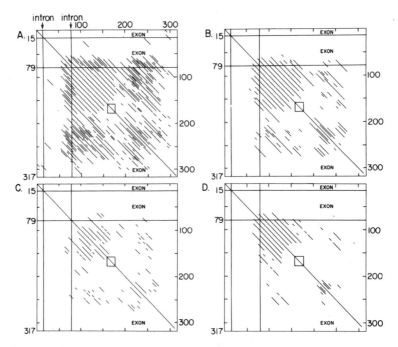

Figure 12: Intrasequence comparison matrices for the primary translation product of human apolipoprotein E (PIR code: LPHUE) using the CMPSEQ84 program (McLachlan, 1983). This figure shows the effects of varying span lengths (window sizes) and plotting thresholds. Panel a: span of 45 residues, threshold score with $p < 10^{-2}$. Panel b: span of 45 residues, threshold score with $p < 10^{-3}$. Panel c: span of 23 residues, threshold score with $p < 10^{-3}$. Panel d: span of 45 residues, threshold score with $p < 10^{-4}$. The p values were estimated based on McLachlan's "double matching probability" function (McLachlan, 1971; McLachlan, 1972; McLachlan, 1983). The LDL receptor-binding domain is represented by a box on the main diagonal. [Reprinted from Boguski et al. (1986c), *J. Lipid Research*, Vol. 27, p. 1020, Fig. 4.]

sequences can evolve specialized functions as a result of sequence divergence (Boguski et al., 1986c). Single amino acid substitutions in this zone correspond to naturally-occurring alleles of the apoE gene and are associated with defective receptor binding, type III hyperlipoproteinemia and coronary artery disease (Breslow, 1988).

The LDL receptor itself has two distinct types of internal repeats that have been mapped using dot matrix methods (Herz et al., 1988; Yamamoto et al., 1984). The amino terminus of the receptor constitutes its ligand-binding domain and consists of seven tandem copies of a 40-residue, cysteine-rich, acidic sequence (Figure 13). This domain interacts with positively-charged repeats in apoE and apoB and represents an interesting

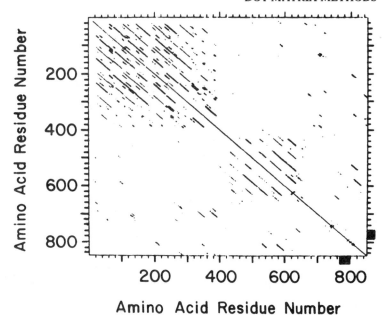

Figure 13: Intrasequence dot matrix analysis of the human LDL receptor (PIR code: QRHULD) using the NBRF DOTMATRIX program (George et al., 1982). The window size is 25 residues with minimum score of 20. Two unrelated sets of internal repeats are seen. The N-terminal (extracellular) repeat domain interacts with apolipoproteins B and E; the central repetitive domain contains several copies of EGF-related sequences (see Chapter 4). The small black boxes on the bottom right axes depict the membrane-spanning region. [Reprinted from Yamamoto et al. (1984), *Cell*, Vol. 39, p.32 , Fig. 8].

case of two unrelated families of sequence repeats that have coevolved to interact with one another as receptor and ligand. Curiously, homologs of the LDL receptor, cysteine-rich acidic repeat are also found in a number of complement components (Herz et al., 1988). This phenomenon was also first described using dot matrix methods (Stanley et al., 1985). The second type of internal repeat in the LDL receptor (Figure 13) consists of three copies of the nearly ubiquitous epidermal growth factor (EGF) repeat (see Theoretical Foundations of Molecular Evolution).

Eukaryotic Transcription Factors. Transcription factor IIIA (TFIIIA) from *Xenopus laevis* binds to the internal promoter of 5S RNA genes and is essential for their transcription by RNA polymerase III (Geiduschek and Tocchini-Valentini, 1988). TFIIIA is historically significant because it was the first eukaryotic transcription factor for which an amino acid sequence became available (Ginsberg et al., 1984). Dot matrix analyses of the TFIIIA sequence by two different groups (Brown et al., 1985; Miller et al., 1985) were instrumental in the discovery of the now-famous zinc finger DNA-binding motif of which there are presently 900 examples in 120 different

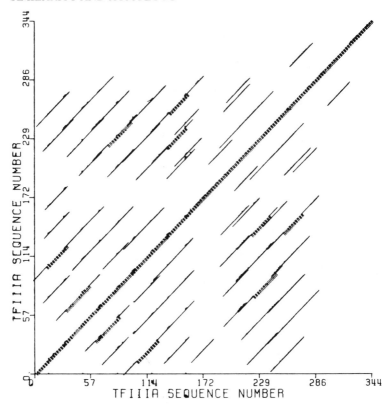

Figure 14: Intrasequence comparison of *Xenopus laevis* transcription factor IIIA (PIR code: TWXL3) using a window of 20 residues and the PAM-250 ("Dayhoff relatedness odds") matrix for scoring. The plot is scaled to represent two levels of similarity: Plain diagonal lines represent local window scores with values between 3.0 and 5.0 standard deviations above the mean; scores > 5 s.d. are represented by short orthogonal bars. (Reprinted by permission of the publisher from "The Primary Structure of Transcription Factor TFIIIA Has 12 Consecutive Repeats," Brown et al., *FEBS Letters* 186, p. 272 . Copyright 1985 by Elsevier Science Publishing Co., Inc.).

proteins.[20]

Figure 14 shows a self-comparison matrix for TFIIIA. Apart from the main diagonal, eight or nine prominent, regularly-spaced parallel diagonals are seen. These correspond to the approximately 30 residue long tandem "finger" repeats that constitute most of the sequence of this 344 residue protein. Note that a narrow blank zone, centered about residue 172, represents a region of sequence divergence where scores have fallen below the plotting threshold. When the diagonals resume distal to this zone, they are slightly displaced indicating deletions or insertions have occurred as well.

[20] Dr. George Michaels, personal communication, based upon current entries in the Zinc Finger Gene Database (Jacobs, 1990).

A. Protein Comparison Matrices

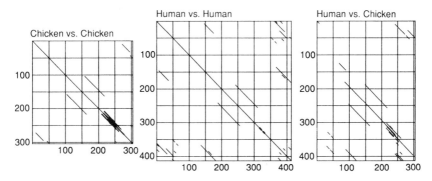

B. Human Erythroid Factor: alignments of internal repeats

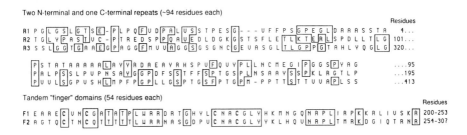

C. Modular Structure of Mammalian Erythroid Transcription Factors

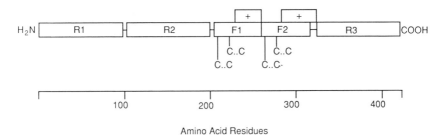

Amino Acid Residues

Figure 15: Comparison matrix and multiple alignment analyses of the chicken (PIR code: A32993) and human (SWISS-PROT ID:GFl$HUMAN) erythroid transcription factors. The top panel shows two intrasequence and one intersequence comparisons computed using CMPSEQ84 (McLachlan, 1983) with a window of 53 residues and the PAM-250 matrix with a plotting threshold of > 3 s.d. above the mean. The chicken self-comparison shows three features: the central tandem finger domain; a shorter diagonal in the upper right/lower left corner indicating homology between the N and C termini; and a dense zone of diagonals just distal to the finger domain that represents multiple oligoglycine and oligoproline peptides in this region. Self-comparison of the human sequence again shows the central tandem finger domain but evidence for another, separate internal repeat begins to emerge with two copies proximal to the tandem finger sequences and a third copy distal to this domain. Alignments of these internal repeats and a schematic diagram of their organization are shown in the bottom two panels. The human vs. chicken comparison shows that the sequences are significantly related but have diverged considerably in their N-terminal domains. [Reprinted with permission from Trainor et al. (1990), *Nature*, Vol. 343, p. 95. Copyright (C) 1990 Macmillan Magazines Ltd].

This region of TFIIIA contains finger units 6 and 7 which have diverged considerably in sequence and length from the other finger units (Brown et al., 1985; Miller et al., 1985).

Several other transcription factors and even RNA polymerase II itself

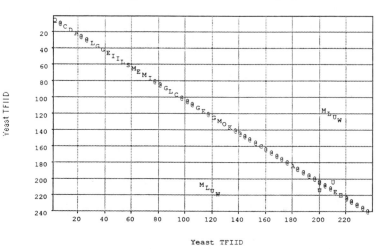

Figure 16: Intrasequence comparisons of transcription factor TFIID from yeast (PIR codes: A30365, A30366) using the "Pustell Protein Matrix" from the MacVector package of sequence analysis software (International Biotechnologies, Inc, New Haven, CT). The default parameters for "window size" (8 residues), "min. % score" (60 %), and "Scoring matrix file" (PAM-250) were used. Pustell uses character-based scaling to indicate different degrees of local similarity at increments of two percentage points: an "A" represents a 100% within the window, "B" = 96%, ..., "Z" = 50%, "a" = 48%, ..., "z" = 0%. Note that for the main (or identity) diagonal, every local similarity score should be 100% yet this diagonal is largely populated by characters other than "A." This phenomenon is an artifact of adjusting the local similarity scores by comparison to a "theoretical maximum score" based on amino acid composition and sequence length. Scores >100% are indicated by "@." Using this manner of scoring, it is also possible to have scores <100% for exact matches.

The short, symmetric diagonals, centered about residues 120 and 210 and signified by the characters "MLUW," represent a portion of the 77-residue internal sequence repeat (Hoeijmakers, 1990; Nagai, 1990). "M" = 76% similarity across an 8-residue window, "L" = 78%, "U" = 60% and "W" = 58% . Because the plot is compressed, "MLUW" actually represents the longer diagonal "MU_SLGIMUOOOW" when one magnifies the local area to its highest resolution or inspects the accompanying "Aligned sequences" display (not shown). By convention, the highest score from each of the regions being compressed is used as the score for that region. This longer diagonal represents the following alignment of internal residues within TFIID:

```
         110                      128
         KTTALIFASGKMVVTGAKSE
         MU_SLGIMUOOOW
         KIVLLIFVSGKIVLTGAKQR
         201                      220
```

Note that the alignment extends -4 and +3 residues beyond the ends of the plotted diagonal. Recall that an important characteristic of all window-based methods is that the residues used to compute the local score extend approximately half a span length in either direction from the plotted character or dot.

Finally, only 20 of the 77 residues that make up each internal repeat are apparent using default parameters. Larger windows and/or lower thresholds can be used to reveal the full extent of the internal duplication (not shown).

have internal homology or repeats. For example, the erythroid-specific, trans-acting factor Eryf1 has recently been shown to contain two distinct types of repeated domains, one of which is a tandemly-duplicated, 54-residue "finger" sequence (Trainor et al., 1990). Two copies of this finger domain are present in avian, human and murine Eryf1 along with a second, unrelated internal sequence repeat (Figure 15). Molecular evolutionary analysis of the Eryf1 tandem finger domains indicates a relatively ancient ancestor (Trainor et al., 1990). Interestingly, single copies of the Eryf1 finger were subsequently found in two fungal genes (*A. nidulans areA* and *N. crassa nit-2*) that regulate nitrogen metabolism (Fu and Marzluf, 1990; Kulda et al., 1990).

The well-known "TATA" box is an essential control region for polymerase II transcription units, and the protein factor that binds to this region (TFIID) is required for the first step of transcription initiation. The 240-residue sequence of yeast TFIID was reported late in 1989 by three independent groups (Hahn et al., 1989; Horikoshi et al., 1989; Schmidt et al., 1989). Early in 1990, two different investigators simultaneously published a finding, apparently overlooked by the original authors, that TFIID contains two 77-residue internal repeats (Hoeijmakers, 1990; Nagai, 1990). These repeats are obvious using default parameters for window and stringency on a dot matrix plot (Figure 16) and underscore the importance of performing this type of analysis on every new sequence.

RNA polymerase II has a carboxy-terminal repetitive sequence domain that consists of a species-specific variable number of copies of a seven-residue repeat unit, sometimes known as the "tail piece" (Sawadogo and Sentenac, 1990). An intersequence comparison of polymerase II from yeast and mouse shows the highly-repetitive C-terminus present in both species as well as the absence of internal repeats in other areas of the sequences (Figure 17). The main diagonal displays considerable, but nonuniform, sequence conservation and an absence of large deletion or insertion mutations. Dot matrix comparisons have been very helpful in analyzing evolutionarily conserved domains among polymerase subunits (see Figure 1 in Sawadogo and Sentenac, 1990). The precise biochemical function of the tail piece is as yet unknown, but Ohno and Ohno (1986) have transformed its coding sequence into a musical score "according to the modus operandi of Chopin's Nocturne." According to Ohno and Ohno (1986), when played on the piano: "This composition has a lively dance cadence, which is not altogether surprising because RNA polymerase is not a nocturnal creature, having instead to engage in transcriptional activity day and night." [Reprinted from Ohno and Ohno (1986), *Immunogenetics*, Vol. 24, p. 74.]

Finally, many transcription factors contain homopolymer and alternating copolymer tracts and/or regions enriched in particular residues (Brendel and Karlin, 1989; Mitchell and Tijan, 1989). Although these "low entropy"[21] subsequences are often readily identified by visual inspection, dot

---

[21] In information theory, entropy is the measure of the information content of a message (Pierce, 1980).

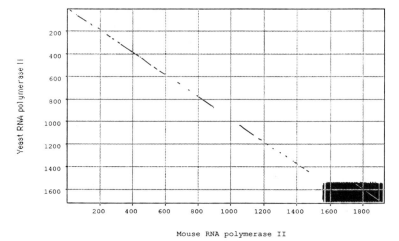

Figure 17: Intersequence comparison of yeast (PIR code: RNBR2L) and mouse (PIR code: A28490) RNA polymerase II, large subunit, using the MacVector/Pustell Protein Matrix with a window of 16 residues, plotting threshold of 60% and the PAM-250 matrix. See Figure 1 in Sawadogo and Sentenac (1990) for more extensive and detailed interspecies comparisons.

matrix plots are useful for mapping the boundaries of low entropy and high entropy domains and visualizing the overall sequence organization (see Cell Division Cycle Gene Products).

Cell Division Cycle (CDC) Gene Products. A large number of gene products are required for normal progression through the eukaryotic cell cycle, and more than 50 of these genes have been identified through genetic analysis in yeast (Nurse, 1985; Pringle and Hartwell, 1981). Subsets of genes act at different points in the cell cycle. For example, passage from interphase into mitosis appears to be universally regulated by a protein kinase, first identified as the product of the *cdc28* gene in the budding yeast *S. cerevisiae* . *cdc28* is homologous to the *cdc2* gene in the fission yeast *S. pombe*.[22]

Another subset of CDC genes[23] function at the G2/M boundary after DNA replication but prior to mitotic spindle elongation (Pringle and Hartwell, 1981). Database searching and dot matrix analysis of the derived amino acid sequence of *cdc23* uncovered a new repetitive sequence motif and a new relationship among a number of genes required for mitosis and RNA synthesis[24] (Sikorski et al., 1990). This repeating, 34-amino acid motif, known as "TPR," has also been identified in proteins involved in *Drosophila*

[22] For several recent reviews and a source of original literature citations, see the special issue of Science,"Frontiers in Biology: The Cell Cycle," vol. 246, 1989.

[23] *S. cerevisiae cdc13, cdc16, cdc17, cdc20* and *cdc23*.

[24] The CDC subset of TPR proteins includes *cdc23, cdc16* (*S. cerevisiae*), *nuc2+* (*S. pombe*), *bimA* (*A. nidulans*); the RNA regulation subset includes *ski3* and *SSN6* (*S. cerevisiae*). See Legend to Figures 18 and 19 for database retrieval codes.

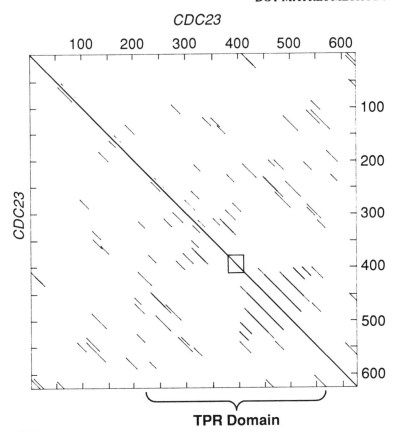

CDC23

TPR Domain

Figure 18: Intrasequence comparison of *S. cerevisiae cdc23* (PIR code: A32697, JS0435) using CMPSEQ84 (McLachlan 1983) with a span of 35 residues and the PAM-250 matrix. Thinner and thicker lines represent spans with scores with $p < 0.01$ and $p < 0.001$, respectively. The most significant diagonals (thicker lines) represent the TPR domain although a blank zone shows local repeat divergence. The box on the main diagonal shows the location of clustered temperature-sensitive mutations and this overall pattern is similar to that seen in apoE (Figure 12). Independent analysis, using the NBRF RELATE program, confirmed the significance of the internal repeats and indicated that the repeat unit length was 34 residues (Sikorski et al., 1990).

neurogenesis, mitochondrial transmembrane transport and the stress response (Boguski et al., 1990). Figure 18 shows a self comparison of *cdc23*. Eight tandem TPR repeats span residues 295-569 with a ninth copy present at residues 215-248. In between, there is a blank zone reminiscent of the type seen in the apoE self-comparison (see Figure 12) suggesting that this region may be functionally distinguishable from flanking sequences in the TPR domain. Consistent with this idea is the fact that temperature-sensitive point mutations (resulting in single amino acid substitutions) cluster in this region of the *cdc23* sequence (Sikorski et al., 1990).

Another interesting member of the TPR family is *SSN6* (also known as

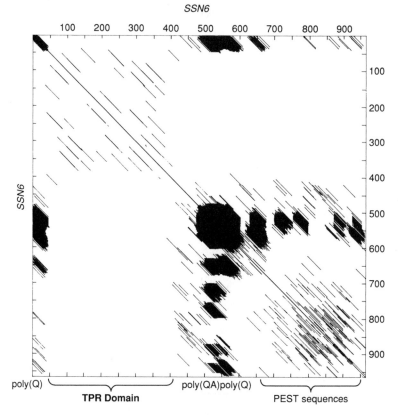

Figure 19: Intrasequence comparison of *S. cerevisiae SSN6* (PIR code: A30906) using CMPSEQ84 (McLachlan, 1983). Span length, plotting thresholds and scoring matrix were identical to those used in Figure 18. Note the striking "ink blot" appearance of the "low entropy" poly(Q) and poly(QA) regions. The N-terminal, tandem TPR domain is much easier to appreciate than in the case of *cdc23* (Figure 18) and this reflects the fact that among TPR proteins, *SSN6* has the most highy-conserved repeats (Sikorski et al., 1990). The C-terminal PEST domain (Schultz et al., 1990), has many closely and irregularly-spaced diagonals indicating a complex pattern of short, degenerate repeats. Contrast this with the more orderly and regular appearance of the TPR domain.

cyc8), a nuclear phosphoprotein of *S. cerevisiae* that acts as a negative regulator of a variety of genes required for normal growth, mating and sporulation (Schultz et al., 1990). The self-comparison matrix of *SSN6* is quite striking (Figure 19) and indicates the presence of four separate regions. The region containing 10 tandem TPR repeats (Sikorski et al., 1990) extends from about residue 50 to 400, and is flanked by a polyglutamine tract at the amino-terminus and a long segment containing poly(glutamine-alanine) and polyglutamine sequences in the central region of the protein. Note the "ink blot" appearance of the poly(QA) and poly(Q) regions. The carboxyl-terminal domain contains many short, degenerate repeats and clusters of charged residues. Schultz et al. (1990) have noted that this domain has a high content of proline, glutamate, serine and threonine (PEST) residues that are thought to be characteristic of proteins with short half-lives (Rechsteiner, 1988). Another important feature of the comparison matrix is the presence of absolutely blank zones in the symmetric right upper and left lower quadrants. This demonstrates quite clearly that the N-terminal TPR domain is not homologous to the C-terminal domain and suggests that *SSN6* is a mosaic protein formed by a gene fusion event involving the central poly(QA)•poly(Q) region.

Interestingly, the poly(Q) and poly(QA) regions of *SSN6* appear to be entirely dispensable for function (Schultz et al., 1990). Although such homopolymer tracts and/or alternating copolymers have received much recent attention because of their occurrence in a variety of transcription factors and developmental control proteins (e.g., Hoffman et al., 1990), they are actually found in hundreds of sequences, most notably a variety of plant seed nutrient storage proteins.[25]

Repetitive sequence characterization. Methods for more detailed characterization of internal repeats are not formally part of dot matrix analysis, but often go hand in hand with this technique and are thus briefly discussed here. Determining the unit length and copy number of an internal repeat is not always as easy as one might imagine. This is especially true in cases where repeats display length variability and/or considerable sequence divergence, where several distinct types of repeats are present in the same sequence, or where repeats are superimposed on a simpler, underlying pattern. Perhaps one of the best studied cases of the latter phenomenon is that of the myosin rod which contains a 197-residue period superimposed on a 28-residue repeat which in turn is superimposed on a 7-residue motif (McLachlan, 1983).

Usually one relies upon visual inspection to define an individual repeat unit and evidence for internal repeats may even be apparent in the restriction map of a cDNA. For example, the cDNA for rat apo-AIV contained an unexpectedly large number of evenly-spaced PstI sites which, retrospectively, were noted to correspond to codons for a conserved leucine-glutamine dipeptide in the 22-residue repetitive unit (Boguski et al., 1984). More typically, however, one searches for well-conserved or invariant "landmark" amino acid residues such as the "punctuating" prolines in apo-AI and AIV (Boguski et al., 1986c), the conserved tryptophan residue among TPRs (Sikorski et al., 1990), and the cysteine-histidine or cysteine-cysteine pairs found in finger proteins (Brown et al., 1985; Miller et al., 1985). Such landmark residues are then often used to estimate repeat boundaries and serve as anchor points for alignments.

A more objective and sensitive method for determining repeat unit length is to perform an intrasequence sliding window comparison (of exactly

---

[25] Using the 87-reside poly(QA)•poly(Q) region of *SSN6* as a query, the BLASTP program reports 506 matches in PIR release 26.0. FASTA gives 322 matches with a ktup of 2.

the same type used to compute a dot matrix) and note the average displacements of the highest-scoring segments. This is conveniently done using NBRF's RELATE program. The average displacements of high-scoring segments tend to be multiples of the repeat unit length. For example, RELATE analysis of apo-AIV which contains a fundamental 11-residue repeat, showed additional displacements of 22, 44, 55, 66, etc. residues (Boguski et al., 1986b). Likewise, analysis of *cdc23* which contains a 34-residue repeat, resulted in additional displacements of 68 and 102 amino acids (Sikorski et al., 1990). Finally, both autocorrelation[26] (Kubota et al., 1981) and Fourier methods have been used to determine the period of sequence repeats.

Summary and Future Developments

Dot matrix analysis is a simple, yet powerful, technique for sequence comparison. To paraphrase Collins and Coulson (1987), any comparison of two sequences (or of a sequence with itself) should start with a dot plot. We have seen multiple instances in which failure to heed this advice has delayed the identification of important sequence features.

As useful as dot matrix methods are, there is still considerable room for improvement. No present implementation takes full advantage of modern computer hardware and graphical user interface technology. Dot matrix analysis would also benefit from integration with other types of data analysis and image display tools. The incorporation of multi-length probes (Argos, 1987; Argos and Vingron, 1990) and customized scoring matrices (Altschul, 1991) would improve sensitivity and specificity. Finally, although dot matrix analysis will fundamentally remain a heuristic method of exploratory data analysis, the ability to estimate the statistical significance of the patterns one observes is highly desirable and might be accomplished using a combination of new and traditional methods.

DYNAMIC PROGRAMMING METHODS

Dot matrix methods rely on the power of the human brain to recognize patterns indicative of similarity and to add gaps to the sequences to achieve an alignment. It is, however, quite difficult to be sure that one has obtained the highest scoring, or optimal, alignment when it is made by hand. Because assessments of homology are almost always made on the basis of alignments produced by dynamic programming approaches, we will discuss the method in detail.

---

[26] Autocorrelation analysis is available in Amos Bairoch's PC/GENE, marketed by IntelliGenetics, Inc. (Mountain View,CA)

A brute force approach of aligning sequences with the automatic insertion of gaps shows that the problem is very difficult. Simply comparing two sequences, without gaps, is equivalent to the computation that takes place in dot matrix analysis, and requires time proportional to the product of the lengths of the sequences (i.e., time proportional to NM, where N=length of sequence 1, and M=length of sequence 2). If the sequences are assumed to be approximately the same length (N), then time proportional to N^2 is required. To account for the presence of gaps, we would have to repeat this calculation 2N times to examine the possibility of gaps in each position of each sequence, for time proportional to N^{4N}. In actuality, the situation is not quite so bad since some of these alignments would be nonsensical, for instance aligning gaps with gaps. An explicit equation has been derived for the number of comparisons that would be required (Waterman, 1989). For two sequences 300 residues long about 10^{88} comparisons would be required, which compares favorably to the estimated 10^{80} elementary particles in the universe.

Fortunately, there is a more efficient way of aligning sequences based on an approach known as dynamic programming. Needleman and Wunsch (1970) introduced this approach to molecular biologists, which is, to this day, frequently referred to as the Needleman-Wunsch algorithm. The dynamic programming method requires only time proportional to N^2, and is based on a simple realization of what the term optimal alignment implies.

Derivation of Dynamic Programming Alignment

If we consider the optimal, or highest scoring, alignment shown in A (below), we can break the alignment into two parts as shown in B. The overall alignment score is the score for the left-hand alignment of four bases plus the score for aligning the two bases on the right. If we assume that the 5 base alignment in A is optimal, we must conclude that the four base alignment in B is also an optimal alignment. If it was not (for example, if we gave a positive score for aligning G with T), the alignment shown in C would give a higher score than the one shown in A. Then C rather than A would be the optimal alignment.

```
AATGC          AATG     C        AATGC
|  ||           |  |  +  |        | .||
AG-GC          AG-G     C        A-GGC
  A               B                C
```

In plain English then, the best alignment that ends at a given pair of bases or residues is the best alignment of the sequences up to that point, plus the score for aligning the two additional bases or residues. Mathematically, we might say that, for sequence 1 and sequence 2 numbered 1 to i and 1 to j respectively

$$S_{ij} = s_{ij} + \max_{\substack{1 \le k < i \\ 1 \le l < j}} S_{kl} \tag{3}$$

where S_{ij} is the score for the alignment ending at i in sequence 1 and j in sequence 2

         s_{ij} is the score for aligning i with j.

Removing another pair of bases from B gives us the situation shown in D (below). The next step would require inserting a gap in sequence 2. Brief consideration shows that, at any step, there are only three possibilities: aligning the next base from sequence 1 with the next base from sequence 2; aligning the next base from sequence 1 with a gap; or aligning a gap in sequence 1 with the next base from sequence 2.

```
AAT        G        C
 |    +    |    +   |
AG-        G        C
```

D

This allows us to rewrite equation (3) in a more detailed form:

$$S_{ij} = s_{ij} + \max \begin{cases} S_{i\text{-}1\,j\text{-}1} & \text{or} \\ \max_{2<x<i} S_{i\text{-}x\,j\text{-}1}+w_{x\text{-}1} & \text{or} \\ \max_{2<y<i} S_{i\text{-}1\,j\text{-}y}+w_{y\text{-}1} & \end{cases} \tag{4}$$

where S_{ij} is the score for the alignment ending at i in sequence 1 and j in sequence 2

         s_{ij} is the score for aligning i with j

         w_x is the score for making a x long gap in sequence 1

         w_y is the score for making a y long gap in sequence 2 allowing gaps to be any length in either sequence.

The scores for gaps, w, are negative and are often referred to as gap penalties. This constitutes a virtually complete mathematical description of dynamic programming alignments since each of the terms on the right of equation 4 can, itself, be calculated from equation 4.

Simple Example of Dynamic Programming Alignment

Actual alignments are calculated in two stages. First, the two sequences are arranged on a lattice in much the same way as in dot matrix methods. For each point in the lattice, the alignment score, S_{ij}, is calculated. At the same time, the position of the best alignment in the previous row or column, i.e., the score of the best previous alignment which was used to calculate S_{ij}, is stored. This stored value is called a pointer and is represented by an arrow. In the second stage, the alignment is produced by starting at the highest alignment score in the lattice, and building up the alignment from right to left by following the pointers. This second stage is called the traceback. A graph of the pointers is sometimes referred to as a path graph because it defines the path through the lattice that corresponds to the optimal alignment.

Figure 20 shows a simple example of a dynamic programming alignment of the sequences AGGC (sequence 1) and AATGC (sequence 2). In this example no penalty is applied for introducing gaps so that the optimal alignment is simply the alignment with the most matches. The score matrix,

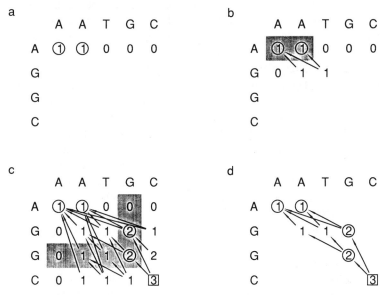

Figure 20: Calculation of dynamic programming alignments. The score matrix and path graph at several stages during the calculation of the alignment. In this calculation only identical matches receive positive scores, and no penalty is applied for gaps. The numbers represent the scores, S_{ij}, in the score matrix, and give the score for the best alignment ending at that pair of aligned residues. The alignment scores at positions where the comparison score for the corresponding two residues, s_{ij}, are positive are circled. The path graph is shown as arrows indicating the best previous alignment at each position in the path graph. a. after calculating the first row of the score matrix. b. after calculation of $S_{2,3}$, and the first several pointers in the path graph. c. after calculation of the last position, $S_{4,5}$, in the score matrix, and completed path graph. d. simplified score matrix and path graph showing only the best path or paths passing through each positive score, s_{ij} (circled).

containing the S_{ij} values, is filled in from left to right and top to bottom. Figure 20a shows the score matrix after filling the first row (i=1). Two positions, indicated by circled scores, are matches and receive a score of 1. All other positions receive scores of zero. The alignment score, S_{ij}, is the sum of the score for comparing the bases at i and j, plus the best previous alignment. Since all of these elements correspond to the first base in sequence 1, there are no best previous alignments and no pointers are saved at this point.

Figure 20b shows a later stage in the calculation of the score matrix. $S_{2,1}$ is an edge and therefore there is no best previous alignment to consider. $S_{2,2}$ has only one position that could contain a previous alignment, $S_{1,1}$, and this is therefore the position used for the pointer. To calculate $S_{2,3}$ we add the score for comparing the G in sequence 2 and the T in sequence 1 (mismatch so $s_{2,3}$=0), to the best previous alignment. The best previous alignment must end in either the previous row or the previous column, above and to the left of $S_{2,3}$. Therefore, we must look for the best previous alignment in both $S_{1,1}$ and $S_{1,2}$ (shown shaded). Since the scores for these positions are the same (in the absence of gap penalties), we store a pointer for each of them.

The final step in the generation of the score matrix is shown in Figure 20c. Setting the pointers for $S_{4,5}$ requires examination of the entire previous row and column (shown shaded) for the best previous alignments. Two equivalent positions are found at $S_{2,4}$ and $S_{3,4}$ and pointers set accordingly. The alignment is generated by following the pointers from the highest score in the score matrix, along a path leading up and to the left. Because an alignment must end in either the last base of sequence 1 or the last base of sequence 2 (the only other possibility being that both sequences end in a gap), the highest score in the score matrix is constrained to lie in either the last row (the last pair of bases in the alignment contain the last base of sequence 1) or the last column (the last pair of bases in the alignment contains the last base of sequence 2). In our example, the highest scoring position is found at $S_{4,5}$ and therefore aligns the last base from each sequence. This position is shown boxed.

Figure 20c is confusing because of the large number of unproductive paths, that is to say, paths that after an early match contain only mismatches. Because optimal alignments must contain matches, it is sufficient to show only the best path or paths passing through each matching position. This simplification applied to Figure 20c gives us Figure 20d. We now perform the traceback to generate the final alignment. Starting from the highest scoring position, $S_{4,5}$, we follow the pointers back, building up the alignment one pair of residues at a time, from right to left. If we follow the lower pointer at each position, we generate the following alignment in four steps:

C	GC	G.GC	AG.GC	**Sequence 1**
|	||	||	| ||	
C	GC	ATGC	AATGC	**Sequence 2**
step 1	step 2	step 3	step 4	

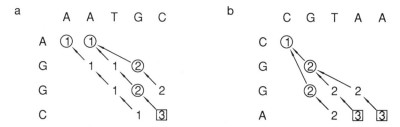

Figure 21: Effect of not saving all path pointers. The alignment in Figure 20 is repeated, but only one path pointer, the one which would introduce the shortest gap, is saved for each position, S_{ij}, in the score matrix. a. forward alignment b. reverse alignment - the same alignment with each sequence reversed. This will often, but not always, give a different alignment when only one pointer is saved for each position.

At step 3 we skip from the G in sequence 2 to the A, leaving the T unmatched. This is a gap, indicated by aligning the T with a null character, in this example a period. The final alignment, as indicated by the score for the alignment, $S_{4,5}$, contains 3 matches. There are actually five equivalent alignments beginninbg with $S_{4,5}$ in Figure 20d, all contatining three matches:

```
AG.GC     A.GGC     .AGGC     A..GGC     .A.GGC     Sequence 1
|  ||     |  ||     |  ||     |   |      |   |
AATGC     AATGC     AATGC     AATG.C     AATG.C     Sequence 2
  1         2         3         4          5
```

There are no other ways to align these sequences and get three matches unless gaps are aligned with gaps.

Many alignment programs allow only a single pointer to be set for each position in the score matrix. When two previous alignments have the same score, an arbitrary decision must be made about which pointer to store. Figure 21a shows an alignment example of the same two sequences used above, but storing only the pointer that corresponds to the shorter gap. The resulting optimal alignment is number 3 above and appears to be unique, judging from the path matrix.

This brings to light an important point about alignment programs. Although dynamic programming alignment techniques are guaranteed to find an optimal alignment, there may be other equally optimal alignments, and some of them may be more biologically relevant. The GCG program GAP[27] approaches this problem in a unique way, allowing the option to control which equivalent pointers are saved. The "highroad" option always saves the "upper" pointer, and would result in alignment 5 above, while the "lowroad" option, which always saves the "lower" pointer, would result in

[27] Genetics Computer Group, Inc., Madison, WI.

alignment 1 (Figure 20c). The highroad/lowroad options will always give different alignments if there are equivalent alignments. For long sequences there could be hundreds of equivalent alignments and it is prohibitive and confusing to list them all. The highroad/lowroad procedure can be thought of as establishing an upper and lower bound for the variation of the alignments.

Another way of detecting possible equivalent alignments is shown in Figure 21b. Simply perform the alignment a second time, keeping all parameters the same, but reverse both sequences. This method is not foolproof, as Figure 21b shows, since depending on which of the two optimal paths is reported, the result might be the same as that of 21a.

The problem of equivalent alignments is worse for nucleic acid sequences than for protein sequences because nucleic acids are usually aligned using a scoring system that gives all identical comparisons the same score (usually 1). In combination with the four character nucleic acid alphabet, this makes multiple equivalent paths common. Protein alignments are usually made based on a scoring system that gives a partial score for amino acid residues that are chemically or mutationally similar (see Scoring Systems). In combination with the larger 20 character protein sequence alphabet, this makes equivalent alignments less likely (although still possible).

More Complicated Alignments

The simple alignment shown in Figures 20 and 21 applied no penalties for the introduction of gaps. For longer sequences, gap penalties must be used to produce sensible alignments. For instance, when human pancreatic hormone precursor and chicken pancreatic hormone are aligned without gap penalties (Figure 22a), the high similarity of these homologous peptide hormones does not immediately strike the eye. However, when penalties are applied for the introduction of gaps, as shown in Figure 22b, the similarity is clear. It is worth noting that the last four residues of the chicken sequence are aligned in a non-homologous position in Figure 22a, but correctly in Figure 22b.

Gap penalties were originally applied either as a single penalty, regardless of the length of the gap (Needleman and Wunsch, 1970), or as penalty for each gap character inserted into the sequences (Sellers, 1974). More recently,

```
        Human ALLLQPLLGAQGAPLEPVYPGDNATP.EQMAQ.YAAD.LRRYINMLTRPRYGKRHKEDTLAF
A             :   | : |  |    ||||:| | |::    |  | |  |:|::|      ||:      :
      Chicken G....P..S.Q..P..T.YPGDDA.PVEDLIRFY..DNLQQYLNVVT......RHR.....Y

        Human ALLLQPLLGAQGAPLEPVYPGDNATPEQMAQYAADLRRYINMLTRPRYGKRHKEDTLAF
B             :| :| ||||:| |::  :  :|  |:|::|| ||
      Chicken ............GPSQPTYPGDDAPVEDLIRFYDNLQQYLNVVTRHRY..........
```

Figure 22: Gap penalties are required for sensible alignments. The alignment of the human pancreatic hormone precursor and chicken pancreatic hormone are shown. Identical matches are shown as 'I', and conservative substitutions as ':'. a. alignment without gap penalties. b. alignment with gap penalty of 1.0 + 0.1 x gap length.

most programs have relied on gap penalties with both a length-dependent and a length-independent term (equation 5).

$$w_x = g + lx \qquad (5)$$

where w_x is the penalty for a gap of length x
       g is the length-independent term (gap opening penalty)
       l is the length-dependent term (gap extension penalty)

The length-independent term of the penalty (g) is applied to all gaps regardless of their length. It can be considered a penalty that is paid when the first base or residue is aligned with a gap character, and is therefore sometimes called a gap opening or gap creation penalty. The length-dependent term (l) of the gap penalty increases with the length of the gap and can be considered to be a penalty paid as each successive position is added to the gap. For this reason, it is sometimes called a gap extension penalty. Fitch and Smith (1983) showed that for globin mRNA sequences, correct alignments could only be made if both terms were non-zero. As can be seen from the Figure 22, gap penalties have a large effect on alignments and it is wise to sample a wide range of values in order to find the most interesting optimal alignments.

Typical values for the gap creation penalty are in the range of one half to five times the score for a match. The gap extension penalty is usually smaller than the gap creation penalty, often in the range of a tenth to one times the score of a match. When these gap penalty values are used, an alignment must gain a substantial number of matches to be worth adding a gap, but a long gap costs only slightly more than a short gap. This coincides with our knowledge of the mutational process which suggests that long insertions and deletions of various lengths can be produced by single mutational events.

Alignment programs vary in their treatment of gaps introduced at the ends of the sequences (end-gaps). If the gap penalties are applied for end-gaps, they are referred to as weighted end-gaps. If the penalties are not applied, we call them unweighted-end gaps. For sequences that are known to be homologous, it makes sense to weight end-gaps. However, if the sequences are different lengths, or of unknown homology, it is probably a good idea to not weight end-gaps. If you are unsure whether the program you are using weights end-gaps, you may be able to find out by adding small amounts of additional sequence to the ends of one sequence and observing the effect on the alignment.

The alignment procedures described above are known as global alignment algorithms, because the resulting alignments contain all characters in both sequences. Short but highly similar subsequences may not be aligned in a global alignment because they are outweighed by the rest of the sequence. One of the most important advances in dynamic programming sequence alignment techniques was the introduction of local alignment methods (Smith and Waterman, 1981). These methods find the two "most similar" segments of the sequences, and generate an alignment that may contain only part of each sequence. Only small modifications to the algorithm described above are required:

- the scoring system must include negative scores for mismatches
- the minimum score recorded in the score matrix, S, is zero
- the end of the optimal path may be found anywhere in the score matrix, not only in the last row or column.

The key to the local alignment method is point 1. Use of negative scores for mismatches means that once the end of a region of similarity is reached, the scores along the path will begin to decrease. Because we want each short segment of similarity to start from zero, positions in the score matrix which would have a negative score are given a value of zero. A position in the score matrix will either be close enough to an existing path to be linked to it by a gap, or it will be the beginning of an independent region of local similarity.

Local alignment programs are probably the method of choice for unknown sequences, since they will find something quite close to a global alignment if the sequences are highly similar, or the region of highest similarity if they are not. Global alignment of distantly related sequences, on the other hand, may entirely miss their similarity. Figures 23a and 23b show global alignment and local alignments of segments of the phi-X174 A gene and *lac* promoters. The global alignment misses the similarity of the -35 regions of the promoters, which is found by the local alignment. Although the -35 regions of the promoters have 6 out of 7 identical bases (86% identical), the optimal global alignment matches only 7 out of 15 (47% identical). This clearly shows the differences between the approaches. The local algorithm finds the segment with the highest local similarity, while the global algorithm chooses a different alignment with higher overall similarity (7 matches) but lower local similarity (only 47% identical versus 86% identical).

Other Derivations

The presentation above follows the original Needleman and Wunsch paper, particularly in finding the alignment that optimizes the similarity between the sequences. Their paper, however, presented neither a mathematical outline of the algorithm nor a proof, and much of the early mathematical work centered on versions of the algorithm presented in terms of distance rather than similarity. In terms of distances, the alignment program finds the alignment that minimizes the distance between the sequences rather than maximizes the similarity, but the procedure is basically the same. The scores for matches are thus 0, and the scores for mismatches some larger value (dissimilar residues are more distant). Path matrices are often shown in a slightly different form, as well, with gaps shown as a series of horizontal and vertical steps along the lattice, rather than a single diagonal jump.

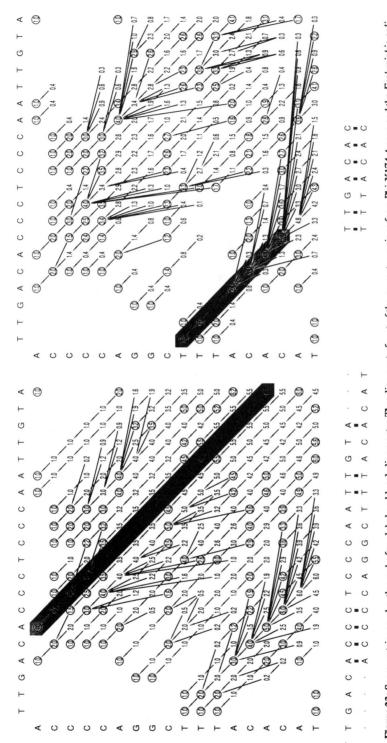

Figure 23: Score matrices and path graphs for global and local alignments. The alignment of part of the promoter regions from Phi-X174 A gene and the *Escherichia coli lac* gene. For both alignments, matches receive a score of 1, the gap opening penalty is 1.2 and the gap extension penalty is 0.3. In the local alignment, mismatches receive a score of -0.6. The best paths are shaded, and the highest scoring positions shown in a square. The corresponding alignments are shown below the score/path matrices.

Extensions

The primary drawback to dynamic programming methods is that they require a considerable amount of computation. This limits their usefulness for tasks such as database searching. One simple way to speed up the alignment is to calculate only part of the score matrix, usually a diagonal band down the center (e.g., Sankoff and Kruskal, 1983). This can be safely done, for instance, if you know the sequences are homologous and do not require large gaps in their alignment, or if you have information from a faster method, such as hashing (see Hashing and Neighborhood Algorithms) that tells you where the most similar regions of the sequences are. Several methods that perform a banded alignment and iteratively increase the width of the band until the optimal alignment is found have been presented (Ukkonen, 1983).

A further great increase in alignment speed can be achieved through subdivision. If segments in each sequence can be identified, for instance by hashing methods (see Hashing and Neighborhood Algorithms), that are so similar they are unlikely to match with anything else, the alignment can be broken down into two smaller alignments, separated by the matching segment. Each equal subdivision increases the speed of the alignment by a factor of two.

Once a cDNA clone is sequenced, one usually wishes to identify the protein encoded by the message. One approach is to translate all three (or six) reading frames of the nucleic acid sequence and use the resulting protein sequences as probes in a fast database search (e.g., TFASTA - Lipman and Pearson, 1985; TBLASTN - Gish et al., in preparation). Unfortunately, this approach can be quite sensitive to frameshift errors in the cDNA sequence. An alternative to this approach (States and Botstein, 1990) uses dynamic programming methods to align the DNA and protein sequence.

SCORING SYSTEMS

The simplest scoring systems for molecular sequence analysis give positive scores only to comparisons of identical bases or residues. These scoring tables are referred to as an identity or unitary matrices and are still the primary scoring systems used for nucleic acid sequences.

The average rate of transition (purine to purine or pyrimidine to pyrimidine) mutations is about three times the average rate of transversion (purine to pyrimidine and vice versa) mutations. The rates of insertion/deletion mutations can also be determined from known homologous sequences. These values have been used to calculate scoring tables for nucleic acid sequences based on maximum likelihood methods (Bishop and Thompson, 1986). However, mutation rates and characteristics vary dramatically from species to species, from coding to non-coding regions, and from gene to gene, making it impossible to define a single best scoring system by this approach.   In the absence of a single appropriate scoring table, most nucleic acid sequence alignments continue to be based on identity scoring systems.

Identity-based scoring systems often do not give the desired sensitivity when comparing distantly related sequences, especially for protein sequences. There is a strong consensus that, for proteins, scoring systems based on the chemical or mutational similarity of the amino acid residues are much better than identity scoring systems (Schwartz and Dayhoff, 1978; Feng and Doolittle, 1987). One early method of scoring the similarity of amino acid residues is known as the minimum base change or genetic code matrix. This scoring system calculates the similarity between residues as the minimum number of base changes required to change a codon for one residue to a codon for another. This system seemed especially plausible for evolutionary studies because it allowed the difference in amino acid residues to be stated in terms of the minimum number of mutational events needed to convert one residue to another.

The most commonly used scoring systems for protein sequences are based on the MDM_{78} table (mutation data matrix, 1978) of Dayhoff and coworkers (Schwartz and Dayhoff, 1979; George et al., 1990; see Appendix IV). Often called simply the "Dayhoff" table, this scoring table is derived using the "accepted point mutation" model of evolution (Dayhoff et al., 1978). A dataset was compiled from a group of closely related proteins (less than 15% amino acid differences), that could be unambiguously aligned. From these aligned sequences, Dayhoff and coworkers calculated a matrix describing the probability, for each residue, that a mutation would change the residue to each of the other possible residues. The matrix was calculated such that the probabilities represent the average mutational change that will take place when 1 residue out of 100 undergo mutation (1% accepted mutations or 1 PAM). This matrix is called the mutation probability matrix at 1 PAM, or simply the PAM-1 matrix. The specific model of evolution used by Dayhoff and coworkers assumes that more distantly related proteins arise by a series of uncorrelated mutations that can be described by the PAM-1 matrix. Mathematically, this is called a first order Markov chain transition model. To derive a mutational probability matrix for a protein sequence that has undergone N percent accepted mutations, a PAM-N matrix, the PAM-1 matrix is multiplied by itself N times. This results in a family of scoring matrices often referred to as PAM-120, PAM-250, etc.

Because one often desires to know if an alignment is more likely than one between unrelated sequences, scoring systems are often converted to a log-odds matrix. In a log-odds matrix, each element of the matrix, representing the probability that the two corresponding characters are evolutionarily related, is divided by the probability that the two characters could be aligned by chance. To aid in the calculation of probabilities, the values are converted to logarithms. The log-odds form of the PAM-250 matrix is called MDM_{78} and Dayhoff and coworkers recommend using it for all sequence comparisons although it has been argued that it may be better to use an equivalent log-odds matrix calculated for a lower PAM for alignments of unknown sequences (Altschul, personal communication). The log of the probability of two sequences being evolutionarily related can, in principle, be calculated as the sum of the scores for each aligned pair of residues, i.e., the alignment score if a log-odds matrix is used as the scoring system for the alignment. However, this is overly simplistic since it ignores the effect of insertions and deletions on the probability.

The accepted point mutation model of protein sequence evolution is known to be imperfect in a number of ways. One common criticism is that the frequencies of mutations that require more than one base change in the DNA sequence is higher than would be expected for a simple Markovian model of DNA sequence evolution (Dayhoff and Eck, 1968; Wilbur,1986). This criticism, however, is based on a specific model of DNA sequence evolution which is, itself, open to criticism (George et al., 1990). More importantly, the accepted point mutation model assumes that all residues in a protein are equally mutable; an assumption that is clearly incorrect. This can be easily seen by examining alignments of families of homologous proteins. For a set of six proteins, each sharing a pairwise sequence identity of 35 % or less, one would expect to find not a single amino acid conserved in every sequence if all positions were equally mutable. In actual families of proteins, however, it is not unusual to find several residues that are absolutely conserved in dozens of distantly related sequences (the active site triad of the serine proteases, for example). Furthermore, by starting from aligned sequences with only one or two differences, Dayhoff and coworkers selected mutations occurring at the most mutable positions as the basis for their calculation. Since the most important features in alignments are those positions that are unusually conserved, it has been argued that scoring systems based on the chemical or structural properties of the amino acid residues may produce better alignments (for example, Kubota et al., 1981; Feng and Doolittle, 1985; Argos, 1987; Risler et al., 1988). Lastly, the matrix may be biased because it was derived using mainly small globular proteins as a basis. In spite of its flaws, the MDM_{78} table, or a scoring table derived from it, remains the only widely accepted means of scoring protein sequence alignments. The important position that the MDM_{78} table occupies in molecular sequence analysis is clearly indicated by the fact that every new scoring system compares itself to the MDM_{78} table as a standard.

A special class of scoring systems known as metric distances merits additional consideration. A metric is a distance measure that has the following properties:

- no distance is less than 0
- identical sequence characters have a distance of 0
- the distance is symmetric; that is, the distance from A to B is the same as the distance from B to A

• the scoring system as a whole obeys the triangle inequality; if you consider any three distances, the distance from A to C must be less than or equal to the distance from A to B plus the distance from B to C

Metric distances have received a great deal of attention by mathematicians and were extensively used in the early development of dynamic programming sequence alignment techniques (Sankoff, 1972; Sellers, 1974). The emphasis on metric distances is due mainly to the early use of sequence alignments to provide a measure of evolutionary distance between two sequences. An alignment score generated using a metric scoring system is itself a metric, and thus the most appropriate kind of measure to use in constructing a phylogenetic tree.

Many alignment programs permit one to use a user-specified scoring system. Usually, the alignment program reads the scoring information from a separate file. It is extremely important to use a scoring system appropriate to the algorithm you are using. For global alignments, all of the values in the scoring table must be greater than zero; if they are not, the highest scoring position is not guaranteed to occur at the last row or column of the score matrix, and the resulting alignment is likely to be less than optimal. Local alignment algorithms require that scores for mismatches be less than zero. If you inadvertently use a table with only positive scores with a local alignment program, the result is not so disastrous — the resulting alignment is simply a global alignment.

Fast Methods

To be useful, an algorithm must be able to sensitively and specifically identify sequence relationships while running on available computing systems with satisfactory execution times.[28] Efficiency is a complex issue influenced by many aspects of the computing resources available. High speed microprocessors and dedicated special purpose coprocessors may aide in some phases of a search, while overall performance remains limited by other aspects. I/O requirements, random access memory space and access patterns, and disk access all need to be considered. The dynamic programming algorithm described above is guaranteed to find the optimal alignment between two sequences, but because it requires order N^2 operations, the use of this algorithm for database searching on currently available PCs and workstations is prohibitive. The dynamic programming algorithm is amenable to parallel implementations processing an entire anti-diagonal stripe simultaneously.

---

[28] Although supercomputers, massively paralleled achitectures, and specialized chips all have their niches, the great majority of sequence analysis problems are adequately and efficiently handled using general purpose computers.

The difficulty with these approaches is that they require specialized hardware and software development, although dramatic performance enhancements have been demonstrated (Collins and Coulson, 1990).

Hashing and Neighborhood Algorithms

An alternative strategy which greatly accelerates the initial search while still functioning on standard processors involves the use of hashing or neighborhood tables to screen a set of sequences for possible matches with a query sequence. This is accomplished by building a table of the locations of short subsequences, or *words*, in the query sequence (Dumas and Ninio, 1982; Wilbur and Lipman, 1983; Pearson and Lipman, 1988; see Figure 22).

Segments from the database are then sequentially tested against this hash or neighborhood table. If a match is found, it corresponds to a potential alignment and is saved. If no match is found then the next segment is examined. For large databases the time required to build the hash or neighborhood table is negligible so the computation time is proportional to the size of the database, N, where N is the number of bases in the database. This is a great improvement over the N^2 time requireds for dynamic programming alignments (see Dynamic Programming Methods).

The FASTP (Lipman and Pearson, 1985) and FASTA (Pearson and Lipman, 1988; Pearson, 1990) programs have proven to be very popular and useful implementations of this type of algorithm. In the case of FASTA, the hash table is built to require exact matches between the query and target sequence over the full length of the hash entry. The size of the hash table entry (word size) is adjustable as an input parameter (ktuple). The use of a larger ktuple increases the speed of the algorithm dramatically, but the requirement for an exact match over the entire length of the ktuple means that many significant alignments between moderately diverged sequences will be missed if a large ktuple (greater than two for protein sequences) is used.

The FASTA program passes through four steps as it searches the database for similar sequences. In the first step, regions of diagonals with the highest density of common words are found. In the second step, the ten regions with the highest density of matching words are rescored using the MDM_{78} matrix (see Scoring Systems). The ends of the regions are then trimmed to remove residues that do not contribute to the highest score, resulting in a set of partial alignments without gaps. The best scoring region from this second step is reported as the "init1" score. In the third step, regions that are near enough together are joined into a single region. The score for this, possibly larger, region, including penalties for gaps needed to join the initial regions, is reported as "initn" and used to sort the output of the search. Finally, in the fourth step, a dynamic programming alignment is performed in a band 32 residues wide in the region around the best (init1) initial region. This is the "opt" or optimized score. This procedure is described in detail by Pearson (1990). Table 3 provides an example where the FASTA algorithm

```
1680 scores better than 27 saved, ktup: 2, fact: 8  scan time:  0:01:13
The best scores are:                                initn init1   opt
KFMS$HUMAN (Swiss) MACROPHAGE COLONY STIMULATING FACTO  422   422   422
KFMS$FELCA (Swiss) MACROPHAGE COLONY STIMULATING FACTO  354   354   355
KFMS$FSVMD (Swiss) FMS TYROSINE KINASE TRANSFORMING PR  353   353   354
KFMS$MOUSE (Swiss) MACROPHAGE COLONY STIMULATING FACTO  335   335   335
FINC$BOVIN (Swiss) FIBRONECTIN (FN).                     64    48    48
HV35$MOUSE (Swiss) IG HEAVY CHAIN V-III REGION (HPC76)   63    46    50
FCE1$RAT (Swiss) HIGH AFFINITY IMMUNOGLOBULIN EPSILON    62    51    60
LSTP$STAST (Swiss) LYSOSTAPHIN PRECURSOR.                61    61    61
LSTP$STASI (Swiss) LYSOSTAPHIN PRECURSOR.                61    61    61
VGLC$HSVE1 (Swiss) GLYCOPROTEIN 13 PRECURSOR (GP13).     59    59    60
PGDR$MOUSE (Swiss) PLATELET-DERIVED GROWTH FACTOR RECE   59    44    56
ARS$CHLRE (Swiss) ARYLSULFATASE PRECURSOR (EC 3.1.6.1)   58    58    58
FINC$HUMAN (Swiss) FIBRONECTIN (FN).                     56    48    48
FCEA$HUMAN (Swiss) HIGH AFFINITY IMMUNOGLOBULIN EPSILO   55    40    44
API$ACHLY (Swiss) PROTEASE I PRECURSOR (EC 3.4.21.50)    54    54    67
GLGB$ECOLI (Swiss) 1,4-ALPHA-GLUCAN BRANCHING ENZYME (   54    54    55
TEGU$HSV11 (Swiss) LARGE TEGUMENT PROTEIN (VIRION PROT   53    39    46
HV33$MOUSE (Swiss) IG HEAVY CHAIN V-III REGION (W3082)   53    37    51
ENV$HIV1J (Swiss) ENVELOPE POLYPROTEIN GP160 PRECURSOR   53    53    57
HV28$MOUSE (Swiss) IG HEAVY CHAIN V-III REGION (U61).    53    37    51
```

Table 3: The FASTA search performed using the first immunoglobulin domain of the fms (CSF-1 receptor) extracellular domain as defined by exon-intron junctions (Hampe, 1989) against the SWISS-PROT sequence database identifies many significant pairwise and three way alignments. The beginning of the listing indicates the total number of scores saved for more detailed analysis after the initial hash table search (1680), the score used to define that list (27), and the ktuple size used in building the table (2). The scores in columns labeled "initn," "init1," and "opt" are the scores for the best single diagonal identified in the hash table search, "initn," a heuristically defined score based on combining the best 10 hash table hits, "init1," and the best score identified using a limited dynamic programming analysis, "opt." Scores were calculated using the PAM-250 matrix.

was used to search the SWISS-PROT database (see Appendix VIII) using a ktuple of 2 and the CSF-1 (cfms) receptor as a query sequence. This domain is known to be a member of the immunoglobulin family of protein domains. Although the search does identify significant similarity to other immuno-globulin-like proteins, this search misses many significant similarities (for examples, see Multiple Alignment for Database Searching).

The probability of missing a significant alignment in a hash table based method has been theoretically evaluated (Karlin and Altschul, 1990) and it is possible to explicitly balance search time against the possibility of missing a relevant alignment. Alignments where there are extensive regions of low similarity, but few exact ktuple matches are unusual enough that hashing methods have proven to be effective in the majority of cases. The reliability of the hash table methods may be improved by building the table based on both approximate and exact matches, in other words, around a neighborhood of the exact match. This permits the use of a much larger ktuple size (and performance enhancement) while preserving alignment reliability to a greater extent. A finite state machine algorithm has been implemented in the BLAST algorithm (see below).

Finite State Machines

To this point, all of the algorithms have been presented as taking sequences a single base or amino acid at a time. This is inefficient from a computational point of view because it takes only 2 or 5 bits of information to represent a base or amino acid, respectively. Modern computers manipulate data in chunks of 16, 32, or even 64 bits. One way in which the capabilities of available processors can be better exploited is with an algorithm known as a finite state machine. Implementation of a neighborhood or hash table algorithm involves stepping between a limited number of states (the sequence matches a pattern to this point or it does not). This can be exploited by calculating a state transition table that tells what state to go to based on the next data element or elements that are read (Altschul et al., 1990; Hopcroft and Ullman, 1979). By taking the data several bases or amino acids at a time, several state transitions may be considered in one step and the rate of progress is effectively multiplied. The state table is smaller than the hash or neighborhood table for single transitions, but grows exponentially with the number of transitions being considered in each step.

Statistical Approaches - BLAST

The algorithm employed in a sequence search may have a significant impact on its discriminatory ability. For example, searches based on protein sequences are frequently able to recognize significant matches that are not apparent in the analyzing the nucleic acid sequence directly (Doolittle, 1986). Search strategies based on complete or approximate alignment of sequences including the presence of insertions and deletions have been widely utilized (e.g., FASTA). While the statistical characteristics of these algorithms may be empirically characterized (Collins and Coulson, 1990), a rigorous derivation of the significance of observed scores has not been achieved. With the ever-expanding size of sequence databases, the balance between search sensitivity and specificity becomes increasingly critical, and the rigorous application of statistical formalism can help to optimize performance. Recently, Altschul and Karlin have derived a rigorous theory for the significance of ungapped sequence alignments (Karlin and Altschul, 1990). Using these statistics, a very efficient neighborhood search algorithm (Basic Local Alignment Search Tool, or BLAST) has been devised that examines only ungapped segments, but ranks matches statistically (Altschul et al., 1990).

The power of this algorithm is demonstrated by repeating our example using the first extracellular domain of the cfms receptor as a query to search the SWISS-PROT database (see Table 3 and Hashing and Neighborhood Algorithms). As shown in Table 4, the BLAST algorithm correctly identifies a number of significant alignments with immunoglobulin-like domains in other receptors, cell adhesion molecules, and the immunoglobulins themselves. The "Expect" probability values represent the calculated probability

```
>KFMS$HUMAN (Swiss) MACROPHAGE COLONY STIMULATING FACTOR I RECEPTOR
   Score = 449, Expect = 6.2e-60, Poisson P = 6.2e-60, length = 87
>KFMS$FELCA (Swiss) MACROPHAGE COLONY STIMULATING FACTOR I RECEPTOR
   Score = 367, Expect = 1.1e-47, Poisson P = 1.1e-47, length = 87
>KFMS$FSVMD (Swiss) FMS TYROSINE KINASE TRANSFORMING PROTEIN (EC
2.7.1.112)
   Score = 365, Expect = 2.2e-47, Poisson P = 2.2e-47, length = 87
>KFMS$MOUSE (Swiss) MACROPHAGE COLONY STIMULATING FACTOR I RECEPTOR
   Score = 341, Expect = 8.6e-44, Poisson P = 8.5e-44, length = 87
>PGDR$HUMAN (Swiss) PLATELET-DERIVED GROWTH FACTOR RECEPTOR ALPHA
PRECURSOR
   Score = 70, Expect = 0.0026, Poisson P = 0.0026, length = 30
>KKIT$MOUSE (Swiss) KIT PROTO-ONCOGENE TYROSINE KINASE PRECURSOR (EC
   Score = 68, Expect = 0.0053, Poisson P = 0.0053, length = 30
>NCAM$XENLA (Swiss) NEURAL CELL ADHESION MOLECULE PRECURSOR (N-CAM)
   Score = 63, Expect = 0.029, Poisson P = 0.029, length = 35
>FCEA$HUMAN (Swiss) HIGH AFFINITY IMMUNOGLOBULIN EPSILON RECEPTOR
   Score = 62, Expect = 0.041, Poisson P = 0.040, length = 50
>PGDS$HUMAN (Swiss) PLATELET-DERIVED GROWTH FACTOR RECEPTOR BETA
PRECURSOR
   Score = 61, Expect = 0.058, Poisson P = 0.057, length = 37
>NCA2$HUMAN (Swiss) NEURAL CELL ADHESION MOLECULE,
   Score = 59, Expect = 0.12, Poisson P = 0.11, length = 28
>FCE1$RAT (Swiss) HIGH AFFINITY IMMUNOGLOBULIN EPSILON RECEPTOR
   Score = 54, Expect = 0.65, Poisson P = 0.48, length = 20
>LV0A$HUMAN (Swiss) IG LAMBDA CHAIN V REGION (4A).
   Score = 53, Expect = 0.92, Poisson P = 0.60, length = 18
```

Table 4: The BLAST search performed using the first immunoglobulin domain of the fms (CSF-1 receptor) extracellular domain as defined by exon-intron junctions (Hampe, 1989) against the SWISS-PROT sequence database identifies several significant pairwise alignments. The output score is the sum of the PAM-120 matrix values over the identified segment. The "Expect" probability is the number of equally good alignments that would be expected in searching a random sequence database with the query. The "Poisson" statistic attempts to combine significance if multiple diagonals were identified for the pair of sequences. The "length" is the length of the aligned diagonal segment.

of finding similarities with this significance in the entire target database, calculated from the Karlin-Altschul statistics. This avoids reviewing histograms of scores for each search and attempts to theoretically estimate alignment significance.

While the BLAST approach is approximate in the sense that the possibility of gapped alignments is ignored, the statistical ranking and significance tests outweigh this disadvantage. It should be noted that simply because one might expect to find an alignment of similar significance at random (Expect > .5, for example), this does not imply that the alignment is not meaningful, as the bottom line of Table 4 illustrates.

Multiple Sequence Alignment

Multiple alignment has many important applications in sequence analysis. Although it is often used to simply display or summarize the relationships among a group of sequences, multiple alignment also has major roles in protein modeling and structure prediction, studies of molecular evolution, and the detection and quantitation of sequence patterns or motifs. With the explosive growth of sequence databases, it is now common to find several

Global Multiple Alignment

Altschul, S. F. (1989). "Gap costs for multiple sequence alignment." J. Theor. Biol. **138**: 297-309.

Altschul, S. F., R. J. Carroll and D. J. Lipman. (1989). "Weights for data related by a tree." J. Mol. Biol. **207**: 647-653.

Altschul, S. F. and D. J. Lipman. (1989). "Trees, stars, and multiple biological sequence alignment." SIAM J. Appl. Math. **49**: 197-209.

Barton, G. J. and M. J. E. Sternberg. (1987). "A strategy for the rapid multiple alignment of protein sequences. Confidence levels from tertiary structure comparisons." J. Mol. Biol. **198**: 327-337.

Carrillo, H. and D. J. Lipman. (1988). "The multiple sequence alignment problem in biology." SIAM J. Appl. Math. **48**: 1073-1082.

Feng, D. and R. F. Doolittle. (1987). "Progressive sequence alignment as a prerequisite to correct phylogenetic trees." J. Mol. Evol. **25**: 351-360.

Fredman, M. L. (1984). "Algorithms for computing evolutionary similarity measures with length independent gap penalties." Bull. Math. Biol. **46**: 553-566.

Gotoh, O. (1986). "Alignment of three biological sequences with an efficient traceback procedure." J. Theor. Biol. **121**: 327-337.

Johnson, M. S. and R. F. Doolittle. (1986). "A method for the simultaneous alignment of three or more amino acid sequences." J. Mol. Evol. **23**: 267-278.

Lipman, D. J., S. F. Altschul and J. D. Kececioglu. (1989). "A tool for multiple sequence alignment." Proc. Natl. Acad. Sci. USA. **86**: 4412-4415.

Murata, M., J. S. Richardson and J. L. Sussman. (1985). "Simultaneous comparison of three protein sequences." Proc. Natl. Acad. Sci. USA. **82**: 3073-3077.

Sankoff, D. (1975). "Minimal mutation trees of sequences." SIAM J. Appl. Math. **28**: 35-42.

Sankoff, D. and R. J. Cedergren. (1983). Simultaneous comparison of three or more sequences. Time Warps, String Edits and Macromolecules: The Theory and Practice of Sequence Comparison. Reading, MA, Addison-Wesley.

Sobel, E. and H. Martinez. (1986). "A multiple sequence alignment program." Nucleic Acids Res. **14**: 363-374.

Taylor, W. R. (1987). "Multiple sequence alignment by a pairwise algorithm." Comput. Appl. Biosci. **3**: 81-87.

Vingron, M. and P. Argos. (1989). "A fast and sensitive multiple sequence alignment algorithm." Comput. Appl. Biosci. **5**: 115-121.

Waterman, M. S. and M. D. Perlwitz. (1984). "Line geometries for sequence comparisons." Bull. Math. Biol. **46**: 567-577.

Local Multiple Alignment

Bacon, D. J. and W. F. Anderson. (1986). "Multiple sequence alignment." J. Mol. Biol. **191**: 153-161.

Galas, D. J., M. Eggert and M. S. Waterman. (1985). "Rigorous pattern-recognition methods for DNA sequences. Analysis of promoter sequences from *Escherichia coli*." J. Mol. Biol. **186**: 117-128.

Posfai, J., A. S. Bhagwat, G. Posfai and R. J. Roberts. (1989). "Predictive motifs derived from cytosine methyltransferases." Nucleic Acids Res. **17**: 2421-2435.

Queen, C. M., N. Wegman and L. J. Korn. (1982). "Improvements to a program for DNA analysis: a procedure to find homologies among many sequences." Nucleic Acids Res. **10**: 449-456.

Schuler, G. D., S. F. Altschul and D. J. Lipman. (1990). "A workbench for multiple alignment construction and analysis." Proteins Struct. Func. Genet., *In press.*

Smith, H. O., T. M. Annau and S. Chandrasegaran. (1990). "Finding sequence motifs in groups of functionally related proteins." Proc. Natl. Acad. Sci. USA. **87**: 826-830.

Stormo, G. D. and G. W. Hartzell. (1989). "Identifying protein-binding sites from unaligned DNA fragments." Proc. Natl. Acad. Sci. USA. **86**: 1183-1187.

Waterman, M. S., R. Arratia and D. J. Galas. (1984). "Pattern recognition in several sequences: consensus and alignment." Bull. Math. Biol. **46**: 515-527.

Table 5: Selected bibliography on multiple sequence alignment.

significant matching sequences in a search of the databases. Further, given a particular clone of interest, screening libraries under conditions of reduced stringency may be used to identify additional, related macromolecules. The alignment of an entire family of proteins or nucleic acids may provide more information than the alignment of any pair of those sequences. Relations between multiple sequences may improve the accuracy of alignment, and the increased sample size improves the chance that a representative range of the permissible sequence variation will be observed. Multiple alignment has been the subject of a large number of research and development efforts over the years and a comprehensive review of this literature is beyond the scope of this primer. However, we provide a selected bibliography in Table 5 for access to this considerable body of work.[29]

There are several approaches to multiple alignment that need to be considered in the context of the sequences under study. Global alignment methods are most appropriate to sequences that are small (< 500 residues), approximately equal in length and share a global, but perhaps distant, relationship (Lipman et al., 1989). Local alignment methods, on the other hand, are preferable for longer sequences that vary greatly in length and may share only isolated regions of similarity separated by variable-length segments of little or no sequence conservation (Posfai et al., 1989; Schuler et al., 1990). Finally, the progressive alignment strategy (see Extension of Pairwise Alignment Techniques to Higher Dimensions) is the only one that is practical for large numbers (dozens to hundreds) of sequences.

A major advantage of local alignment methods is that a new theory for estimating the statistical significance of sequence similarities (Karlin and Altschul, 1990) can be applied to the ungapped homology blocks obtained. However, global alignment methods using dynamic programming are superior for determining the locations and extents of insertion and deletion mutations (Lipman et al., 1989), and also allow for the application of

[29] Also, Sections V and VII in Methods in Ezymology Vol. 183 have a number of articles that address multiple alignment and its applications (Doolittle, 1990).

sequence weighting to control for redundant data (Altschul et al., 1989). However, it is possible to combine the two approaches by first applying local alignment methods to identify highly-significant, ungapped segments and then performing an optimal alignment on individual sequence domains or a subset of the sequences. (See Boguski and States, 1991 and Ballester et al., 1990 for recent examples of the combined application of local and global alignment techniques for protein modeling and the design of complementation experiments.)

Multiple sequence alignment, as a completely connected (all pairwise comparisons) alignment of the individual component sequences in a gene family, ultimately does not model evolution. Gene families evolve as trees (or graphs if recombination occurs). Different branches of the evolutionary tree may be subject to differing selective pressures and differing constraints on sequence conservation, and the occurrence of random events will obviously differ from one branch of the tree to another. Detailed analysis of large protein families, such as the globins (Bashford et al., 1987), has demonstrated that the conserved residues in one branch of the family are not the same as the conserved residues in other branches of the family.

Extension of Pairwise Alignment Techniques to Higher Dimensions

Multiple sequence alignment can be viewed as a generalization of simple pairwise sequence alignment, but the complexity of the computation grows exponentially with the number of sequences being considered. One approach to multiple sequence alignment has always been manual editing (Barber and Maizel, 1990). Unfortunately, given the enormous complexity of the problem, the multiple sequence alignments generated by hand are rarely, if ever, optimal when tested with a defined scoring system. By analogy with the pairwise case, dynamic programming techniques can be applied to align sequences in multiple dimensions, but the exponential growth in the complexity of the computations limited early implementations to no more than three dimensions (sequences) (Gotoh, 1986; Murata et al., 1985). Carillo and Lipman (1988) introduced a bounding procedure that uses pairwise alignments to limit the volume of the N-dimensional space that needs to be searched in the full alignment, thereby greatly improving overall speed and making larger problems tractable. The Carrillo-Lipman algorithm is implemented in the program MSA (Lipman et al., 1989) and has been used effectively for protein modeling and molecular evolutionary studies (e.g., Peitsch and Boguski, 1990; Trainor et al., 1990).

It is usually not possible to simultaneously align more than ten sequences by the rigorous approach used in the MSA program. For larger numbers of sequences, a variety of approximate methods have been proposed (see Table 5). The most useful approaches seem to be those based on clustering and have been termed progressive alignment methods (Feng and Doolittle, 1987). In this approach each pair of sequences is aligned to give a measure of the similarity of the sequence pair. The sequences are then grouped into clusters based on the similarity. The multiple alignment is produced by performing a pairwise alignment of the two most closely related sequences, and then adding in additional sequences, or clusters of sequences, one at a time according to the clustering pattern. The resulting alignment is not guaranteed to be optimal — there may be multiple alignments for which the sums of the pairwise similarities are higher. However, the alignments are often quite sensible biologically, and it is possible to align hundreds of sequences by this method (e.g., Barton and Sternberg, 1987; Taylor, 1987).

Incorporating chemical and biological knowledge into multiple sequence alignment can greatly improve the reliability of results, but this may require manual intervention. An important advance in this area is the development of hybrid approaches. One of these, the Multiple Alignment Construction and Analysis Workbench (MACAW) (Schuler et al., 1991), provides statistically based alignments on segments of a multiple alignment while allowing the user to interactively define, lock, and shift different portions of the data. Chemical, functional and structural information not directly expressible in sequence form may be used to guide the alignment process and ensure that active sites and other features are preserved. At the same time, the basic alignment procedure remains automated with rigorous statistical criteria applied. Because the user may limit the automated alignment to small blocks of sequences, computational demands are manageable, and good response may be achieved even with PC-based implementations. Using blocks of highly significant alignment, it is possible in MACAW to progressively limit the portions of the sequences which are unaligned. As the calculation progresses, the length and number of sequences that need be examined both decrease so that computations become much quicker, and many alternatives for the poorly defined regions of the structure may be explored. Conserved regions of a multiple alignment may be highly significant with little uncertainty as to position while the intervening segments are quite variable. This may correlate with surface accessibility and the location of intron/exon junctions (Craik et al., 1983). By highlighting the well defined portions of the multiple alignment, MACAW guides subsequent structural studies and may delineate these highly divergent features.

Data Interdependence and Sequence Weighting

Finally, multiple alignment differs from pairwise alignment in a very important respect: the problem of bias introduced by data interdependence. For any group of homologous sequences, it is usually the case that certain subsets of sequences are much more closely related to each other than to other sequences in the family. Yet in most multiple alignment procedures, all sequences are treated as independent variables and given equal weight in the construction of an alignment, thus biasing the alignment in favor of sequences that have the greatest pairwise similarities. The progressive alignment strategy is particularly prone to this type of artifact.

One obvious way of dealing with this problem is to simply exclude highly correlated sequences from the data set. This solution, however, suffers from arbitrariness and the loss of information. Felsenstein has dealt with the data weighting problem in the context of phylogenetic tree reconstruction (Felsenstein, 1973; Felsenstein, 1985). More recently, Altschul et al. (Altschul et al., 1989) have devised similar strategies for weighting sequence alignments in terms of their pairwise interdependence. These strategies have been implemented in the MSA program (Lipman et al., 1989) and have important applications in profile analysis and the derivation of sequence motifs (see Chapter 2).

Examples of Multiple Sequence Alignment

Figure 24 illustrates the type of analysis that can be accomplished with the MACAW tool. In this example, a group of serine proteases are being examined. Using data from the known sequences, it is possible to recognize regions of conserved sequence around the catalytic residues. MACAW identifies related sequence in the unknown sequences and gives a global view of the locations of insertions and deletions without worrying about detailed calculation of specific indel sites. Since the optimal indel site is frequently less well defined than the fact that an insertion or deletion must have taken

Comparison of MSA Dynamic Programming and
MACAW Maximal Diagonal Sets
Multiple Sequence Alignment

MSA alignment	IVGGYTCGANTVPYQVSL--NSGY---HFCGGSLINSQWVVSAAHC--YKSGIQVRLGED IVNGEEAVPGSWPWQVSLQDKTGF---HFCGGSLINENWVVTAAHC--GVTTSDVVVAGE VVGGTEAQRNSWPSQISLQYRSGSSWAHTCGGTLIRQNWVMTAAHCVDRELTFRVVVGEH IIGGVESIPHSRPYMAHLDIVTEKGLRVICGGFLISRQFVLTAAHC--KGREITVILGAH VVGGTRAAQGEFPFMVRL--SMG------CGGALYAQDIVLTAAHCV-SGSGNNTSITAT

MACAW alignmnet block	...sgyhfCGGSLINSQWVVSAAHCyksgi... ...tgfhfCGGSLINENWVVTAAHCgvtts... ...swahtCGGTLIRQNWVMTAAHCVDrel... ...glrviCGGFLISRQFVLTAAHCkgrei... ...rlsmgCGGALYAQDIVLTAAHCVSsgs...

Figure 24: The multiple sequence alignments generated with MSA (or other variations of the N-dimensional dynamic programming approach) differ from MACAW alignments in the inclusion of gaps and the lack of clearly defined blocks of significance. The MACAW output highlights the regions of sequence similarity, but makes no attempt to define the optimal placement of gaps in the regions which are not highly conserved.

place, this level of analysis is of great biological utility.

Multiple Alignment for Database Searching

An important new application of multiple sequence alignment is sensitive database searching. By looking simultaneously for similarity to two sequences, it is possible to find alignments which are clearly significant even though none of the pairwise comparisons would themselves be considered statistically significant (Altschul and Lipman, 1990). Table 6 shows the summed scores necessary to achieve statistical significance in multiple alignments involving various numbers of sequences.

This multiple alignment search approach has been implemented in a program, BLAST3, which is internally very similar to the BLAST algorithm for pairwise comparisons. First, a very low threshold pairwise search of the database is performed, saving many matches which are probably not significant. By definition, all of these pairs have the query sequence in common. The list of pairs is then processed to see if the other sequences, in the specified alignment, also form a significant pairing. The result is a computationally efficient and sensitive search tool. The power of these methods can be seen by comparing the results of searches performed using the different tools. In the examples below, the first immunoglobulin domain of the CSF-1 receptor (cfms) is used as a query sequence to search the SWISS-PROT protein sequence database.

In the FASTA search of the database (see Table 3), the four top scoring sequences are clearly homologous to the CSF-1 receptor (see Hashing and Neighborhood Algorithms). The remainder of the list contains a mixture of meaningful and false positive matches which is confusing at best.

In the search performed using the pairwise BLAST algorithm (see Statistical Approaches-BLAST), the closely related homologs are again

Segment in pairwise	Parameters		Score at 95%	Average
multiple alignment	λ	K	significance level	score
2	0.336	0.179	64	64
3	0.255	0.177	141	47
4	0.202	0.137	246	41
5	0.165	0.096	384	38
6	0.137	0.068	577	37

Table 6: Multiple sequence alignment scores can be calculated by summing all pairwise comparison scores at each position along an aligned segment and used to calculate statistical significance (Altschul, 1990). The scores necessary to achieve statistically significant multiple alignment scores for searching a database of 4,000,000 protein residues with a 150 amino acid query are shown in the right middle column, and the average pairwise score is shown in the rightmost column. The λ and K parameters refer to the prefactor and exponential used in the statistical significance calculation. The score at 95% significance is the sum of all pairwise scores in the multiple alignement which would be significant at a 95% level when searching a database of the indicated size. The average pairwise score is the overall sum divided by the number of pairs in the alignment. [Reprinted from Altschul and Lipman (1990), *Proc. Natl. Acad. Sci USA*, Vol. 87, p. 5510, Table 1.]

observed, as well as several shorter but still statistically significant alignments with other receptors (PDGF receptor) and cell surface proteins (NCAMs), and a marginally significant match with an immunoglobulin (0.92 probability of observing a similar alignment against random sequence). These results suggest that the CSF-1 receptor domain may be part a larger gene family, but the relationship to the immunoglobulins is only suggestive.

The results using the multiple sequence alignment tool BLAST3 are shown in Table 7. It is immediately apparent that the CSF-1 receptor domain is part of a large and diverse family of immunoglobulin-like domains. The combination of BLAST and BLAST3 gives a rapid and informative assessment of the sequence relationship and is much more powerful than earlier algorithms such as FASTA. The final column gives the expectation of finding a three-way alignment with this significance in the database search.

There are two problems apparent in the FASTA output (see Table 3). First, a number of high scoring alignments were missed, and second, the ranking of the relative significance of matches was erroneous. The fact that FASTA missed a number of significant alignments can be attributed to the use of a ktuple of 2 in performing the search. While the use of a large ktuple in building the hash table greatly accelerates the speed of the algorithm, it also increases the probability that significant alignments will be missed (Lipman and Pearson, 1985; Pearson and Lipman, 1988). The relatively poor ranking of matches in FASTA when compared to BLAST suggests that the scoring algorithm used in FASTA is not optimal. BLAST was run using the PAM-120 matrix while FASTA used the PAM-250 matrix, the default choices from the publications describing each algorithm. (Altschul has demonstrated, based upon information theoretic considerations, that the PAM-120 matrix is probably more appropriate for database searching (Altschul, 1990).

Similarity and Significance

Theoretical Foundations of Molecular Evolution

Establishing a significant sequence relationship usually has one of two goals, one more practical and the other more theoretical. Most molecular biologists want to know if a similarity is *significant enough* to predict the function of a newly-discovered sequence by analogy to other sequences of known function. The other goal of sequence comparison is to understand how sequences have evolved. These two goals are interrelated, however, and a knowledge of molecular evolution can often be of great help in making functional inferences. While a thorough discourse on molecular evolution is beyond the scope of the present work, we include a brief discussion of evolutionary concepts and classifications to aid in the understanding of sequence relationships.

The development of molecular evolutionary studies as a distinct discipline is generally attributed to Linus Pauling and Emile Zukerkandl's seminal

Database Search performed using BLAST3

```
>Human                              7 IEPSVPELVVKPGATVTLRCVGNGSVEWDGPASPHWTLYSDGSSSIILSTNNATFQNTGTYRCTEPGDP    74   S     E
[>LV0A$HUMAN    28] >KV3J$HUMAN    29 PTLSLSPGERVTLSCRASQSV                                                49 147 0.0052
[>KV3J$HUMAN    29] >LV0A$HUMAN    28 PSLTVSPGGTVTLTCASSTGA                                                48 147 0.0052
[>CD83$HUMAN    91] >NCA2$HUMAN    71                                             VVWNDDSSSTLTIYNANIDDAGIYKCVVTGED   102 146 0.0067
[>NCA2$HUMAN    71] >CD82$HUMAN    91                                             AVFRDASRFIlNLTSVKPEDSGIYFCMIVGSP   122 146 0.0067
[>NCA2$HUMAN    71] >CD83$HUMAN    91                                             AVFRDASRFIlNLTSVKPEDSGIYFCMIVGSP   122 146 0.0067
[>NCA2$HUMAN    71] >CD81$HUMAN    91                                             AVFRDASRFIlNLTSVKPEDSGIYFCMIVGSP   122 146 0.0067
[>LV0A$HUMAN    28] >TRKB$MOUSE   204 PNLTVEEGKSVTLSCSVGGD                                                223 143 0.015
[>LAR$HUMAN    233] >HV02$CANFA    12 VKPGGSLRLSCVASG                                                      26 143 0.015
[>LAR$HUMAN    233] >HV3A$HUMAN    12 VKPGGSLRLSCVASG                                                      26 143 0.015
[>HV02$CANFA    12] >LAR$HUMAN    233 VMPGGSVNLTCVAVG                                                     247 143 0.015
[>LAR$HUMAN    233] >HV01$CANFA    12 VKPGGSLRLSCVASG                                                      26 143 0.015
[>FCE1$RAT     155] >NCA3$MOUSE    77                                             DSSTLTIYNANIDDAGIYKCV              97 142 0.019
[>FCE1$RAT     155] >NCA2$RAT      77                                             DSSTLTIYNANIDDAGIYKCV              97 142 0.019
[>NCA3$MOUSE    77] >FCE1$RAT     155                                             DSNNISIRKATFNDSGSYHCT            175 142 0.019
[>KV3J$HUMAN    29] >LV1C$MOUSE     8 SALTTSPGETVTLTCRSNTGA                                                28 140 0.032
[>LAR$HUMAN    233] >HV30$MOUSE    12 VQPGGGSMKLSCVASG                                                     26 140 0.032
[>LAR$HUMAN    233] >HV32$MOUSE    12 VQPGGGSMKLSCVASG                                                     26 140 0.032
[>LAR$HUMAN    233] >HV35$MOUSE     7 VQPGGGSMKLSCVASG                                                     21 140 0.032
[>LAR$HUMAN    233] >HV29$MOUSE    12 VQPGGGSMKLSCVASG                                                     26 140 0.032
[>LAR$HUMAN    233] >HV31$MOUSE    12 VQPGGGSMKLSCVASG                                                     26 140 0.032
[>LAR$HUMAN    233] >HV28$MOUSE    12 VQPGGGSMKLSCVASG                                                     26 140 0.032
[>LAR$HUMAN    233] >HV33$MOUSE    12 VQPGGGSMKLSCVASG                                                     26 140 0.032
[>LAR$HUMAN    233] >HV27$MOUSE    12 VQPGGGSMKLSCVASG                                                     26 140 0.032
[>NCA2$HUMAN    75] >B29S$MOUSE    99                                             NGSVYTLTIQNIQYEDNGIYFC           120 138 0.053
[>LAR$HUMAN    233] >HV50$MOUSE    12 VKPGASVNLSCKASG                                                      26 138 0.053
[>NCA2$HUMAN    73] >PIGR$RAT      87                                             FPENSTFVINIAHLTQEDTGSYKC         110 137 0.069
[>NCA2$HUMAN    75] >BGP1$HUMAN   375                                             SQGNTTLSINPVKREDAGTYWC           396 137 0.069
[>FCE1$RAT     156] >NCA1$CHICK    78                                             SSTLTIYNANIDDAGIYKCV              97 137 0.069
[>LV0A$HUMAN    28] >LV4D$HUMAN     7 PSVSVSPGQTAVITCSGD                                                   24 136 0.090
[>LV0A$HUMAN    23] >LV5A$HUMAN     2 VLSQPPSVSVAPGQTARITCGGDG                                             25 135 0.12
[>LV0A$HUMAN    28] >KV6I$MOUSE     9 AIMSASPGQKVTMTCSASSSV                                                29 135 0.12
[>LV0A$HUMAN    28] >KV6J$MOUSE     9 AIMSASPGQKVTMTCSASSSV                                                29 135 0.12
[>LV0A$HUMAN    28] >KV6G$MOUSE     9 AIMSASPGQKVTMTCSASSSV                                                29 135 0.12
[>LV0A$HUMAN    28] >KV6H$MOUSE     9 AIMSASPGQKVTMTCSASSSV                                                29 135 0.12
[>LV0A$HUMAN    28] >KV6F$MOUSE     9 AIMSASPGQKVTMTCSASSSV                                                29 135 0.12
[>LV0A$HUMAN    28] >KV6K$MOUSE     9 AIMSASPGQKVTMTCSASSSV                                                29 135 0.12
[>LV0A$HUMAN    28] >KV3H$HUMAN    29 ATLSVSPGERATLSCRASQSV                                                49 135 0.12
[>FCE1$RAT     159] >FL18CHICK    367                                             LRIQGLTFEDAGMYQCIA               384 135 0.12
[>FCE1$RAT     159] >CONT$CHICK   367                                             LRIQGLTFEDAGMYQCIA               384 135 0.12
[>FCE1$RAT     159] >Y15K$TGMV     41                                             IDCRNNGFTHRGTYHCA                 57 134 0.15
[>LAR$HUMAN    233] >HV07$MOUSE    31 VKPGASVKLSCKASG                                                      45 134 0.15
[>LAR$HUMAN    233] >HV49$MOUSE    31 VKPGASVKLSCKASG                                                      45 134 0.15
[>LAR$HUMAN    233] >HV09$MOUSE    31 VKPGASVKLSCKASG                                                      45 134 0.15
[>LAR$HUMAN    233] >HV08$MOUSE    31 VKPGASVKLSCKASG                                                      45 134 0.15
[>LAR$HUMAN    233] >HV11$MOUSE    31 VKPGASVKLSCKASG                                                      45 134 0.15
[>LAR$HUMAN    233] >HV54$MOUSE    31 VKPGASVKLSCKASG                                                      45 134 0.15
[>LAR$HUMAN    233] >HV04$MOUSE    31 VKPGASVKLSCKASG                                                      45 134 0.15
[>LAR$HUMAN    233] >HV3S$HUMAN    12 VQPGGSLKLSCAASG                                                      26 133 0.20
[>LV0A$HUMAN    28] >KV2F$MOUSE     9 PSALVTPGESVSISCRSSKS                                                 28 132 0.25
[>LAR$HUMAN    233] >HV48$MOUSE    31 VKPGASVQLSCKASG                                                      45 132 0.25
[>NCA1$CHICK    78] >SPF3$MOUSE   373                                             KGELRLYDVTFENAGMYQCI             392 131 0.33
[>LV1C$MOUSE    10] >KV3K$HUMAN    12 LSLSLSPGESATLSCRASQSV                                                49 131 0.33
[>LAR$HUMAN    233] >HV2F$MOUSE    12 VKPSETLSLTCIVSGGP                                                    28 131 0.33
[>LV0A$HUMAN    28] >A1BG$HUMAN   197 SSQVLHPGNKVTLTCVAP                                                  214 130 0.42
[>LAR$HUMAN    233] >HV40$MOUSE    12 VQPGGGSLKLSCAASG                                                     26 130 0.42
[>LAR$HUMAN    233] >HV13$MOUSE    12 VQPGGSVKMSCAASG                                                      26 130 0.42
[>LAR$HUMAN    233] >HV37$MOUSE    12 VQPGGGSLKLSCAASG                                                     26 130 0.42
[>LAR$HUMAN    233] >HV36$MOUSE    30 VQPGGGSLKLSCAASG                                                     44 130 0.42
[>LAR$HUMAN    233] >HV41$MOUSE    12 VQPGGGSLKLSCAASG                                                     26 130 0.42
[>LAR$HUMAN    233] >HV12$MOUSE    12 VKPGGSVKMSCAASG                                                      26 130 0.42
[>LAR$HUMAN    233] >HV38$MOUSE    12 VQPGGGSLKLSCAASG                                                     26 130 0.42
[>LV0A$HUMAN    28] >KV5C$MOUSE    29 ASLSASVGETVTITCRASGNI                                                49 129 0.55
[>PGDR$HUMAN   274] >FLG5$MOUSE   324                                             EVLHLRNVSFEDAGEYTC               341 129 0.55
[>FLG5$MOUSE   324] >PGDR$HUMAN   274                                             SILHIPSAELEDSGTYTC               291 129 0.55
[>PGDR$HUMAN   274] >FLG5$HUMAN   124                                             EVLHLRNVSFEDAGEYTC               141 129 0.55
[>NCA1$CHICK    78] >FCG1$HUMAN   150                                             NSNLTILKTNISHNGTYHCS             169 128 0.71
[>NCA1$CHICK    78] >FCG0$HUMAN   150                                             NSNLTILKTNISHNGTYHCS             169 128 0.71
[>LV0A$HUMAN    28] >OPCM$BOVIN   143 SDVTVNEGSSVTLLCLAIG                                                 161 128 0.71
[>KV6F$MOUSE    11] >LV1B$MOUSE    29 LTTSPGETVTLTCRSSTGA                                                  47 128 0.71
[>KV6F$MOUSE    11] >LV1A$MOUSE    29 LTTSPGETVTLTCRSSTGA                                                  47 128 0.71
[>KV6F$MOUSE    11] >LV1E$MOUSE    29 LTTSPGETVTLTCRSSTGA                                                  47 128 0.71
[>LV0A$HUMAN    30] >IL6R$HUMAN    35 LTSLPGDSVTLTCPG                                                      49 128 0.71
[>LAR$HUMAN    233] >HV05$MOUSE    31 VRPGSSVKLSCKASG                                                      45 128 0.71
[>NCA2$RAT      74] >FCG0$HUMAN    63                                             TQTSTPSYRITSASVNDSGEYRC           85 127 0.92
[>NCA2$RAT      74] >FCG1$HUMAN    63                                             TQTSTPSYRITSASVNDSGEYRC           85 127 0.92
[>NCA2$RAT      77] >FCEA$HUMAN   157                                             ENHNISITNATVEDSGTYYCT            177 127 0.92
[>NCA2$RAT      77] >PGCA$RAT     114                                             SDATLEIQNLRSNDSGIYRC             133 127 0.92
[>LAR$HUMAN    233] >HV3N$HUMAN    12 VQPGGGSLRLSCAASG                                                     26 127 0.92
[>LAR$HUMAN    233] >HV3R$HUMAN    12 VQPGGGSLRLSCAASG                                                     26 127 0.92
[>LAR$HUMAN    233] >HV3E$HUMAN    12 VQPGGGSLRLSCAASG                                                     26 127 0.92
[>LAR$HUMAN    233] >HV3M$HUMAN    12 VQPGGGSLRLSCAASG                                                     26 127 0.92
[>LAR$HUMAN    233] >HV3C$HUMAN    31 VQPGGGSLRLSCAASG                                                     45 127 0.92
[>LAR$HUMAN    233] >HV3O$HUMAN    12 VQPGGGSLRLSCAASG                                                     26 127 0.92
[>LAR$HUMAN    233] >HV3P$HUMAN    12 VQPGGGSLRLSCAASG                                                     26 127 0.92
[>LAR$HUMAN    233] >HV34$HUMAN    12 VQPGRSMKLSCVASG                                                      26 127 0.92
[>LAR$HUMAN    233] >HV3D$HUMAN    12 VQPGGGSLRLSCAASG                                                     26 127 0.92
```

Table 7: The BLAST3 search performed using the first immunoglobulin domain of the fms (CSF-1 receptor) extracellular domain as defined by exon-intron junctions (Hampe, 1989) against the SWISS-PROT sequence database identifies many significant pairwise and three-way alignments. The most significant group of three-way alignments is shown with the accession names of the two sequences which make up the alignment in the left most two columns, the aligned segments in the middle section, and the significance figures on the right. The score (S column) is the sum of the PAM-120 scores between each pair of the three way alignment. The expection (E column) is the probability of observing three sequences with that degree of relatedness in searching a database the size of SWISS-PROT. Interestingly, many of the three way alignments which are in the marginally significant region (E = 0.1 or greater) are still biologically significant. The listing of pairwise alignments is not shown.

paper, "Chemical Paleogenetics: Molecular Restoration Studies of Extinct Forms of Life" (Pauling and Zuckerkandl, 1963).[30] Fitch and Margoliash (1970) subsequently formalized the following very useful distinctions among different subtypes of molecular homology. *Orthologous sequences* are homologous sequences whose history reflects the phylogenetic branching order of the species in which they are found, and have identical functions. An example would be human α-hemoglobin and mouse α-hemoglobin. *Paralogous sequences*, on the other hand, are products of a gene duplication that was fixed prior to speciation resulting in the formation of a gene family. Paralogous sequences may be functionally similar, or may have evolved entirely new biochemical roles or different patterns of expression. Erythrocyte α-hemoglobin and muscle myoglobin are paralogs .

In countless papers that describe sequence relationships, investigators refer to sequences as being "highly conserved." One is always tempted to ask: "Compared to what?" It has long been known that genes and their protein products evolve at highly varying rates (Doolittle, 1986), and saying that one's sequence is "highly conserved" has little meaning unless compared to some objective scale. A very useful yardstick is that of Li et al. (1985) who have determined the nucleotide substitution rates for 40 mammalian genes. It is often enlightening to compare these rates to those of other genes to estimate how stringently the latter sequences are really being conserved (Trainor et al., 1990).

There are a number of examples of proteins whose three-dimensional structures are superimposable and yet whose primary sequences appear to show no statistically significant similarity (Creighton, 1984). However, for reasons previously stated, the occurrence of true *convergent* evolution is undoubtedly rare. Indeed, using the structure-based alignment as a starting point, Keim et al. (1981) were able to demonstrate significant sequence similarities between the two domains of rhodanase that were not detectable based on consideration of the primary structure alone. Nevertheless, biological significance is not always reflected in statistical significance and vice versa.

Modularity in protein and gene structure combines with the complex nature of genetic recombination to make a correct inference of homology quite difficult in some cases. In many cases, several domains of a pair of multi-domain proteins may be clearly homologous, while other analogously located domains clearly have different origins. This modular nature of biological sequences raises an important point in sequence comparison. The origin and relationship of the various components of a pair of sequences may differ. Comparison over the entire sequence (global alignment) may then be inappropriate. On the other hand, if two sequences are known to be similar over their entrie length, constraining the alignment to consider the full extent

---

[30]Little did Pauling and Zuckerkandl know at the time that it would one day actually be possible to restore portions of extinct genomes using PCR amplification and molecular cloning techniques [Paabo, 1989].

both sequences may significantly improve the optimal alignment when compared to segmental or local alignments.

For example, in the tyrosine kinase class of membrane receptors, the kinase domains share approximately 50% sequence identity over a 400 residue domain, a degree of similarity that necessarily implies homologous origin of this domain. For some receptors, such as platelet derived growth factor (PDGF) and colony stimulating factor-1 (CSF-1) receptors, the extracellular domains also share a high degree of similarity and by inference are homologous proteins. Other receptors such as the epidermal growth factor (EGF) share a common kinase domain, but the extracellular domain bears no sequence similarity to the extracellular domains of the PDGF and CSF-1 receptors. Thus a rearrangement is likely to have occurred that substituted extracellular domains in the evolution of these receptors.

Comparison of Amino Acid Sequence Conservation by Domain

	extracellular	intracellular (kinase)
cfms vs. PDGFr	21.3%	56.8%
cfms vs. EGFr	none	35.8%

Finally, no discussion of protein evolution is complete without some mention of Dayhoff and coworkers' superfamily classification system (Schwartz and Dayhoff, 1979) that was devised to categorize sequence relationships quantitatively and is still used to organize the annotated portion of the PIR Protein Sequence Database[31] (see Appendix VIII). Dayhoff (1978) devised a procedure for clustering homologous sequences into several groups (e.g., "Superfamilies," "Families," and "Subfamilies") based upon their calculated degrees of pairwise similarity. Proteins in the same subfamily had to have greater than 80% identical residues in their "best alignment" and proteins in the same family had to be greater than 50% identical. For proteins more distantly related than this, statistical criteria were applied, using the Z score approach, and proteins that had a less than 10^{-6} probability[32] of being similar by chance were assigned to the same superfamily. Individual protein superfamilies were each assigned a numerical identifier and a common name usually based on the first member of the superfamily to be identified.[33] Currently, there are 2,350 protein superfamilies (PIR release 26.0). It is interesting to think about the extent to which these represent all protein

---

[31] Due to the sheer volume of new data, the current release of PIR (26.0) contains less than a third of the total number of sequence entries in the "Annotated and Classified" subset. The remainder are in the "Preliminary" and "Unverified" categories.

[32] This p-value corresponds to a z score of about 4.75 and was estimated based on the *normal distribution*.

[33] The superfamily numbers and names can be found in the PLACEMENT and SUPERFAMILY data fields, respectively, of PIR entries.

archetypes that exist.[34]

The superfamily classification system originated during a more innocent age of molecular biology before the promiscuity of protein mosaicism and the dynamics of genome rearrangement were fully appreciated. This system was built on the assumption that evolutionary relationships could be modeled topologically by a *tree*, whereas now a *network* seems to be a more appropriate representation. But Dayhoff's superfamily classifications are of great historical importance and are still the benchmark for determining the sensitivity and specificity of any new algorithm for database searching.

Statistical Analysis of Alignments

The goal of sequence analysis is seldom to produce an alignment or to find a homologous sequence for its own sake, but rather to find out something interesting about the biology of the protein or DNA molecules. Although statistical calculations can be a guide, they are wayward guides at best since some biologically relevant similarities are not statistically significant, and some significant similarities are biologically very unlikely. In some cases the similarity between the sequences is so great that there is no need to evaluate the similarity statistically, nor to consider the possible biological relationship between the molecules. In many cases, however, the similarity is weak and must be evaluated using statistical techniques (described below). In cases where significant similarity can not be demonstrated, one must consider the likelihood that there is some biological similarity between the molecules that justifies considering the relationship, even though the significance of the sequence comparison is marginal. A major focus of ongoing work involves the integration of sequence and bibliographic databases (Boguski and States, 1990), and should greatly increase the ease with which this can be done.

One major tool that is often overlooked in evaluating alignments is common sense. Examine alignments carefully; if they require more than about one gap for every twenty residues, they may be suspicious. We expect that a significant alignment will not be sensitive to small changes in the gap penalties applied during the alignment. If you find that an alignment changes drastically when you change the gap penalties by small amounts (say 10%), it suggests that the alignment being presented is not very different from many other possible alignments. This, in turn, suggests that the alignment may not be very significant.

Monte Carlo methods (also known as randomization, or permutation methods) are probably the most common methods of calculating the sig-

---

[34] It has been estimated (Zuckerkandl, 1975; Dayhoff, 1974; Doolittle, personal communication) that the number of classes of proteins is less than a thousand, perhaps considerably less, and that as more data and more sensitive methods for establishing distant relationships become available, we will learn how to collapse all of the 50 to 100 thousand human gene products into this much smaller number of categories. But in our experience, more than half of the new sequences we are asked to examine have no demonstrable homologs in the current databases.

nificance of sequence comparisons. In these methods, one or both sequences are randomized (or shuffled or scrambled) and the analysis repeated a sufficient number of times to calculate a mean and a standard deviation for the distribution of the scores for comparison to an unrelated (scrambled) sequence of the same composition. These methods date back to the early days of sequence analysis (Needleman and Wunsch, 1970) and are still in use today. The major drawback to these methods is that they are computationally intensive. Accurate calculation of the mean and standard deviation require the analysis to be repeated several hundred times, and this is often prohibitive.

The scores of sequence alignments are often assumed to be normally distributed, and sometimes pass tests of normality (e.g., Needleman and Wunsch, 1970; May et al., 1985). However, recent experimental (Smith et al., 1985; Waterman, 1989) and theoretical investigations (Arratia et al., 1985; Waterman, 1989; Karlin and Altschul, 1990) suggest that this may not be the case, and that the tails of the distribution are significantly larger than those of a normal distribution. Significance estimated from Monte Carlo simulations must therefore be taken as approximate when calculated in terms of standard normal deviates or Z scores, unless the score distribution has been shown to be normal.

Another common method of evaluating alignments, often used for database searches (e.g. Pearson, 1990; Gribskov et al., 1990) is to compare the score for the sequence comparison to the distribution of scores seen in the database search. This method has the advantage that weak similarities between sequences that are due to intrinsic properties of macromolecular structure are implicitly included in the analysis. For instance, in proteins an amphipathic helix is a common structural motif (see Chapter 4) and gives rise to a characteristic pattern of hydrophilic and hydrophobic residues. Many unrelated proteins, especially those rich in alpha helices, would be expected to share this similarity and thus seem weakly similar. Although score distributions for dynamic programming sequence alignments seem to be approximately normal (subject to the comments in the previous paragraph), they do show a systematic dependence on the sequence length (Waterman, 1989; Gribskov et al., 1989). The FASTA program gives distributions that decidedly are not normal, and it is therefore difficult to use them for statistical analyses.

If the program one is using does not provide a plot of the distribution, it is a good idea to make one yourself if you evaluate significance in comparison to a database search. One particularly useful way of plotting the distribution is to plot the logarithm of the number of occurrences of a score, or scores in a narrow range, against the score. A least-squares fit can be used to identify the randomly expected component of the distribution and to identify significant outliers (Collins and Coulson, 1990).

A more recent development in analyzing the significance of sequence comparisons arises from a statistical analysis by Karlin and Altschul (1990). They derive an explicit equation that gives the probability that a comparison score will be greater than a specified value for two random sequences (equation 6). In this derivation the comparison score is the highest score for aligning any segment of the first protein with a segment of the second, but without gaps (maximum segment score). The resulting equation depends on two parameters, K and λ, which depend on the scoring system and the frequencies of the residues or bases in the sequences.

$$P(S > x) \sim 1 - e^{-Ke^{-\lambda x}} \qquad (6)$$

where P(S>x) is the probability that the maximum segment score will be greater than x.

Significance calculated by this approach is limited to alignments that do not include gaps. An additional drawback of this approach is that unrelated sequences are considered to be random with respect to one another, an assumption that may be incorrect for protein sequences (see above) due to intrinsic constraints imposed by protein structure. Nevertheless, this is an important advance that will be widely used, and useful.

Examples

To demonstrate the relative discriminatory power of the several traditional and new tests of statistical significance, several protein sequence alignments are shown below comparing the NAS score, the Karlin-Altschul significance calculated by BLAST, and Monte Carlo simulations carried out by the programs RDF2 (Pearson and Lipman, 1988; Pearson, 1990), ALIGN, and RELATE (NBRF). The first example shows the human high affinity immunoglobulin receptor aligned with the first domain of the human CSF-a receptor.

It is possible to make a rough estimate of sequence alignment significance using very simple rule (Doolittle, 1986), but this may result in a significant loss of sensitivity, particularly where short regions of alignment are present. For example, the "normalized alignment score" (NAS) method of Doolittle scores a 10 for each identical amino acid in a pair of aligned protein sequences, adds an additional 10 for each aligned pair of cystines, and subtracts 25 for each gap that is introduced in the alignment. This score is then divided by the sequence length, multiplied by 100, and compared against a

```
>FCEA$HUMAN (Swiss) HIGH AFFINITY IMMUNOGLOBULIN EPSILON RECEPTOR
Length = 257
Score = 62, E = 0.0036, D = 0.0036, P = 1.9e-07, length = 50
Query:    14 GATVTLRCVGNGSVEWDGPASPHWTLYSDGSSILSTNNATFQNTGTYRC 63
              G  VTL C GN   E +    H   S+ ++S L+  NA F+++G Y+C
Sbjct:    44 GENVTLTCNGNNFFEVSSTKWFHNGSLSEETNSSLNIVNAKFEDSGEYKC 93
```

Table 8: Alignment of fms with the FC receptor.

reference curve.

The alignment of fms with the FC receptor has 18 matches with 2 cysteines in 50 amino acids to give an NAS of 400, which is marginally significant. The more detailed analysis of this segment (BLAST) which incorporates information from the PAM-120 amino acid exchange probability matrix and the biases introduced by amino acid composition in the query sequence shows that this is a clearly significant alignment (Table 8).

A detailed, but empirical analysis of the alignment was performed using the RDF2 (Pearson, 1990) program to compare the true alignment with a series of alignments against randomly shuffled sequences using the FASTA algorithm. This method gives an alignment score of 2.31 SD above the mean, which is not significant. However, with ktup=1, RDF2 shows a clearly significant similarity (alignment score of 7.33SD).

Using the NBRF ALIGN program to analyze this pair by comparing the observed alignment to a series of random sequence alignments, but using a full dynamic programming alignment, the fms/FCEA alignment has a score 4.16 standard deviations above the mean as is shown in Figure 25. The fms/FCEA alignment illustrates an interesting problem that can arise in alignments between repeated sequences. Although only a single Ig domain of fms was used as a query, FCEA has two such domains. In this case, ALIGN matched the beginning of the fms domain with the beginning of the first FCEA domain, but the end of the fms domain is matched with the end of the

```
KFMS    ------------------GQGIPVIEPSVPELVVKP-------GATVTLRCVGN
FCEA    MAPAMESPTLLCVALLFFAPDGVLAV-PQKP.KVSLNPPWNRIFKGENVTLTCNGN
Common                       G         P  P      P        G  VTL C GN

KFMS    -----GSVEW--DGPAS------------------------------------
FCEA    NFFEVSSTKWFHNGSLSEETNSSLNIVNAKFEDSGEYKCQHQQVNESEPVYLEVF
Common       S   W   G  S

KFMS    PHWTL---------------------------YSDGSS------SILSTN
FCEA    SDWLLLQASAEVVMEGQPLFLRCHGWRNWDVYKVIYYKDGEALKYWYENHNISIT
Common     WL                              Y DG              S

KFMS    NATFQNTGTYRCTEP-------GDPLGGSA--------------------AIH
FCEA    NATVEDSGTYYCTGKVWQLDYESEPLNITVIKAPREKYWLQFFIPLLVVILFAVD
Common  NAT    GTY CT        PL                          A

KFMS    --*LYV---------------------------KD-
FCEA    TGLFISTQQQVTFLLKIKRTRKGFRLLNPHPKPNPKNN
Common    L                             K
```

```
Mutation Data Matrix (250 PAMs)+2 Penalty for a break=6
100 random runs
34 identities out of 86 possible matches between residues
11 breaks
Total score (R) =  326        Mean score (M) =   281.31
R-M =   44.69                 Standard deviation =   10.73
Alignment score =     4.16 SD
```

Figure 25: The alignment of the first immunoglobulin domain of the fms (CSF-1 receptor) extracellular domain (KFMS) with the high affinity Fc receptor (FCEA) generated with the NBRF ALIGN program is shown. The default PAM-250 matrix with a gap initialization penalty of 6 and extension penalty of 2 were used in generating this alignment. The significance of the alignment is evaluated in the information listed at the bottom of the figure, comparing the observed alignment against 100 trials against randomly generated sequences.

```
>KKIT$MOUSE (Swiss) KIT PROTO-ONCOGENE TYROSINE KINASE
Length = 975
Score = 64, E = 0.0018, D = 0.0018, P = 3.6e-07, length = 28
Query:     2 IEPSVPELVVKPGATVTLRCVGNGSVEW 29
             I P+ +EL+V +G T++L C+    V W
Sbjct:    39 IHPAQSELIVEAGDTLSLTCIDPDFVRW 66
```

Table 9: Alignment of CFS-1 receptor and the kit proto-oncogene.

second FCEA domain. By using a higher gap penalty as described above in the FASTA section, this type of error might be reduced, but for this analysis the default parameters were used.

The NBRF RELATE program does a sliding window alignment and can also be used to screen for sequence relationships. In the case of fms and FCEA, it gives a score of 6.03, indicating significance. This may be misleading, however, because the program is adding alignments between the one fms domain and each of the two FCEA domains as if they were originating from a single domain comparison.

Repeating this analysis for the *kit* proto-oncogene compared to the CSF-1 receptor, a segment in the extracellular domains aligns as shown using BLAST (Table 9). In this case the NAS is 429, and the scoring curve predicts that this is unlikely to be a significant alignment. The RDF2 score is only 0.26 standard deviations away from the random sequence mean, again not significant. ALIGN gives this pair a score of 3.05 SD, which is only marginally significant. RELATE and BLAST analysis predict a much greater level of confidence that the alignment is meaningful.

Finally, an even shorter segment arises in comparing the CSF-1 receptor with the neural cell adhesion protein (Table 10). In this case, the NAS is 556, which again falls in the unlikely to be significant scoring region. RDF2 and ALIGN also fail to demonstrate significance, but RELATE gives a score of 6.8 SD from the mean, which, like the BLAST analysis, strongly suggests significance.

All of these molecules are cell surface receptors, and all three show extensive regions of similarity to members of the immunoglobulin family of proteins. It is clear, therefore, from the biologic context that all are of homologous origin and that the alignment is in fact meaningful. As this series of comparisons demonstrates, biologically significant sequence similarities may not be found using simplified analytical methods. In particular, this appears to be a problem where short lengths of aligned sequence are exam-

```
>NCA3$MOUSE (Swiss) NEURAL CELL ADHESION PROTEIN
Length = 725
Score = 61, E = 0.0077, D = 0.0077, P = 1.1e-06, length = 18
Query:    16 SGTLLCAASGYPQPNVTW 33
             S TL+C A G+P+P ++W
Sbjct:   230 SVTLVCDADGFPEPTMSW 247
```

Table 10: Alignment of CFS-1 receptor with the neural cell adhesion protein.

ined. It should also be noted that while BLAST is an improvement over the less sophisticated tools, it still remains an imperfect tool. Many sequence similarities which are clearly of biological importance fail to meet statistical tests of significance even with the BLAST analysis scoring systems.

SUMMARY AND CONCLUSIONS

The basic methods of sequence comparison have now been available for some time, and there is a considerable aggregate experience in their use which we have tried to impart in this chapter. Nevertheless, sequence comparison continues to be an active area of mathematical, statistical, and computational research and development, and the current generation of database search and sequence alignment tools offer considerable improvements in both efficiency and reliability. A relatively underdeveloped capability, however, is the integration of molecular sequence data with other types of data in the scientific literature. We also lack hybrid bioinformatics tools for more general information retrieval and data analysis. Such integrated resources will become ever more important as the data rich future of molecular biology unfolds.

Acknowledgements: We thank Stephen Altschul, Jean-Michel Claverie, Warren Gish, David J. Lipman, James Ostell, Greg Schuler and John Wootton for suggestions on the manuscript.

4 Practical Aspects: Analysis of *Notch*

Lisa Caballero

Using a computer to analyze genetic sequences is most fruitful when the investigator is familiar with the standard algorithms used by sequence analysis programs. This includes understanding the effects that input parameters have upon the results and, what can be more difficult, interpreting the results. The selection of one algorithm over another depends upon the question being asked, and ultimately, on the sequence being analyzed. The key to success is to realize that the computer will only answer the questions one asks of it, and that it may take a little work to find the right question.

The goal of this chapter is to show the process of sequence analysis through examples. It demonstrates, in practical terms, how to set parameters and evaluate results by reproducing the steps a researcher might take in analyzing a newly determined sequence.

Background

The *Notch* sequence from *Drosophila* is used as the sample data. *Notch* is thought to control cell fate decisions in development. It encodes a large, transmembrane protein which may function through cell adhesion, and it was cloned and sequenced in 1985 (Wharton et al., 1985a & b; Kidd et al., 1986). *Notch* is an ideal sequence to analyze because it contains many features that computers are good at finding. Figure 1 shows a schematic of the *Notch* protein and its major features.

The *Notch* sequence is available in the Genbank and EMBL sequence database under accession numbers M16153, M16149, M16150, M16151 and M16152 (see Appendix VIII). The most successful way to approach this chapter is to reproduce the analyses. This will familiarize one with a specific

159

software package, and offers a more accurate picture of the volume of output data produced by many programs than could be allowed in the figures in this chapter.

Programs for most of the analyses used in this chapter are widely available on IBM PCs, Macintoshes and mainframe computers. The examples have intentionally been kept generic, but programs from the following sources were used: Genetics Computer Group Sequence Analysis Software (Devereux et al., 1984; Genetics Computer Group Inc., Madison, WI), Genbank Online Services (Benton, 1990), National Library of Medicine Services (Benson et al., 1990), and PC Gene (A. Bairoch, University of Geneva; ™ Intelligenetics Inc., Mountain View, CA and Genofit SA).

Strategy

Unless a researcher is studying nontranslatable segments of DNA, the immediate goal upon the isolation of a new gene is usually to deduce the amino acid sequence of its product. The laboratory approach might go from isolating a cDNA clone, determining its nucleotide sequence, locating a large open reading frame, and translating the sequence into a putative protein. In this case priority is usually given to analyzing the putative protein, with promoter regions introns being sequenced later to elucidate gene regulation. The organization of the following example analysis of *Notch* reflects these laboratory priorities by beginning with cDNA analysis, moving to protein analysis, and then returning to DNA analysis for the genomic sequence.

cDNA SEQUENCE ANALYSIS

Sequencing Project Management

For technical reasons the DNA of a gene or cDNA clone must be cut into smaller pieces before the sequence can actually be determined. The sequences of the fragments are then usually determined by a number of enzymatic sequencing reactions, each of which reveals the sequence of a short stretch of DNA. There are several ways of doing this so that the set of sequencing reactions covers the whole gene: by randomly cloning DNA fragments (shotgun method), by a progressive deletion approach, or by synthesizing oligonucleotides to be used as primers to extend the previously determined sequence (see Chapter 1). The short sequences determined by each of these methods (called 'fragments' or 'gels' by some software packages) are assembled into a complete consensus sequence on the computer.

The job of assembling a sequence can best be explained with an example. If the sentence "I really enjoy reading about computer methods to analyze

Notch Schematic

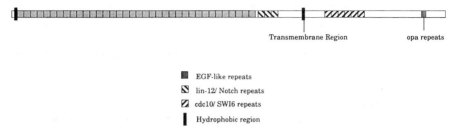

Transmembrane Region   opa repeats

█ EGF-like repeats
▣ lin-12/ Notch repeats
▣ cdc10/ SWI6 repeats
▌ Hydrophobic region

Figure 1: Schematic of the *Notch* protein from *D. melanogaster*.

sequences" were a DNA sequence, the sequence fragments read from its shotgun sequencing might look like Figure 2. The computer's job is to find where these fragments overlap and then to join them into a large consensus sequence corresponding to the full length DNA. Unfortunately, assembling an actual sequence is not as simple as shown in the example. Because of sequencing errors, the overlapping regions between fragments do not perfectly agree. Moreover, a 10 kb sequence like *Notch*, depending on the sequencing method used, can generate between eighty and several hundred sequenced fragments, each generally between 200 and 450 bases long. Because this amount of data is difficult to manipulate, computer database systems for keeping track of the fragments are essential. Fragment assembly systems store the fragments, compare them, keep track of where they overlap and generate consensus sequences (contigs).

Unlike many analysis tasks, for which there are standard algorithms, the organization of a fragment assembly system is up to the programmer. The approach a program uses to deal with sequence alignment, fragment editings, and problems such as cloning artifacts and sequencing errors, is not at all standardized. Therefore, before choosing a system, one should look into how it works. Some questions to ask are: how many fragments will it accept; how easy is it to edit the fragments; will it align the sequences; how automatic

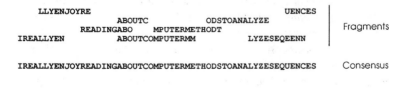

```
LLYENJOYRE                          UENCES
        ABOUTC          ODSTOANALYZE
    READINGABO    MPUTERMETHODT                    Fragments
IREALLYEN       ABOUTCOMPUTERMM      LYZESEQEENN

IREALLYENJOYREADINGABOUTCOMPUTERMETHODSTOANALYZESEQUENCES      Consensus
```

Assembly Project

Figure 2: Fragment assembly project showing constituent fragments and consensus sequence.

is it; is it designed to handle the sequencing protocol (shotgun, deletion, etc.) you intend to use?

Because the details of assembling a sequence are specific to the software package, this section will not give a detailed example of an assembly (see chapter 1); however, here are some guidelines for any system which can prevent many headaches:

1) Use the same software package for entering and assembling the fragments. One of the aggravations of sequence analysis is that each software package and database has its own file format, although progress is being made toward compatibility and standards. If you use more than one package, sequence reformatting can rarely be avoided. Don't make things more difficult than they need to be; enter the sequence into the computer in the format required by the assembly system.

2) Enter the fragments into the project as you go along. It is easier to align and join a few fragments than to load fifty fragments into a project at the same time. Currently, none of the widely available assembly systems can be relied on to automatically churn out a correctly assembled sequence from a set of fragments. In practice, human intervention is required to make decisions about which fragments to join, and this task is most manageable when only a few fragments are added at a time.

3) Don't enter vector sequence into your project. Some systems notify the user if they detect a vector sequence. If your system does not do this, you must use a sequence searching program to scan the fragments for vector sequence before you enter them into the system. Be conservative—if there is any chance that it may be vector sequence (e.g., has a few mismatches or gaps), remove it. Even small amounts of vector sequence will compromise many packages' ability to detect fragment overlaps.

4) Make up a code to easily distinguish sequence changes made with an editor from unedited data. For example, lower case might be used for editings: AAAAaAA. Also, use a different code to distinguish between ambiguities in the sequence data and corrections made to align sequences. An 'X' might be used to indicate an indeterminable base on the autoradiograph, and a '.' as an edited gap in the sequence. If you do this, you must understand how the '.' or 'X' will be treated by the system. The system may prevent other fragments from matching to ambiguous regions, or inversely, consider the symbol a wildcard to which anything can match.

5) Keep the original sequence data separate from the edited versions. As an assembly progresses, it will become apparent that some gels were read incorrectly due to poor quality or human error. Assembly systems provide an editor for correcting these mistakes. Remember, however, that these flawed original readings are the primary data. Often, after a fit of over-zealous editing, one realizes that the fragment is actually in the wrong place and probably shouldn't have all those "fixes" inserted into it. It is important to be able to recover the original fragment reading. Some systems automatically keep the original or archive sequence separate from the edited or working version. Others do not.

6) Make the strongest joins first. Most systems work by joining two or more fragments and comparing their consensus sequence with the other fragments. These joined fragments are called "contigs" (Staden, 1980). A consensus sequence is the majority consensus of bases at each position along the entire length of the contig. If two fragments have previously been incorrectly joined, they will have an incorrect consensus which may prevent the program from finding the correct overlap. To avoid this problem, one should work from the strongest to the weakest alignments.

7) Sequences with repeats in them are the hardest to assemble. This is because it can be hard to distinguish between poor quality sequence data and an imperfect repeat. If you suspect that your sequence has repeats, it is particularly important to make the strongest joins first.

8) Save versions of the entire database. Inevitably, at some point during the course of reconstructing a sequence, one will want to undo the last several hours worth of work. Either because fragments have been incorrectly joined, or because some other mistake was made. When this happens, the easiest way to handle it is often to go back to an earlier version of the project. Some packages record a history of the work as it progresses, others allow a current project to be saved. If the software does not offer a way of saving a databases' contents, then this should be done periodically using the facilities provided by the operating system.

Restriction Map

A computer-generated restriction enzyme map provides essential information for manipulating pieces of DNA. A restriction map lists the sequence and marks the cleavage sites of selected enzymes. It often includes a protein translation in all six frames. Many programs allow one to select enzymes which cut the sequence only once or twice. A database of enzymes, their sites and commercial sources is available (Roberts, 1988). Figure 3 shows a portion of the *Notch* restriction map. Predicted restriction enzyme maps

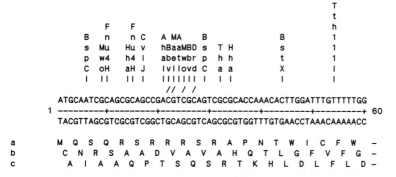

Figure 3: Computer generated restriction enzyme map for a portion of the *Notch* sequence.

provide an important means of checking a sequencing project as it progresses. Restriction enzyme maps of the contigs should be checked against the known map of the original clones.

Finding Open Reading Frames

Once a cDNA sequence has been assembled, it can be examined for its protein coding potential. The cDNA should first be scanned for open reading frames, or ORFs. An open reading frame is a region that lies between an AUG start codon and ends with either a UAG, UGA or UAA stop codon. Figure 4a shows a plot of the three possible translation frames for start and stop codons. The "boxes" indicate ORFs. Notice that there are two large ORFs, one in the first reading frame and the other in the second. This configuration typifies a shift in the protein reading frame caused by a sequencing error, such as a base missed due to band compression. The corrected sequence produces the plot in Figure 4b and results in a more than 8 kb ORF in translation frame 1.

Codon Preference

One way to confirm that an open reading frame actually encodes a protein is to examine its codon usage. Codon preference is based on the observation that organisms prefer to use certain codons for amino acids over other

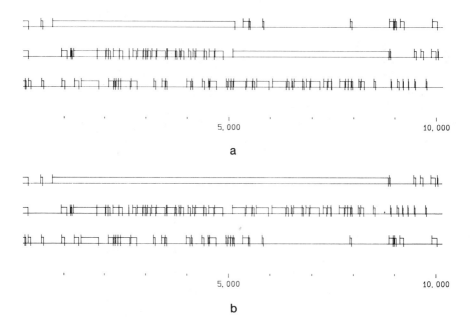

Figure 4: a. Open reading frame plot for the forward translation frames of the *Notch* cDNA. There is a large ORF in both the first and second translation frames due to a sequencing error which caused a shift in the translation reading frame. b. ORF plot with the sequencing error corrected.

AmAcid	Codon	Number	/1000	Fraction
Gly	GGG	11.00	2.60	0.03
Gly	GGA	92.00	21.74	0.28
Gly	GGT	86.00	20.33	0.26
Gly	GGC	142.00	33.56	0.43
Glu	GAG	212.00	50.11	0.75
Glu	GAA	69.00	16.31	0.25
Asp	GAT	110.00	26.00	0.43
Asp	GAC	144.00	34.03	0.57

Figure 5: Portion of a codon frequency table for *D. melanogaster*. The third column is the number of observations for each codon. The fourth column is the observations normalized to a frequency per thousand. The fifth column is the fraction of each codon within its synonymous family

synonymous codons (see Chapter 1). This is especially true for highly expressed genes and reflects the need for rapidly translated messages to use the major isoaccepting tRNAs. For example, the codon GGG and GGC both code for glycine. The partial codon usage table in Figure 5 indicates that, in *Drosophila*, glycine is usually encoded by a GGC and only rarely is it encoded by GGG. By verifying that its codon usage agrees with the general codon preference of the species, codon usage tables can help determine if an open reading frame is likely to encode a protein. In other words, an open reading frame from *Drosophila* which recurrently codes glycine with GGG is suspicious. Codon preference tables for different organisms are provided with some software packages or may be available from colleagues. It is also possible to make a codon usage table. This is done with a program which calculates codon frequencies from known coding regions.

Figure 6 shows the results of a scan of the three forward reading frames of *Notch* with a *Drosophila* codon preference table. The curve plotted is the codon preference statistic. It is based on the ratio between the occurrence of a codon and its synonymous family, and the calculated occurrences of the codon and its synonymous family in a random sequence of the same composition (Gribskov et al., 1984). Expressing the preference by this ratio assures that the statistic is not biased by the amino acid composition of the encoded protein. A value of one is a neutral score. A value over one indicates that the codon preference is similar to that of the table. A value under one means that it is different. The large open reading frame in frame 1 consistently scores above one, increasing our confidence that this ORF encodes the *Notch* product.

TestCode Statistic

An elegant method for finding coding regions is the TestCode statistic (Fickett, 1982). Fickett found that nucleotides in protein coding regions have

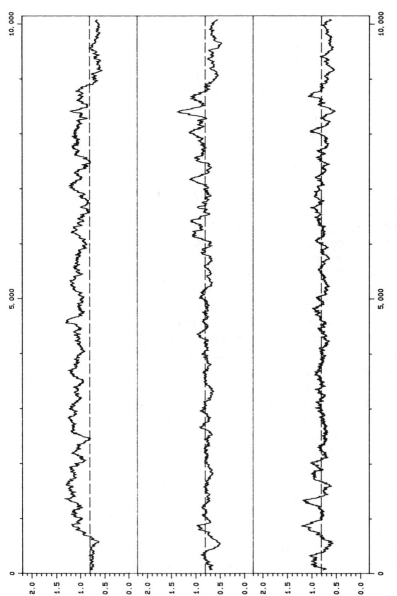

Figure 6: Codon preference plot of the *Notch* cDNA. Each window represents a translation frame. The statistic plotted is p= (f/F)/(r/R), where f is the codon's frequency of occurrence, F is the total occurrences of its synonymous family, and r and R are those values for a random sequence of the same composition as the sequence being analyzed.

a period-of-three bias which is absent in non-coding regions. That is, any given base will be found preferentially in either the first, second or third position of the sequence. For example, in the sequence segment

ACTAGTGGTTATAG
12312312312312

the 'A' prefers position 1, the 'C' prefers position 2, 'T' prefers position 3 and 'G' prefers position 2. The TestCode statistic measures this bias and uses it to

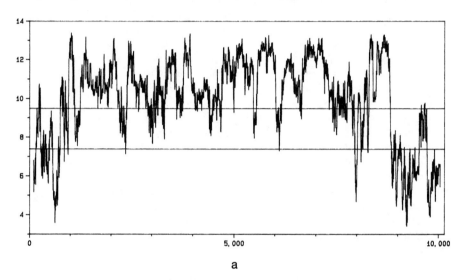

a

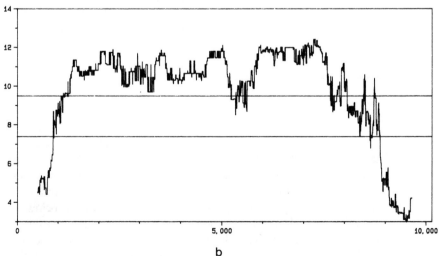

b

Figure 7: Plot of Fickett's period-of-three-bias statistic for predicting coding regions. a. Statistic is calculated within a window of 200. b. Same plot with a window of 1000.

```
                                                          ↰EGF 1
   1  MQSQRSRRRSRAPNTWICFWINKMHAVASLPASLPLLLLTLAFANLPNTVRGTDTALVAASCTSVGCQNGGTCVTQLNGK    80
                   ↰EGF 2                                  ↰EGF 3
  81  TYCACDSHYVGDYCEHRNPCNSIRCQNGGTCQVTFRNGRPGISCKCPLGFDESLCEIAVPNACDHVTCLNGGTCQLKTLE   160
                   ↰EGF 4                                  ↰EGF 5
 161  EYTCACANGYTGERCETKNLCASSPCRNGATCTALAGSSSFTCSCPPGFTGDTCSYDIEECQSNPCKYGGICVNTHGSYQ   240
                   ↰EGF 6                                  ↰EGF 7
 241  CMCPTGYTGKDCDTKYKPCSPSPCQNAGICRSNGLSYECKCPKGFEGKNCEQNYDDCLGHLCQNGGTCIDGISDYTCRCP   320
                   ↰EGF 8                                  ↰EGF 9
 321  PNFTGRFCQDDVDECAQRDHPVCQNGATCTNTHGSYSCICVNGWAGLDCSNNTDDCKQAACFYGATCIDGVGSFYCQCTK   400
                  ↰EGF 10                                 ↰EGF 11
 401  GKTGLLCHLDDACTSNPCHADAICDTSPINGSYACSCATGYKGVDCSEDIDECDQGSPCEHNGICVNTPGSYRCNCSQGF   480
                  ↰EGF 12                                 ↰EGF 13
 481  TGPRCETNINECESHPCQNEGSCLDDPGTFRCVCMPGFTGTQCEIDIDECQSNPCLNDGTCHDKINGFKCSCALGFTGAR   560
                  ↰EGF 14                                 ↰EGF 15
 561  CQINIDDCQSQPCRNRGICHDSIAGYSCECPPGYTGTSCEININDCDSNPCHRGKCIDDVNSFKCLCDPGYTGYICQKQI   640
                  ↰EGF 16                                 ↰EGF 17          EGF 18↴
 641  NECESNPCQFDGHCQDRVGSYYCQCQAGTSGKNCEVNVNECHSNPCNNGATCIDGINSYKCQCVPGFTGQHCEKNVDECI   720
                   ↰EGF 19                                 ↰EGF 20
 721  SSPCANNGVCIDQVNGYKCECPRGFYDAHCLSDVDECASNPCVNEGRCEDGINEFICHCPPGYTGKRCELDIDECSSNPC   800
                  ↰EGF 21                                 ↰EGF 22
 801  QHGGTCYDKLNAFSCQCMPGYTGQKCETNIDDCVTNPCGNGGTCIDKVNGYKCVCKVPFTGRDCESKMDPCASNRCKNEA   880
                  ↰EGF 23                                 ↰EGF 24
 881  KCTPSSNFLDFSCTCKLGYTGRYCDEDIDECSLSSPCRNGASCLNVPGSYRCLCTKGYEGRDCAINTDDCASFPCQNGGT   960
                  ↰EGF 25                                 ↰EGF 26
 961  CLDGIGDYSCLCVDGFDGKHCETDINECLSQPCQNGATCSQYVNSYTCTCPLGFSGINCQTNDEDCTESSCLNGGSCIDG  1040
                  ↰EGF 27                                 ↰EGF 28
1041  INGYNCSCLAGYSGANCQYKLNKCDSNPCLNGATCHEQNNEYTCHCPSGFTGKQCSEYVDWCGQSPCENGATCSQMKHQF  1120
                  ↰EGF 29                                 ↰EGF 30
1121  SCKCSAGWTGKLCDVQTISCQDAADRKGLSLRQLCNNGTCKDYGNSHVCYCSQGYAGSYCQKEIDECQSQPCQNGGTCRD  1200
                  ↰EGF 31                                 ↰EGF 32
1201  LIGAYECQCRQGFQGQNCELNIDDCAPNPCQNGGTCHDRVMNFSCSCPPGTMGIICEINKDDCKPGACHNNGSCIDRVGG  1280
                  ↰EGF 33                                 ↰EGF 34
1281  FECVCQPGFVGARCEGDINECLSNPCSNAGTLDCVQLVNNYHCNCRPGHMGRHCEHKVDFCAQSPCQNGGNCNIRQSGHH  1360
                  ↰EGF 35                                 ↰EGF 36
1361  CICNNGFYGKNCELSGQDCDSNPCRVGNCVVADEGFGYRCECPRGTLGEHCEIDTLDECSPNPCAQGAANCEDLLGDYECL  1440
                                                                                          EGF-like
                                                                                          Repeats
1441  CPSKWKGKRCDIYDANYPGWNGGSGSGNDRYAADLEQQRAMCDKRGCTEKQGNGICDSDCNTYACNFDGNDCSLGINPWA  1520
          ↰LNR 2                          ↰LNR 3                                          lin 12/
1521  NCTANECWNKFKNGKCNEECNNAACHYDGHDCERKLKSCDTLFDAYCQKHYGDGFCDYGCNNAECSWDGLDCENKTQSPV  1600   Notch
                                                                                          Repeats
1601  LAEGAMSVVMLMNVEAFREIQAQFLRNMSHMLRTTVRLKKDALGHDIIINWKDNVRVPEIEDTDFARKNKILYTQQVHQT  1680
1681  GIQIYLEIDNRKCTECFTHAVEAAEFLAATAAKHQLRNDFQIHSVRGIKNPGDEDNGEPPANVKYVITGIILVIIALAFF  1760   TM
1761  GMVLSTQRKRAHGVTWFPEGFRAPAAVMSRRRRDPHGQEMRNLNKQVAMQSQGVGQPGAHWSDDESDMPLPKRQRSDPVS  1840
                                                          ↰cdc 1
1841  GVGLGNNGGYASDHTMVSEYEEADQRVWSQAHLDVVDVRAIMTPPAHQDGGKHDVDARGPCGLTPLMIAAVRGGGLDTGF  1920
         ↰cdc 2                             ↰cdc 3                                        cdc 10/
1921  DIENNEDSTAQVISDLLAQGAELNATMDKTGETSLHLAARFARADAAKRLLDAGADANCQDNTGRTPLHAAVAADAMGVF  2000   SWI 6
         ↰cdc 4                          ↰cdc 5                               ↰cdc 6       Repeats
2001  QILLRNRATNLNARMHDGTTPLILAARLAIEGMVEDLITADADRNAADNSGKTALHWAAAVNNTEAVNILLMHHANRDAQ  2080
2081  DDKDETPLFLAAREGSYEACKALLDNFANREITDHMDRLPRDVASERLHHDIVRLLDEHVPRSPQMLSMTPQAMIGSPPP  2160
2161  GQQQPQLITQPTVISAGNGGNNGNGNASGKQSNQTAKQKAAKKAKLIEGSPDNGLDATGSLRRKASSKKTSAASKKAANL  2240
2241  NGLNPGQLTGGVSGVPGVPPTNSAAQAAAAAAAAVAAMSHELEGSPVGVGMGGNLPSPYDTSSMYSNAMAAPLANGNPNT  2320
2321  GAKQPPSYEDCIKNAQSMQSLQGNGLDMIKLDNYAYSMGSPFQQELLNGQGLGMNGNGQRNGVGPGVLPGGLCGMGGLSG  2400
2401  AGNGNSHEQGLSPPYSNQSPPHSVQSSLALSPHAYLGSPSPAKSRPSLPTSPTHIQAMRHATQQKQFGGSNLNSLLGGAN  2480
                                                                                          opa
2481  GGGVVGGGGGGGGVGQGPQNSPVSLGIISPTGSDMGIMLAPPQSSKNSAIMQTISPQQQQQQQQQQQQQHQQQQQQQQQQ  2560   Repeats
2561  QQQQQQQQLGGLEFGSAGLDLNGFCGSPDSFHSGQMNPPSIQSSMSGSSPSTNMLSPSSQHNQQAFYQYLTPSSQHSGGH  2640
2641  TPQHLVQTLDSYPTPSPESPGHWSSSSPRSNSDWSEGVQSPAANNLYISGGHQANKGSEAIYI                     2703
```

Figure 8: Annotated *Notch* protein sequence.

predict coding potential. The program slides a window along the sequence and plots the TestCode within that window. It does not predict the reading frame or an exact boundary of the ORF. Figure 7a shows the Fickett statistic for the *Notch* cDNA. Values above the upper line represent regions with a greater than 95% probability of being coding regions. Values below the lower line are, to 95% accuracy, non-coding regions. Values in the middle are indeterminate. This plot, along with the codon preference and the open reading frame, suggests the presence of an approximately 8 kb coding region in the *Notch* cDNA. This large ORF can be translated into the 2703 residue protein sequence shown in Figure 8.

Windows

At this point, it is worth explaining window calculation schemes in general. Many sequence analyses, including dotplots, secondary structure predictions, and hydropathy plots, work by calculating some value within a window at each position in the sequence. Therefore, it helps to understand a few basic concepts about windows. The window below is 14 bases long.

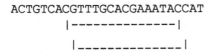

As it is moved one base at a time along the sequence, the average value of some property can be calculated and plotted. As for any plotted average, the size of the window within which it is calculated affects the smoothness of the plot. Figure 7a was plotted with a window of 200, Figure 7b with a window of 1000. Notice that Figure 7a is much more jagged. Thus, increasing the window size smooths the plot. A rule of thumb is that the window size should be about one half to two thirds the size of the structure to be found. For example, the membrane-spanning region of a protein is approximately 20 amino acids long. To detect it on a dotplot or hydrophobicity plot, the window size should be 10 to 15 residues long.

PROTEIN ANALYSIS: DETERMINING STRUCTURE AND FUNCTION

Database Searches

The first indication of the function and structure of a newly determined sequence is often similarity to sequences in a DNA or protein database, or to other characterized patterns in a DNA or protein motif database. This will become increasingly true as the sequence database continues to grow. A database search for similarity to known sequences is therefore a good first step in any analysis. Because the smaller DNA alphabet causes more false positives, searches at the protein level are less subject to "noise." Moreover, the physical and chemical attributes of amino acids can offer insight into three-dimensional structure. Therefore, protein sequence searches are recommended over DNA sequence searches whenever possible. A number of programs are available to search both sequence and motif databases.

Database searches are probably the most important and least understood kind of sequence analyses. Not only are the algorithms complicated, but the results can be difficult to interpret. One reason the algorithms seem nonintuitive to biologists is because programmers have introduced concepts foreign to biology to optimize the speed of the searches. Terms such as "word," "ktup," "hashing," "lookup-table," and "dictionary" are associated with most searching programs and pertain to computer data structures for fast searching techniques (see Chapter 3). They have nothing to do with biology. However, because there is a trade-off between search speed and search sensitivity, it is important for the biologist to understand what these terms mean.

Adding to the difficulties, determining a match's biological significance based on its search score is not straightforward. Although assessing a rudimentary statistical significance for search scores is not difficult (most programs calculate a mean score and standard deviation and provide a histogram of score distribution), it is very important to approach search results with a clear realization that statistical and biological significance are not equivalent. Beginners often want to know if a database search or an alignment score is "good." The answer is: it depends on what you are looking for. Biologically important matches can have relatively low scores on a database search, as will be startlingly demonstrated by the match between *Notch* and the *cdc10* protein from the fission yeast *S. pombe*. Although sophisticated statistical methods of evaluating sequence similarity are being developed (Karlin and Altschul, 1990; Altschul and Lipman, 1990), the scoring methods of most available database search programs are still quite basic. The following discussion of statistical significance refers to these basic methods.

The following section will demonstrate three different database search programs: FASTA, BLAST and PROSITE. FASTA and BLAST are DNA and protein database searching programs. FASTA-type algorithms (Pearson and Lipman, 1988; Wilbur and Lipman, 1983) have been the standard method for database searching (see Chapter 3). BLAST (Altschul et al., 1990) is a recent program which has not yet become widely available, but which has many advantages over existing methods (see Chapter 3). PROSITE (Bairoch, 1990) is a database of protein motifs that can be scanned with a number of different programs and is a useful addition to the standard DNA and protein libraries (see Chapter 2).

FASTA

FASTA is the most widely used of the word/dictionary-based database search programs. Like most search programs, it lists the names, scores and a brief description of the highest scoring sequences from the search; after this list, it displays the alignments between a specified number of the high scoring sequences and the query sequence. The major weakness of this type of search is that it reports only the "best" region of similarity between two sequences and thus may miss weaker similarities in other regions, or repeated features.

To run FASTA-like searches, you will need to decide on a "word size" or "ktup." This section will explain what those terms mean.

The algorithm. Computer scientists judge the speed or "time" (technically, the complexity) of an algorithm in terms of the number of operations (additions, multiplications, comparisons) it must make. Although this concept may seem abstract, it allows them to classify the difficulty of computing problems independently of the speed of a particular machine. For example, if "N" and "M" are the lengths of two sequences, filling the grid of a dotplot requires N x M comparisons, one for each point in the grid. So the dotplot is an order N^2 problem.[1] Because of the size of sequence databases, order N^2 is an unacceptable speed for a database search. FASTA reduces the database search problem from order N^2 to the linear order N + M, where M is the sum of the lengths of all sequences of the database (Order N + M can be referred to as order N). It does this by using a "look-up table" or "dictionary." This dictionary is sometimes referred to as a hash table.

A dictionary is simply a list of all of the possible oligonucleotides or polypeptides (words) of a given length. Figure 9a shows a dictionary of oligonucleotides of length 6. These entries in the dictionary are called "words," or in FASTA "ktups," which is short for k-tuple. When a program asks for a word or ktup size, it wants to know the length of the entries. It follows that the size of the dictionary depends on the word size. A DNA dictionary of words of length 6 will have 4^6 or 4096 entries.

The program works by recording in each dictionary entry the position of every matching word in the query sequence. For example, the short sequence shown on the horizontal axis in Figure 9b contains the word "ACGATA" in positions 1 and position 27, and "GATACC" occurs in position 3. Those positions are recorded after the entry. This table of positions is the lookup table. After this table has been filled for the entire query sequence, the searching can begin. Notice that the number of operations required to fill the lookup table is approximately equal to the length of the sequence. This is the "N" in "N + M."

An important feature of a dictionary is that its contents can be numbered. AAAAAA is entry 0. AAAAAT is entry 1. Thus, each word acts as an index into the dictionary list. Moreover, the index can be calculated from the word. For example, assign 'A' the number '0', 'T' - '1', 'C' - '2' and 'G' - '3.' With these equivalences, each word can be described numerically. ACGATA becomes 023010, a number in base four. This number is used as an index into the lookup table.

The actual search is done with the lookup table, not the query sequence. The first word of the first sequence in the database is looked up in the table based on its unique index. The offset between the positions of the word in the query and the database entry are calculated and saved. For example, if the word occurred at position 20 in the query sequence, the offset would be 20-1, or 19. An intuitive way to think of an offset is as a diagonal on a dotplot (Figure 9b). Then the next word in the database is looked up. If that word occurs at position 21 of the database entry, this would mean that the offset was again 19 (21-2) and might indicate the beginning of a segment of similarity.

---

[1] Although N x M may not equal N^2, they are problems of the same magnitude.

Dictionary	Query		Entry			Diagonal			
AAAAAA	15	–	15	16	=	0	–1		
AAAAAT	16	–	17		=	–1			
AAAAAC									
.									
.									
.									
ACGATA	1	–	1	28	=	0	–27		
ACGATT									
.									
.									
GATACC	3	29	–	3	30	=	0	–27	26 –1
GATACG									
.									
.									
GGGGGG									

a

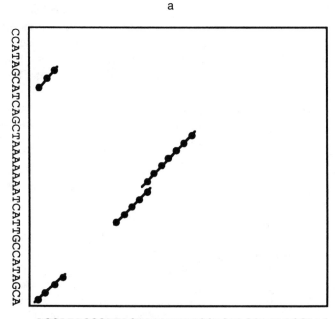

ACGATACCGATACTAAAAAATCGACTACGATACCCAAA

b

Figure 9: a. Schematic of the "dictionary" and "lookup table" structures used in database search algorithms. These have been calculated for the sequences listed on the axes of figure 9b. b. Offsets "0", "-1" and "-27" viewed as a dotplot.

These matching words are often called "hits." The entire database is scanned this way, with the program keeping track of the longest similar segments. Notice that the "time" this requires is proportional to "M," the length of the database.

After the program has compared the query and a sequence entry, the matches must be scored. How this is done varies between programs, but FASTA proceeds through three more steps. The scores from each of the steps are reported as the INIT1, INITN and OPT scores in the output file. The INIT1 score is calculated by joining nearby contiguous stretches of similarity with the same offset, or diagonal. This joins together similar regions separated by short regions of mismatch. Next, FASTA tries to join similar regions from nearby adjacent diagonals into a single long region of similarity. This corresponds to introducing gaps into the sequences. The length of the gaps is limited by applying a penalty based on the distance between the diagonals. This is the INITN score. Finally, FASTA performs a dynamic programming algorithm of the highest scoring regions to determine the OPT score.

There are a couple rules of thumb for choosing word size. First, the smaller the word, the slower and more sensitive the search is. A word size of six is common for DNA searches, two for protein. However, if you are not paying for computer time, you should probably use more sensitive limits such as 4 for DNA and 1 for protein. Also, remember that word size indicates the minimum number of contiguous matching characters needed to score a hit. The larger the word size, the more unlikely it is to find a match, even in similar sequences.

Interpreting the results. Figure 10 shows the results of a FASTA search of the SWISS-PROT database with the *Notch* protein. Clearly, the number of matches can be overwhelming, even without displaying sequence alignments. The short descriptions displayed for each sequence can be helpful in identifying unfamiliar sequences. Figure 11 shows the SWISS-PROT database entry for the *lin12* sequence from the nematode *C. elegans*, one of the high scoring matches.

According to their documentation in the database, all of the sequences with INITN scores above 155 contain EGF-like motifs. EGF (epidermal growth factor) is a soluble peptide derived by proteolytic cleavage from a larger precursor on the cell surface. Its contains nine sequence repeats with a highly conserved spacing of six cysteines: $C-X_7-C-X_5-C-X_{10}-C-X-C-X_8-C$. This same sequence motif is found in an extraordinarily diverse group of proteins (Davis, 1990). The pattern of cysteines in several of the top-scoring alignments (Figure 12) verifies the presence of this motif in *Notch* (see below for an explanation of alignment algorithms). The PROSITE database can help establish the position and number of these and other motifs.

Scan for Motifs with PROSITE

The PROSITE database is a collection of protein signatures (Bairoch, 1990; see Appendix VIII and Chapter 2). As a matter of course, each new protein

		initn	init1	opt
EGFH$STRPU	EPIDERMAL GROWTH FACTOR HOMOLOG (UEGF-1) (F	958	958	1191
LIN1$CAEEL	LIN-12 PROTEIN PRECURSOR (GENE NAME: LIN12)	609	400	853
GLP1$CAEEL	GLP-1 PROTEIN PRECURSOR (GENE NAME: GLP-1).	601	412	578
NODL$DROME	NEUROGENIC LOCUS DL PROTEIN PRECURSOR (GENE	491	491	839
CRB$DROME	CRUMBS PROTEIN (95F) (GENE NAME: CRB) (FRAG	380	380	518
EGF$HUMAN	EPIDERMAL GROWTH FACTOR PRECURSOR, KIDNEY (	303	126	238
PGCS$HUMAN	CHONDROITIN SULFATE PROTEOGLYCAN CORE PROTE	296	296	296
EGF$MOUSE	EPIDERMAL GROWTH FACTOR PRECURSOR (EGF).	270	129	253
PRTS$BOVIN	VITAMIN K-DEPENDENT PROTEIN S (BLOOD CLOTTI	236	146	253
PRTS$HUMAN	VITAMIN K-DEPENDENT PROTEIN S (BLOOD CLOTTI	226	145	255
FA12$HUMAN	COAGULATION FACTOR XII PRECURSOR (EC 3.4.21	220	145	167
TENA$CHICK	TENASCIN (FRAGMENT).	216	91	314
LMB2$DROME	LAMININ B2 CHAIN PRECURSOR.	191	89	214
NIDO$HUMAN	NIDOGEN PRECURSOR (GENE NAME: NID).	190	144	201
ENTA$MOUSE	ENTACTIN PRECURSOR.	183	132	184
EGF2$STRPU	EPIDERMAL GROWTH FACTOR-RELATED PROTEIN PRE	177	85	107
UROM$HUMAN	UROMODULIN PRECURSOR (TAMM-HORSFALL URINARY	175	107	244
LMBS$RAT	S-LAMININ PRECURSOR.	173	91	255
OS25$PLAGA	25 KD OOKINETE SURFACE ANTIGEN PRECURSOR (P	173	90	120
LMB2$HUMAN	LAMININ B2 CHAIN PRECURSOR.	170	110	163
FA9$HUMAN	COAGULATION FACTOR IX PRECURSOR (EC 3.4.21.	168	168	193
THBS$HUMAN	THROMBOSPONDIN PRECURSOR.	167	85	194
LMB1$DROME	LAMININ B1 CHAIN PRECURSOR (GENE NAME: LAMB	167	76	256
FA9$BOVIN	COAGULATION FACTOR IX (EC 3.4.21.22) (CHRIS	163	163	181
PRTZ$BOVIN	PROTEIN Z.	160	160	187
TRBM$BOVIN	THROMBOMODULIN (FRAGMENT).	159	101	249
LMB2$MOUSE	LAMININ B2 CHAIN PRECURSOR.	158	98	186
UROT$MOUSE	TISSUE PLASMINOGEN ACTIVATOR PRECURSOR (EC	158	120	130
FA10$BOVIN	COAGULATION FACTOR X PRECURSOR (EC 3.4.21.6	157	157	194
FA7$HUMAN	COAGULATION FACTOR VII PRECURSOR (EC 3.4.21	156	156	179
FA10$HUMAN	COAGULATION FACTOR X PRECURSOR (EC 3.4.21.6	155	155	185
ANK2$HUMAN	ANKYRIN 2.1 AND 2.2.	154	154	163
LMB1$MOUSE	LAMININ B1 CHAIN PRECURSOR.	149	92	301
OS25$PLAFO	25 KD OOKINETE SURFACE ANTIGEN PRECURSOR (P	144	92	125
DORS$DROME	EMBRYONIC POLARITY DORSAL PROTEIN (GENE NAM	142	142	153
LMB1$HUMAN	LAMININ B1 CHAIN PRECURSOR (GENE NAME: LAMB	141	87	256
TRBM$HUMAN	THROMBOMODULIN PRECURSOR.	141	87	200
UROT$HUMAN	TISSUE PLASMINOGEN ACTIVATOR PRECURSOR (EC	140	115	123
TRBM$MOUSE	THROMBOMODULIN PRECURSOR.	140	86	244
PGCA$HUMAN	CARTILAGE-SPECIFIC PROTEOGLYCAN CORE PROTEI	140	140	140
LDLR$HUMAN	LOW-DENSITY LIPOPROTEIN (LDL) RECEPTOR PREC	139	101	189
YB07$FOWPM	HYPOTHETICAL BAMHI-ORF7 PROTEIN.	137	137	158
CA24$HUMAN	PROCOLLAGEN ALPHA 2(IV) CHAIN PRECURSOR (GE	136	63	74
CYC8$YEAST	GLUCOSE REPRESSION MEDIATOR PROTEIN (GENE N	133	133	151
ITB4$HUMAN	INTEGRIN BETA-4 SUBUNIT PRECURSOR.	133	80	151
PSTA$DICDI	PRESTALK PROTEIN PRECURSOR.	133	80	487
GUX1$HUMGR	EXOGLUCANASE I PRECURSOR (EC 3.2.1.91) (EXO	129	63	63
VWF$HUMAN	VON WILLEBRAND FACTOR PRECURSOR (GENE NAME:	129	66	100
ELAM$MOUSE	ENDOTHELIAL LEUKOCYTE ADHESION MOLECULE 1 P	128	128	150
74E$DROME	74E PROTEIN (GENE NAME: 74E).	128	128	149
UROK$MOUSE	UROKINASE-TYPE PLASMINOGEN ACTIVATOR PRECUR	128	85	86
SP96$DICDI	SPORE COAT PROTEIN SP96 (GENE NAME: SP96).	127	63	133
THYG$BOVIN	THYROGLOBULIN PRECURSOR.	127	60	60

Figure 10: Results of a FASTA search of the SWISS-PROT database with a ktup of 1.

	initn	init1	opt
GDA5$WHEAT ALPHA/BETA-GLIADIN PRECURSOR (PROLAMIN) (CL	126	126	130
GMP1$HUMAN GRANULE MEMBRANE PROTEIN 140 PRECURSOR.	126	126	132
G$PARPR G SURFACE PROTEIN PRECURSOR.	125	81	261
PRTC$HUMAN PROTEIN C PRECURSOR (EC 3.4.21.-) (AUTOPROT	125	125	143
FSH1$DROME FSH MEMBRANE PROTEIN (7.6 KB MRNA).	124	124	196
VGL2$CVMJH E2 GLYCOPROTEIN PRECURSOR (SPIKE GLYCOPROTE	124	82	90
ITB1$MOUSE FIBRONECTIN RECEPTOR BETA SUBUNIT PRECURSOR	124	78	126
UROT$DESRO SALIVARY PLASMINOGEN ACTIVATOR PRECURSOR (E	122	122	131
ITB2$HUMAN CELL SURFACE ADHESION GLYCOPROTEINS LFA-1,	122	71	117
THYG$HUMAN THYROGLOBULIN PRECURSOR (FRAGMENT).	120	66	68
LAM1$HUMAN LEUKOCYTE ADHESION MOLECULE-1 PRECURSOR (LA	119	119	143
PRTC$BOVIN PROTEIN C PRECURSOR (EC 3.4.21.-) (AUTOPROT	119	119	122
ANDR$RAT ANDROGEN RECEPTOR (GENE NAME: AR).	119	119	120
LNHR$HUMAN LYMPH NODE HOMING RECEPTOR PRECURSOR (GENE	119	119	137
VGLM$BUNSH M POLYPROTEIN PRECURSOR (CONTAINS: NONSTRUC	119	81	83
AGI3$WHEAT AGGLUTININ ISOLECTIN 3 PRECURSOR (WGA3) (FR	119	82	127
PA2H$LATCO PHOSPHOLIPASE A2 HOMOLOG I (PLH-I).	118	87	109
PA22$LATCO PHOSPHOLIPASE A2 II (EC 3.1.1.4) (PHOSPHATI	118	87	102
VGL2$CVMA5 E2 GLYCOPROTEIN PRECURSOR (SPIKE GLYCOPROTE	118	87	98
VGLM$BUNL7 M POLYPROTEIN PRECURSOR (CONTAINS: NONSTRUC	118	72	81
CA13$HUMAN PROCOLLAGEN ALPHA 1(III) CHAIN PRECURSOR (G	117	61	118
PRP1$HUMAN SALIVARY PROLINE-RICH PROTEIN PRECURSOR (PR	117	92	92
PERT$RAT THYROID PEROXIDASE PRECURSOR (EC 1.11.1.8)	117	117	126
ITB1$HUMAN FIBRONECTIN RECEPTOR BETA SUBUNIT PRECURSOR	117	77	128
SWI6$YEAST TRANS-ACTING ACTIVATOR OF HO ENDONUCLEASE G	116	80	95
VGLM$RVFV M POLYPROTEIN PRECURSOR (CONTAINS: NONSTRUC	116	83	87
POLG$WNV GENOME POLYPROTEIN (CAPSID PROTEIN C; ENVEL	116	59	59
GRP2$PHAVU GLYCINE-RICH CELL WALL STRUCTURAL PROTEIN G	115	75	77
COAC$RAT ACETYL-COA CARBOXYLASE (EC 6.4.1.2) (ACC).	113	54	54
POLS$WEEV STRUCTURAL POLYPROTEIN (CONTAINS: COAT PROT	113	55	58
GDA7$WHEAT ALPHA/BETA-GLIADIN PRECURSOR (PROLAMIN) (CL	112	112	130
FSA1$PIG FOLLISTATIN A (FS).	112	72	110
FSA2$PIG FOLLISTATIN A' (FS).	112	72	107
ELSC$BOVIN ELASTIN C PRECURSOR.	111	81	162
IOV7$CHICK OVOINHIBITOR PRECURSOR.	111	53	59
PERU$HUMAN THYROID PEROXIDASE PRECURSOR (EC 1.11.1.8)	111	111	143
ELSA$BOVIN ELASTIN A PRECURSOR.	111	81	162
PERT$HUMAN THYROID PEROXIDASE PRECURSOR (EC 1.11.1.8)	111	111	143
ELSB$BOVIN ELASTIN B PRECURSOR.	111	81	162
ENV$MLVRD ENV POLYPROTEIN PRECURSOR (COAT POLYPROTEIN	111	55	59
CA14$HUMAN PROCOLLAGEN ALPHA 1(IV) CHAIN PRECURSOR (GE	111	53	87
INSR$RAT INSULIN RECEPTOR PRECURSOR (EC 2.7.1.112) (	110	51	69
HUNB$DROVI HUNCHBACK PROTEIN (GENE NAME: HB).	110	110	126
SP60$DICDI SPORE COAT PROTEIN SP60 PRECURSOR (GENE NAM	110	66	134
POLG$KUNJM GENOME POLYPROTEIN (CAPSID PROTEIN C; ENVEL	110	52	54
GDA6$WHEAT ALPHA/BETA-GLIADIN PRECURSOR (PROLAMIN) (CL	109	109	109
INSR$MOUSE INSULIN RECEPTOR PRECURSOR (EC 2.7.1.112) (	108	69	104
LP61$EIMTE ANTIGEN LPMC61 (FRAGMENT).	108	108	113
ITB1$CHICK INTEGRIN BETA-1 PRECURSOR (CSAT ANTIGEN) (J	108	77	130
ANDR$HUMAN ANDROGEN RECEPTOR (GENE NAME: AR).	107	107	107
ELF1$DROME DNA-BINDING PROTEIN ELF1 (FOR ELEMENT I-BIN	107	107	133
GLTA$WHEAT LOW MOLECULAR WEIGHT GLUTENIN PRECURSOR.	105	105	105
POLS$RUBVT STRUCTURAL POLYPROTEIN (CONTAINS: NUCLEOCAP	105	52	53
CC10$SCHPO CDC10 START CONTROL PROTEIN (GENE NAME: CDC	105	67	90

```
ID   LIN1$CAEEL      STANDARD;      PRT;   1429 AA.
AC   P14585;
DT   01-JAN-1990   (REL. 13, CREATED)
DE   LIN-12 PROTEIN PRECURSOR (GENE NAME: LIN12).
OS   CAENORHABDITIS ELEGANS.
OC   EUKARYOTA; METAZOA; ACOELEMATES; NEMATHELMINTHES.
RN   [1] (STRAIN N2 BRISTOL, SEQUENCE FROM N.A.)
RA   YOCHEM J., WESTON K., GREENWALD I.;
RL   NATURE 335:547-550(1988).
CC   -!- FUNCTION: LIN-12 IS IS INVOLVED IN SEVERAL CELL FATES DECISIONS
CC       THAT REQUIRES CELL-CELL INTERACTIONS. IT IS POSSIBLE THAT LIN-12
CC       ENCODES A MEMBRANE-BOUND RECEPTOR FOR A SIGNAL THAT ENABLES
CC       EXPRESSION OF THE VENTRAL UTERINE PRECURSOR CELL FATE.
CC   -!- SIMILARITY: HIGH, TO C.ELEGANS GLP-1.
CC   -!- SIMILARITY: THIS PROTEIN INCLUDES 13 EGF-LIKE DOMAIN.
CC   -!- SIMILARITY: THIS PROTEIN INCLUDES 3 COPIES OF A LIN/NOTCH REPEAT.
CC   -!- SIMILARITY: THIS PROTEIN CONTAINS 6 ANKREPEAT SEQUENCES, THESE
CC       REPEATS ARE GENERALLY FOUND IN TISSUE-DIFFERENTIATION AND CELL-
CC       CYCLE CONTROL PROTEINS (ANKYRIN, NOTCH, LIN-12, GLP-1, CDC10,
CC       SWI14, SWI16, ETC.).
DR   EMBL; M21478; M21478.
DR   PROSITE; PS00022; EGF.
KW   DIFFERENTIATION; TANDEM REPEAT; EGF-LIKE DOMAIN; TRANSMEMBRANE;
KW   GLYCOPROTEIN; SIGNAL.
FT   SIGNAL         1     15        PUTATIVE
FT   CHAIN         16   1429        LIN-12.
FT   DOMAIN        16    908        EXTRACELLULAR.
FT   TRANSMEM     909    931        PUTATIVE.
FT   DOMAIN       932   1429        INTRACELLULAR.
FT   DOMAIN        24    618        13 EGF-TYPE REPEATS.
FT   DOMAIN       631    750        3 COPIES OF A LIN/NOTCH REPEAT.
FT   DOMAIN      1046   1266        6 REPEATS OF THE ANKREPEAT MOTIF.
FT   REPEAT        24     60        EGF-LIKE 1.
FT   REPEAT       118    149        EGF-LIKE 2.
FT   REPEAT       156    189        EGF-LIKE 3.
FT   REPEAT       205    245        EGF-LIKE 4.
FT   REPEAT       254    284        EGF-LIKE 5.
FT   REPEAT       291    322        EGF-LIKE 6.
FT   REPEAT       327    362        EGF-LIKE 7.
FT   REPEAT       369    401        EGF-LIKE 8.
FT   REPEAT       408    440        EGF-LIKE 9.
FT   REPEAT       453    491        EGF-LIKE 10.
FT   REPEAT       507    540        EGF-LIKE 11.
FT   REPEAT       547    578        EGF-LIKE 12.
FT   REPEAT       586    618        EGF-LIKE 12.
FT   REPEAT       635    669        LIN/NOTCH REPEAT 1.
FT   REPEAT       670    710        LIN/NOTCH REPEAT 2.
FT   REPEAT       711    750        LIN/NOTCH REPEAT 3.
FT   REPEAT      1046   1078        ANKREPEAT MOTIF 1.
FT   REPEAT      1079   1119        ANKREPEAT MOTIF 2.
FT   REPEAT      1120   1152        ANKREPEAT MOTIF 3.
FT   REPEAT      1153   1188        ANKREPEAT MOTIF 4.
FT   REPEAT      1189   1232        ANKREPEAT MOTIF 5.
FT   REPEAT      1233   1266        ANKREPEAT MOTIF 6.
SQ   SEQUENCE    1429 AA;  157114 MW;  9796870 CN;
```

Figure 11: The documentation section of the SWISS-PROT database entry for the *lin12* sequence of *C. elegans*.

sequence should be scanned with it. A protein signature is a short pattern that arises from tight constraints on the three-dimensional structures of binding or active sites. PROSITE release 5.0 comprises 338 signature sequences, including the EGF motif. The patterns are compiled from multiple sequence alignments and tend to fall into five general categories: enzyme catalytic sites, prosthetic group attachment sites, residues involved in binding a metal ion, cysteine patterns, protein or molecule binding sites and protein modification sites.

PROSITE uses certain conventions to express the variability or ambiguity of some positions in the motifs. For example, the consensus pattern for a putative N-glycosylation site is "N-{P}-[ST]-{P}," which means: asparagine (N), followed by anything but proline (P), followed by serine (S) or threonine (T), and anything other than proline. The EGF pattern is based on a conserved cysteine pattern "C-X-C-X_5-G-X_2-C." The "X" means any amino acid and the subscript specifies the number of amino acids, so that X_5 means any 5 amino acid residues, and X_2 means only 2 residues.

Figure 13a shows a portion of the output from a scan of the predicted *Notch* protein against the PROSITE database. The most interesting result is the presence of 34 EGF-like repeats occurring between amino acids 83 and 1450. Note that the repeats are almost always spaced at intervals of 38 residues. There is a problem, however; as we will see later, *Notch* has 36 EGF-like repeats. PROSITE did not identify the 2nd and 18th repeats because they do not have a glycine (G) in position 9. Although in this case the oversight is not very important, there is a lesson to be learned from it: computers very precisely answer the questions asked of them. Therefore, it is critical that you understand the assumptions a program is making, in this case, that an EGF-like motif must have a glycine. In particular, the signature sequences in PROSITE are finely tuned to detect known sequences possessing a motif, and therefore may miss similar, but novel, sequences representing a given motif.

This scan also detected several other patterns, including casein kinase II phosphorylation sites (Figure 13b). Their significance will be discussed later (see Protein Degradation: PEST Sequences).

BLAST

The EGF-like repeats dominated the search results. In fact, it was not until the 33rd match, ankyrin2.1, that FASTA reported a non-EGF-like similarity (Figure 12c). Below that point, the alignments show non-cysteine-rich matches interspersed with cysteine-rich EGF-like matches. The easiest way to get around the problem of the EGF-like repeats overwhelming the search is to repeat it with this region removed from the sequence.

This third search gives the opportunity to present an innovative and recently developed database search program, BLAST or "Basic Local Alignment Search Tool" (Altschul et al., 1990; see Chapter 3). BLAST is an order of magnitude faster than other search programs, and can also report

```
LIN1$CAEEL LIN-12 PROTEIN PRECURSOR (GENE NAME: LIN12)
                            .
                            .
                            .

dronot    989 LSQPCQNGATCSQYVNSYTCTCPLGFSGINCQTNDEDCTESSCLNGGSCIDGINGYNCSC
               .  .:. :.   ..  .:. .     : .: :...: .. :.    :  ...: .:.
LIN1$C    445 --PIGFGGVRCDLRLEIGICSRQ----GGKC-FNGGKCLSGFCV----CPPDFTGNQCE-


dronot   1049 LAGYSGANCQYKLNKCDSNPCLNGATCHEQNNE--YTCHCPSGFTGKQCSEYVDWCGQSP
               .. .....    . : : :.::.:.::: ....   :.: :  ::.:. :. . : :  ..:
LIN1$C    493 -VNRKNGKSSLSENLCLSDPCMNNATCIDVDAHIGYACICKQGFEGDICERHKDLCLENP


dronot   1107 CENGATCSQMKHQFSCKCSAGWTGKLCDVQTI-SC-QDAADRKGLSLRQLCNNGTCK-DY
               :.::..: :  .. :::.:.:. :. :. ... .: ...  .. :..... .. .:. .:
LIN1$C    552 CSNGGVCHQHRESFSCDCPPGFYGNGCEQEKMFRCLKSTCQNGGVCINEEEKGRKCECSY


dronot   1164 GNSHVCYCSQGYAGSYCQKEI---DECQSQPC---QNGGTCRDLIGAYECQCRQGFQGQN
               : :  . .   ... .:.    . :... :   .:.:.: :   .:. .:. :.: .
LIN1$C    612 GFSGARCEEKINLTGFTEKDSLLRSVCEKRKCSERANDGNC-DADCNYA-ACK--FDGGD


dronot   1218 CELNIDDCAPNPCQNGGTCHDRVMNFSCSCPPGTMGIICEINKDDCKPGACHNNGSCIDR
               :. . .  .. :. :. : :   :    : ..  . :  . :: :... .   .  ..
LIN1$C    668 CSGKRE--PFSKCRYGNMCADFFAN--GVCNQACNNEECLYDGMDCLPAVVRCPVKIREH


dronot   1278 VGG-F-ECVCQPGFVGARCEGDINECLSNPCSNAGTLDCVQLVNNYHCNCRPGHMGRHCE
               .. :  .:.:.  .. :. : .  ..:
LIN1$C    724 CASRFANGICDPECNTNGCGFDGGDCDNETNATIITNIRITVQMDPKEFQVTGGQSLMEI
```

a

Figure 12: Alignments between *Notch* and sequences with EGF-like repeats. ":" is an exact match between residues; "." is a match between similar amino acids according to the MDM$_{78}$ table; "X" is the boundary of the initial region associated with the INIT1 score; "-" is a gap added to the sequence. a. *Notch* and *lin12*. Continued on page 179.

more than one match per sequence. Rather than showing a single "best" match between a query and a database sequence, BLAST may report several. This prevents one region of similarity between two sequences from obscuring others.

Using BLAST, the SWISS-PROT database was searched with a subset of the *Notch* sequence which excluded the EGF-like repeats. Similarity to several interesting proteins was found (Figure 14a & b). In particular, the alignments with *lin12* point out a weakness of the FASTA program and illustrate the advantages BLAST provides by reporting several matches per sequence. Both *Notch* and *lin12* have two distinct cysteine-rich repeats: the EGF-like repeats and a less extensively repeated group immediately following them, the *Notch/lin12* repeats. *Lin12* has less than half as many EGF-like

FA12$HUMAN COAGULATION FACTOR XII PRECURSOR

```
dronot 265  QNAGICRSNGLSYECKCPKGFEGKNCEQNYDDCLGH-LCQNGGTCIDGISDYTCRCPPNF
              :.:   :   X:.::::..   :.   :  ::...
FA12$H  66  RPGPQPWCATTPNFDQDQRWGYCLEPKKVKDHCSKHSPCQKGGTCVNMPSGPHCLCPQHL


dronot 324  TGRFCQDDVDECAQRDHPVCQNGATCTNTHGSYS-CICVNGWAGLDCSN-NTDDCKQAAC
              ::. ::..     .:  .   .:.  . ......  : :  .. ..:  . .....:. ..:
FA12$H 126  TGNHCQKEKCFEPQLLRFFHKNEIWYRTEQAAVARCQCKG--PDAHCQRLASQACRTNPC


dronot 382  FYGATCIDGVGSFYCQCTKGKTGLLCHLDDACTSNPCHADAICDTSPINGSYACSCATGY
              ..:. :..  :   :.:.  :  ::  .:..X
FA12$H 184  LHGGRCLEVEGHRLCHCPVGYTGPFCDVDTKASCYDGRGLSYRGLARTTLSGAPCQPWAS
```

b

ANK2$HUMAN ANKYRIN 2.1 AND 2.2.

```
dronot 1974  GADANCQDNTGRTPLHAAVAADAMGVFQILLRNRATNLNARMHDGTTPLILAARLAIEGM
               :::  .....:.   ..X . : ::..  .    :
ANK2$H    1  PYSVGFREADAATSFLRAARSGNLDKALDHLRN-GVDINTCNQNGLNGLHLASKEGHVKM


dronot 2034  VEDLITADADRNAADNSGKTALHWAAAVNNTEAVNILLMHHANRDAQDDKDETPLFLAAR
               :  .:.  .    .......:.:::: ::  ....:.:. :. .  :: .:!...:. :::...:!.
ANK2$H   60  VVELLHKEIILETTTKKGNTALHIAALAGQDEVVRELVNYGANVNAQSQKGFTPLYMAAQ


dronot 2094  EGSYEACKALLDNFANREITDHMDRLPRDVASERLHHDIVRLLDEHVPRSPQMLSMTPQA
               :.  :.  : ::.: ::......  .  .  .:: .. .:..:  :  ..  ...  .:X
ANK2$H  120  ENHLEVVKFLLENGANQNVATEDGFTPLAVALQQGHENVVAHLINYGTKGKVRLPALHIA
```

c

Figure 12 (continued from page 178): b. *Notch* and coagulation factor XII. c. *Notch* and *Ankyrin.*

repeats as *Notch.* FASTA aligned the *lin12* EGF-like repeats at the 14th *Notch* EGF-like repeat and aligned the *Notch /lin12* repeats with the remaining *Notch* EGF-like repeats. Figure 15 shows a schematic of this alignment. Thus, the FASTA alignments missed this important additional similarity between the sequences. Figure 14a shows the proper alignment between the two *lin12/Notch* repeat regions.

Aligning *Notch* and *Xotch*

The Algorithm

We have been discussing sequence alignments without considering how they are produced. Alignment algorithms find the best possible alignment between sequences by penalizing gaps and rewarding matches (Needleman

EGF-like cysteine motif

```
        CXCXXXXGXXC .....
   83: NGKTY CACDSHYVGDYC EHRNP
  164: LEEYT CACANGYTGERC ETKNL
  203: SSSFT CSCPPGFTGDTC SYDIE
  241: HGSYQ CMCPTGYTGKDC DTKYK
  279: GLSYE CKCPKGFEGKNC EQNYD
  317: ISDYT CRCPNFTGRFC QDDVD
  358: HGSYS CICVNGWAGLDC SNNTD
  396: VGSFY CQCTKGKTGLLC HLDDA
  435: NGSYA CSCATGYKGVDC SEDID
  474: PGSYR CNCSQGFTGPRC ETNIN
  512: PGTFR CVCMPGFTGTQC EIDID
  550: INGFK CSCALGFTGARC QINID
  588: IAGYS CECPPGYTGTSC EININ
  625: VNSFK CLCDPGYTGYIC QKQIN
  663: VGSYY CQCQAGTSGKNC EVNVN
  701: INSYK CQCVPGFTGQHC EKNVD
  777: INEFI CHCPPGYTGKRC ELDID
  815: LNAFS CQCMPGYTGQKC ETNID
  853: VNGYK CVCKVPFTGRDC ESKMD
  893: FLDFS CTCKLGYTGRYC DEDID
  932: PGSYR CLCTKGYEGRDC AINTD
  970: IGDYS CLCVDGFDGKHC ETDIN
1,008: VNSYT CTCPLGFSGINC QTNDE
1,046: INGYN CSCLAGYSGANC QYKLN
1,084: NNEYT CHCPSGFTGKQC SEYVD
1,122: KHQFS CKCSAGWTGKLC DVQTI
1,169: GNSHV CYCSGQYAGSYC QKEID
1,207: IGAYE CQCRQGFGGQNC ELNID
1,245: VMNFS CSCPPGTMGIIC EINKD
1,283: VGGFE CVCQPGFVGARC EGDIN
1,323: VNNYH CNCRPGHMGRHC EHKVD
1,361: QSGHH CICNNGFYGKNC ELSGQ
1,400: GFGYR CECPRGTLGEHC EIDTL
1,439: LGDYE CLCPSKWKGKRC DIYDA
```

a

Casein kinase II phosphorylation sites

```
          T  E                        T  E
      ..... S XXD..              ..... S XXD..
 133: LGFDE S LCEIA       1074: CLNGA T CHEQN
 158: TCQLK T LEEYT       1105: DWCGQ S PCENG
 248: CPTGY T GKDCD       1139: DVQTI S CQDAA
 307: CQNGG T CIDGV       1159: LCNNG T CKDYG
 386: CFYGA T CIDGN       1197: CQNGG T CRDLI
 457: ECDQG S PCEHI       1235: CQNGG T CHDRV
 502: CQNEG S CLDDP       1273: CHNNG S CIDRV
 521: PGFTG T QCEID       1375: KNCEL S GQDCD
 540: CLNDG T CHDKI       1375: KNCEL S GQDCD
 597: PGYTG T SCEIN       1415: HCEID T LDECS
 691: CNNGA T CIDGI       1466: NGGSG S GNDRY
 752: DAHCL S DVDEC       1523: PWANC T ANECW
 805: CQHGG T CYDKL       1561: LKSCD T LFDAY
 828: GQKCE T NIDDC       1822: PGAHW S DDESD
 843: CGNGG T CIDKV       1858: DHTMV S EYEEA
 860: CKVPF T GRDCE       1918: GGGLD T GEDIE
 866: GRDCE S KMDPC       2297: GGNLP S PYDTS
 960: CQNGR T CLDGI       2327: AKQPP S YEDCI
1,021: GINCQ T NDEDC       2512: GIISP T GSDMG
1,036: CLNGG S CIDGI       2670: SSSPR S NSDWS
```

b

Figure 13: Partial results from a scan of the *Notch* protein with the PROSITE database showing EGF-like cysteine sites and casein kinase II phosphorylation. The pattern consensus sequence is shown on the top line. Each line lists the site position and sequence.

```
>LIN1$CAEEL (Swiss) LIN-12 PROTEIN PRECURSOR (GENE NAME: LIN12). Length = 1429

  Score = 154, E = 1.5e-15, D = 1.5e-15, P = 4.3e-19, length = 80

Query:    74 FKNGKCNEECNNAACHYDGHDCERKLKSCDTLFDAYCQKHYGDGFCDYGCNNAECSWDGL 133
             F NG CN+ CNN  C YDG DC   +  C       C  ++++G CD  CN    C+ DG
Sbjct:   688 FANGVCNQACNNEECLYDGMDCLPAVVRCPVKIREHCASRFANGICDPECNTNGCGFDGG 747

Query:   134 DCENKTQSPVLAEGAMSVVM 153
             DC+N T + ++++  ++V M
Sbjct:   748 DCDNETNATIITNIRITVQM 767

  Score = 131, E = 3.8e-12, D = 2.1e-27, P = 6.0e-31, length = 44

Query:    22 RAMCDKRGCTEKQGNGICDSDCNTYACNFDGNDCSLGINPWANC 65
             R++C+KR C+E+  +G CD+DCN  AC+FDG DCS   +P ++C
Sbjct:   635 RSVCEKRKCSERANDGNCDADCNYAACKFDGGDCSGKREPFSKC 678
```

a

```
>ANK2$HUMAN (Swiss) ANKYRIN 2.1 AND 2.2 Length = 1880

  Score = 126, E = 2.1e-11, D = 2.1e-11, P = 7.9e-15, length = 126

Query:   551 ATNLNARMHDGTTPLILAARLAIEGMVEDLITADADINAADNSGKTALHWAAAVNNTEAV 610
             + ++N+  ++G   L LA++ +   MV +L+ +   ++++ + G+TALH AA    E V
Sbjct:    34 GVDINTCNQNGLNGLHLASKEGHVKMVVELLHKEIILETTTKKGNTALHIAALAGQDEVV 93

Query:   611 NILLMHHANRDAQDDKDETPLFLAAREGSYEACKALLDNFANREITDHMDRLPRDVASER 670
             L+  AN +AQ +K  TPL++AA+E   E  K LL+N AN++++    P  VA ++
Sbjct:    94 RELVNYGANVNAQSQKGFTPLYMAAQENHLEVVKFLLENGANQNVATEDGFTPLAVALQQ 153

Query:   671 LHHDIV 676
             H ++V
Sbjct:   154 GHENVV 159

  Score = 67, E = 0.011, D = 2.4e-08, P = 9.2e-12, length = 123

Query:   560 DGTTPLILAARLAIEGMVEDLITADADINAADNSGKTALHWAAAVNNTEAVNILLMHHAN 619
             D++T+ + AAR +    D +  DIN+ ++G +LH A+   + V LL
Sbjct:    10 DAATSFLRAARSGNLDKALDHLRNGVDINTCNQNGLNGLHLASKEGHVKMVVELLHKEII 69

Query:   620 RDAQDDKDETPLFLAAREGSYEACKALLDNFANREITDHMDRLPRDVASERLHHDIVRLL 679
             ++   K +T+L +AA  G  E  + L++  AN +     P  +A++  H ++V+ L
Sbjct:    70 LETTTKKGNTALHIAALAGQDEVVRELVNYGANVNAQSQKGFTPLYMAAQENHLEVVKFL 129

Query:   680 DEH 682
             E+
Sbjct:   130 LEN 132
```

b

Figure 14: Alignments produced by a BLAST search with *Notch* against the SWISS-PROT database for a. *lin12* and b. *ankyrin*. Exact matches are shown by the corresponding residue between the sequences; conservative substitutions by a "+".

and Wunsch, 1970; Sellers, 1974; Smith and Waterman, 1981). These algorithms are often called dynamic programming methods (see Chapter 3). There are two types of alignment: local and global. A local alignment finds

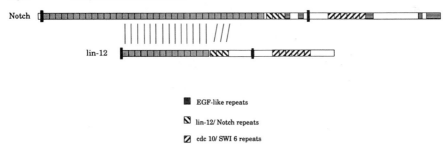

Figure 15: Schematic of the *Notch/lin12* alignment produced by FASTA. The lin12 repeats are aligned to the EGF-like repeats of *Notch*.

the best region of similarity between sequences without insisting that the entire sequence match. The alignments we have shown have been local alignments. A global alignment aligns two entire sequences from beginning to end, insisting that all sequence positions must match. Unless you know that the two sequences you are aligning match along their entire length, you will probably most often use local alignments.

Intuitively, there are a few generalizations that can be made about making alignments. First, the object is to align as many bases or residues as "reasonably" as possible. Second, a gap should be added to a sequence only if it "significantly" increases the number of bases or residues that match. Third, it is better to have a "few" big gaps than a lot of little gaps. Alignment algorithms are a formalization of these rules of thumb. Their parameters are ways of quantifying words like "reasonably," "significantly" and "few." Most implementations assign two gap penalties: one for each gap introduced into a sequence (the gap creation penalty), the other a function of the total length of the gapped regions (the gap extension penalty). For example, in Figure 16a there are two gaps; one is 30 residues long, the other 8. The programs also assign positive scores for matches and negative scores for mismatches. These values are determined by a matrix such as the MDM_{78} table of conservative amino acid substitutions (Dayhoff et al., 1979). Generally, the user has no control over the match and mismatch scores, unless they alter the table; however, they can usually specify a gap creation penalty and a gap extension penalty. One error that is often made is to use the wrong scoring table for local or global alignments. Global alignments require a table with all positive values, and local alignments require one with an average value of less than or equal to zero.

The alignment produced by a program is one of possibly several alignments that have the highest score for the following equation:

Score = Matches - Mismatches - (number of gaps x Gap creation penalty) -

(Gap length x Gap extension penalty)

It is possible, especially with DNA sequences, that the highest score will not be unique, i.e., that there is more than one way to align the sequences and

```
     Gap Weight:   3.000
  Length Weight:   0.100

        Gaps:      1
```

Dronotch.Pep x Xotch.Pep

```
          .          .          .          .          .
  1 MQSQRSRRRSRAPNTWICFWINKMHAVASLPASLPLLLLTLAFANLPNTV 50
                                 ..:.| :|  .:: |...:
  1 ............................MDRIGLAVLLCSLPVLTQGL 20
          .          .          .          .          .
 51 RGTDTALVAASCTSVGCQNGGTCVTQLNGKTYCACDSHYVGDYCEHRNPC 100
    |.|:|| :        | ||| |    .|.. | |:. |.|: |: .|||
 21 RCTQTAEM........CLNGGRCEMTPGGTGVCLCGNLYFGERCQFPNPC 62

                              .
                              .
                              .
```

a

```
     Gap Weight:   2.500
  Length Weight:   0.100

        Gaps:      3
```

Dronotch.Pep x Xotch.Pep

```
          .          .          .          .          .
  1 MQSQRSRRRSRAPNTWICFWINKMHAVASLPASLPLLLLTLAFANLPNTV 50
                    :::: ::|  |  .|||:       |...:
  1 ...................MDRI.GLAVLLCSLPV.........LTQGL 20
          .          .          .          .          .
 51 RGTDTALVAASCTSVGCQNGGTCVTQLNGKTYCACDSHYVGDYCEHRNPC 100
    |.|:|| :        | ||| |    .|.. | |:. |.|: |: .|||
 21 RCTQTAEM........CLNGGRCEMTPGGTGVCLCGNLYFGERCQFPNPC 62

                              .
                              .
                              .
```

b

```
    MQSQRSRRRSRAPNTWICFWINKMHAVASLPASLPLLLLTLAFANLPNTV
                       .. ::| | .|||:| .|
    ...................MDRIGLAVLLCSLPVLTQGLR........

    RGTDTALVAASCTSVG..CQNGGTCVTQLNGKTYCACDSHYVGDYCEHRN
        || .: | ||| |       |.. | |:. |.|: |: .|
    ...........CTQTAEMCLNGGRCEMTPGGTGVCLCGNLYFGERCQFPN

                              .
                              .
```

c

Figure 16: Amino terminal portion of an alignment between *Notch* and its *Xenopus* homolog, *Xotch*. a. Gap creation penalty of 3.0, gap extension penalty of 0.1. b. Gap creation penalty of 2.5, gap extension penalty of 0.1. c. Automatic alignment overridden.

produce the same score. When this happens, only one alignment is generally shown. The user controls the alignment by changing the gap creation and gap extension penalty. For example, Figure 16a shows the amino terminal end of a global alignment between *Notch* and its *Xenopus* homolog, *Xotch* (Coffman et al., 1990). It was run with a gap creation penalty of 3.0 and a gap extension penalty of 0.1.[2] The gap extension penalty is much smaller than the gap creation penalty encouraging a few long gaps, rather than many short gaps. There are some problems with this alignment; the first EGF-like repeat does not line up, and the initial methionine is probably in the wrong place. To allow an extra gap, we can reduce the gap penalty from 3.0 to 2.5, producing Figure 16b. Still, the beginning of the EGF repeat is not in the right place, and subsequent parameter changes do not yield better results. So, as is often the case with an alignment, the user must override the automatic alignment. Some alignment programs let the user anchor regions of the sequence. One trick to force specific positions to align is to add a "new" residue to the comparison matrix with a high score for matching with itself. Next, add that residue to each sequence at the position that should align, and repeat the alignment. This new, heavily-weighted residue will force the regions to line up. The alignment in Figure 16c was produced this way.

The point these figures make is that any program can produce several alignments depending on how the parameters are set, and that the mathematically "best" alignment is not necessarily the one that makes biological sense. Another point to keep in mind is that most programs only report one alignment; they might find one region of similarity and not report a lesser-scoring but significant similarity elsewhere. When using local alignment programs, it is a good idea to check regions not included in the original alignment for further local alignments. For instance, if the best local alignment aligns residues 300 to the end of sequence 1 with residues 450 to the end of sequence 2, try aligning residues 1 to 300 of sequence 1, and 1 to 450 of sequence 2. Dotplots offer another solution to this problem; they show all regions of similarity.

Looking for Internal Repeats

Dotplot

Establishing plot parameters. The simplest way to visualize similarities between two sequences, or internal repeats in a single sequence, is with a comparison matrix or dotplot (Maizel and Lenk, 1981; see Chapter 3). On the two-dimensional grid of the dotplot, stretches of sequence identity appear as diagonal lines parallel to an imaginary main diagonal through the origin; in a sequence plotted against itself, these diagonal lines represent internal

---

[2]In the scoring table used for these analyses (Gribskov and Burgess, 1986), identities receive a score of 1.5, and mismatches a score derived from their similarity in the MDM_{78} table (Dayhoff et al., 1979) and ranging from 1.425 to -1.20. The average score for non-identical comparisons is 0.0.

repeats. Most dotplot programs use a window/stringency method which marks a dot each time a given number of matches occurs within a user-specified window size. For protein sequences the MDM78 matrix of conservative amino acid substitutions (Dayhoff et al., 1979) is often used to score the matches; in that case, the stringency represents the minimum score required for the matches within a given window. This example uses an adaptation of the MDM78 table (Gribskov and Burgess, 1986).

The trickiest part of making a good dotplot is picking the right parameters. A change in the window or stringency dramatically alters a plot's appearance. In fact, entire structures can be missed due to poor settings. For amino acid sequences, good starting parameters for window and stringency (for the scoring table used) are 30 and 9 , but these parameters will rarely produce the nicest plot; usually, it takes several tries to find the best settings. A few rules of thumb in setting the parameters are: 1) the window size should be about half as long as the repeat, 2) raising the stringency reduces the number of points, and 3) increasing or reducing the window size while keeping the window/stringency ratio constant affects the plot definition. The smaller window generally produces more points.

With these guidelines in mind, a dotplot of *Notch* was run with a window of 30 and stringency of 9. These parameters generated more points than this specific dotplot program could accept—an indication of the sequence's highly repetitive structure. Raising the stringency to 13 solved this problem and produced the dotplot in Figure 17a. Although it is a little noisy, this plot indicates four distinct repeat regions from approximately residues 0-1400, 1450-1550, 1900-2100 and 2200-2600.

Ideally, a plot should produce a strong signal for the repeat structure and the background should be clear. In this plot, however, very short diagonals obscure larger structures. To reduce the noise, the stringency was raised from 13 to 18, producing the plot in Figure 17b. This decreased the background noise, but also weakened some of the repeats. Compare the left and bottom margins of the large "box" of repeats between 0 and 1400 in Figures 17a and 17b. Whereas Figure 17a clearly shows repeats beginning at about residue 50, Figure 17b only weakly indicates repeats in the region from residue 50 to 200.

Overall, the plot is good. Nonetheless, a final change in parameters might bring out these weak repeats and improve the display. Figure 17c shows the plot produced by reducing the window size to 20, about half the length of the EGF-like repeat, but maintaining the window/stringency ratio of three to five. A comparison of Figures 17b and 17c illustrates the effect window size has on plot definition. Note that using the smaller window size increased the number of points and made the signals sharper. The plot still may not be perfect; background noise has reappeared. A solution to this might be to raise the stringency by one point at this lower window size, or to increase the window size slightly. However, these window/stringency parameters do a good job of displaying the EGF-like repeat portion of the

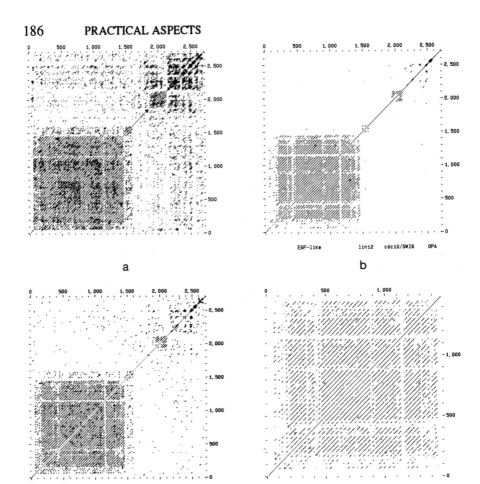

Figure 17: Dotplot of *Notch* protein, self-comparison. a. Window: 30, Stringency: 13. b. Window: 30, Stringency: 18. c. Window: 20, Stringency: 12. d. EGF-like repeats with window of 20 and stringency of 12.

sequence and were used to produce Figure 17d, a close-up of the EGF-like repeat region.

Interpreting the Plot. It is sometimes difficult to translate the geometry of a dotplot into a sequence alignment. This is particularly true for a plot as complex as the *Notch* plot. Figuring out what a plot means is made simpler by keeping three things in mind: 1) a gap in a diagonal line indicates a section of dissimilarity between the sequences, 2) a break and shift in a diagonal indicates an insertion in one of the sequences, and 3) diagonals that cross the same row or column represent an internally repeated segment.

Turning to the first repeated region in *Notch*, the EGF-like repeats (residues 30 - 1420), notice that there are 36 diagonals, indicating 36 repeats.

The interval between diagonals is the length of the repeats. In this case the repeated unit is nearly 40 residues long. Note that the diagonal lines are almost entirely solid. This suggests that the repeat is tandem — a dashed line would have indicated gaps of non-identity between repeats. Of particular interest are the curious white "stripes" that run through the plot. The meaning of these stripes will become more obvious after making a multiple sequence alignment of the EGF-like repeats, but they suggest insertions, deletions or sequence divergence at those positions in the sequence.

The second repeat group consists of three repeats and the third group of six repeats. The fourth group is more difficult to characterize. The big "blot" around residue 2500 is due to a very short repeated unit. Note that there are several smaller "blots" along the diagonal. The very weak repeats immediately amino terminal of the large "blot" may result from a shared biochemical property such as hydrophobicity or just a poorly conserved short repeat.

A scan of the FASTA and BLAST searches show that the second group of repeats are the *lin12/Notch* repeats, the third are the *cdc10/SW16* repeats and the last "blot" is the poly-glutamine, opa repeat. *Cdc10*, a cell cycle control gene from the fission yeast *S. pombe*, is required at the start of the mitotic cell cycle (Aves et al., 1985). *SW16* is a gene from budding yeast *S. cerevisiae* (Breedan and Nasmyth, 1987).

Although dotplots offer an excellent visual overview of the sequence, it is often hard to identify the exact locations of the repeats they reveal. Therefore, programs which scan a sequence for internal repeats and report their position can be a useful addition to the dotplot, particularly if the repeated regions are to be aligned. The RELATE program from NBRF is a widely available program which does this.

Aligning the Repeated Regions

It is estimated that between 10% and 20% of known protein sequences are repetitive (Boguski, 1990). Repeats often have structural importance and should be carefully investigated. Having identified several repeat regions in *Notch*, it is interesting to look at the individual repeats to see how exact they are and which residues are conserved. This is a goal of a multiple sequence alignment. By pointing out conserved amino acids, a multiple alignment can identify active sites and other features that are conserved due to structural constraints. Likewise, when making an alignment, attention should be paid to aligning chemically and structurally similar regions of the sequences.

There are three steps to making a multiple alignment of internal repeats: 1) extracting the repeats from the sequence into a separate file or entry, 2) aligning the repeats, and 3) displaying the alignments. Researchers who frequently make large alignments usually rely on one of the many multiple sequence alignment programs available (Schuler et al., 1990; Feng and Doolittle, 1987; Sobel and Martinez, 1986; Barton and Sternberg, 1987; Taylor, 1987; Carillo and Lipman, 1988; Altschul and Lipman, 1989; Vingron and Argos, 1989; Bacon and Anderson, 1986; see also Chapter 3 Table 5).

The EGF alignments. Because the EGF-like repeats are well-conserved and rather short, the multiple alignment can be done by eye. An efficient way to do this is to use a local alignment program to align one repeat to each of the others; this has the advantage of locating each repeat and aligning it at the same time. The strongest repeat should be chosen as the "master." The approximate location of a strong repeat can be determined from the dotplot, as can the repeat length. Remember, alignment algorithms find one "best" alignment and overlook other significant similarities. If one were to align the master repeat to the entire EGF-like region, the program would align it with

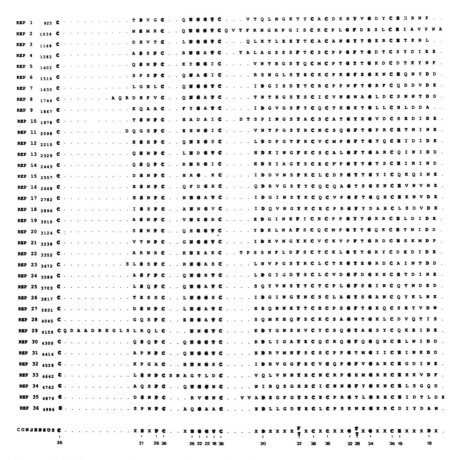

Figure 18: Multiple sequence alignment of the 36 EGF-like repeats in *Notch*. The consensus sequence is based on the presence of an amino acid at a specific position within a repeat at least 50% of the time. [Reprinted from Wharton et al. (1985), *Cell* , Vol. 43, p.576, Fig. 5.]

the most similar repeat, rather than the first repeat. To align to the first repeat, the alignment is restricted to the range where the first repeat is known to lie, approximately from residues 60 to 100. A buffer of 5 to 10 residues should be added to this range to compensate for insertions or deletions. This first repeat should be extracted, and loaded into a multiple sequence editor. This process is repeated for each of the 36 repeats.[3]

Once in the editor, these fragments can be aligned with a program or by eye. Figure 18 shows an alignment of the 36 EGF-like repeats. Notice that repeats 2, 3, 4, 8, 10, 11, 22, 23, 29, 33 and 35 are longer than the other repeats. These slightly longer repeats correspond to the white stripes running through the diagonals of the dotplot (Figure 17). Repeat 29, which is 9 residues longer than the typical EGF-like motif in this group, is responsible for the thickest stripe. The first four repeats, two of which are longer than the norm, produce the weaker signal along the left and bottom margins of the large "box" of EGF-like repeats on the dotplot (Figure 17). This is because with the stringency used to make the plot, a single insertion or deletion causes many adjacent windows to fail to score above the threshold.

The cdc10/SW16 and lin12/Notch alignments. Using RELATE, the exact positions of the *lin12* and *cdc10/SW16* repeats can be determined. The repeats are then extracted and aligned to produce Figure 19a and b. Although it is not known what structures these subsequences form, similarities between

---

[3]If we were dealing with a less conserved repeat group than the EGF-like motif, it would be advantageous to align to a profile (see Profile Analysis) rather than a single repeat.

a

b

Figure 19: a. Multiple sequence alignment of the 3 *lin12/Notch* repeats. b. Multiple alignment of the 6 *cdc10/SW16* repeats. Residue identities are shown in black and residues which are similar, according to the MDM_{78} table, are shaded.

Cons	A	B	C	D	E	F	G	H	I	K	L	M	N	P	Q	R	S	T	V	W	Y	Z	Gap	Len	..
G	50	48	9	57	41	-46	105	-9	-20	-4	-36	-22	32	21	19	-19	42	29	13	-75	-50	27	100	100	
E	8	18	-23	24	36	-18	9	12	-1	21	6	15	5	21	12	7	15	-1	-18	-19	29	100	100		
T	41	22	19	22	22	-30	41	-8	21	21	-9	1	22	31	-8	-9	31	151	21	-62	-30	12	100	100	
P	36	9	10	9	9	-38	23	9	-9	7	-16	-10	5	76	16	14	32	20	6	-42	-42	12	100	100	
L	-9	-48	-81	-48	-28	119	-49	-18	80	-29	150	130	-38	-29	-8	-39	-38	-9	81	48	30	-18	100	100	
H	-5	8	-7	5	8	12	-13	47	8	0	14	6	12	1	18	14	-9	-3	2	-2	18	12	100	100	
L	2	-19	-32	-21	-14	48	-19	-8	33	-9	57	45	-14	-12	-5	-7	-8	-2	30	16	15	-10	100	100	
A	151	22	29	31	31	-50	71	-8	1	1	-9	1	22	50	22	-29	41	41	21	-82	-30	22	100	100	
A	102	14	20	20	20	-33	49	-7	7	0	-1	4	13	34	14	-21	27	29	23	-60	-21	14	100	100	
R	13	7	-6	4	4	-23	2	15	-2	26	-9	11	6	18	16	45	10	5	3	29	-25	10	100	100	
L	8	-1	-9	-1	5	7	1	3	13	1	17	15	-1	1	3	1	1	3	14	1	1	4	22	22	

Figure 20: Profile of the first 11 residues of the *cdc10/SWI6* repeats.

these repeat regions and sequences in the database point out that they are not unique to *Notch*.

Profile Analysis

A profile (Gribskov et al., 1987; Gribskov et al., 1990) is a way of describing a multiple sequence alignment numerically. Without actually predicting a structure, sequence alignments suggest which positions in a sequence may be structurally important. Ideally, one would like to be able to search a database with this structural information; profiles enable you to do this.

The easiest way to think of a profile is as a tabular representation of a multiple sequence alignment. Figure 20 shows a portion of the profile generated by the ProfileMake program for the *cdc10/SWI6* repeat region. The alignment consensus sequence reads down the leftmost column. The top row lists the 22 possible amino acid residues. Each row corresponds to a column of the aligned sequences used to generate the profile, and gives the score for aligning each possible residue at that point in the multiple alignment. For example, if you turn to the alignment (Figure 19b), you will see that the threonine (T) in position 3 (with T in the consensus column) is conserved. The profile reflects this in its scoring. Reading across the third row, notice that any sequence which places a threonine in position three gets a score of 151 for the match. On the other hand, if the sequence cannot put a threonine in that position, it will face penalties of up to -62 in the case of a tryptophan (W). Position eleven in the alignment, on the other hand, is variable. Notice that the profile scores only range from -9 to 17, indicating that this position is less critical to the alignment. The database is searched with a profile by aligning the profile to each sequence entry. The alignment scores are later normalized with respect to sequence length and composition.

Probably the most valuable lesson this chapter has to offer can be seen by comparing the profile search results (Figure 21a) with the original FASTA search results in Figure 10. Sequence alignments (Figure 21b) show that all of the finds on this profile search list have *cdc10/SWI6* repeats. The repeat is named after the fifth sequence in the list, *cdc10*, a yeast protein which regulates the cell cycle. It is hypothesized that *Notch* is involved in the cell cycle, in part, because of its similarity to this protein. However, the FASTA database search ranked *cdc10* the 107th match on the list. The default number of scores listed for most search programs is 100, so it is unlikely that this match

```
        Sequence  Strd ZScore   Orig Length ! Documentation  ..

Swissprot:NOTC$DROME   +   10.47  14.19    2703 ! P07207 FRUIT FLY (DROSOPHILA MELANOGASTER). NEUROGENIC LOCUS NOTCH PROTEIN
Swissprot:ANK2$HUMAN   +    7.43  11.72    1880 ! P16157 HUMAN (HOMO SAPIENS). ANKYRIN 2.1 AND 2.2. 4/90
Swissprot:SWI6$YEAST   +    6.82  11.19     803 ! P09959 BAKER'S YEAST (CEREVISIAE). TRANS-ACTING ACTIVATOR OF HO ENDONUCLEASE
Swissprot:LIN1$CAEEL   +    6.69  11.12    1429 ! P14585 CAENORHABDITIS ELEGANS. LIN-12 PROTEIN PRECURSOR (GENE NAME: LIN12)
Swissprot:GLP1$CAEEL   +    6.43  10.90    1295 ! P13508 CAENORHABDITIS ELEGANS. GLP-1 PROTEIN PRECURSOR (GENE NAME: GLP-1)
Swissprot:CC10$SCHPO   +    6.36  10.80     767 ! P01129 FISSION YEAST (SCHIZOSACCHAROMYCES POMBE). CDC10 START CONTROL PROTEIN
Swissprot:YB13$FOWPM   +    6.11   8.90     172 ! P14368 FOWLPOX VIRUS (ISOLATE HP-438[MUNICH]). HYPOTHETICAL BAMHI-ORF13 PROTEIN
Swissprot:YB07$FOWPM   +    6.10  10.24     410 ! P14360 FOWLPOX VIRUS (ISOLATE HP-438[MUNICH]). HYPOTHETICAL BAMHI-ORF7 PROTEIN
Swissprot:YW01$PARTE   +    6.03   8.09     113 ! P15603 PARAMECIUM TETRAURELIA. HYPOTHETICAL 12.8 KD PROTEIN (ORF1)
Swissprot:VW1$VACCV    +    5.93  10.13     421 ! P14356 VACCINIA VIRUS (STRAIN WR). W1 PROTEIN (GENE NAME: W)
```

a

```
Ank2$Human x Profile

              .                         .
S   110 GFTPLYMAAQENHLEVVKFLLENGANQNVATEDG 143
        ! !!!.!!!.  :  :.!! !!:! !!.!.:.. .
P     1 GETPLHLAARLGSAEAVKILLDNNADRNAQDNSD 34


Swi6$Yeast x Profile

              .                         .
S   470 GDTCLNIAARLGNISIVDALLDYGADPFIANKSG 503
        !:! !.:!!!.!. . !:.!!! !!. ::.!.
P     1 GETPLHLAARLGSAEAVKILLDNNADRNAQDNSD 34


Cc10$Schpo x Profile

              .                         .
S   484 GDTALNIAARIGNKNIVEVLMQAGASAYIPNRAG 517
        !:!!!.:!!!.!. . !::!!:: !.  .: ..
P     1 GETPLHLAARLGSAEAVKILLDNNADRNAQDNSD 34        b
```

Figure 21: a. Top scores from a search of the SWISS-PROT database with the *cdc10/SW16* profile. The Z-score is the search score normalized with respect to length and composition. b. Alignments between the profile and some top-scoring similar sequences.

would have been listed in most output files. Yet this match is one of the most biologically important on the page. This example offers a compelling argument for familiarizing oneself with several database search methods and effectively demonstrates the difference between biological and statistical significance.

Another insight is provided by comparing the profile search results to those of a standard database search done with a simple consensus of the alignment. Figure 22 shows the results of a FASTA search with a consensus of the *cdc10/SW16* repeats. These results are much less significant than the profile search results; *SW16* and *cdc10*, the source of the repeats' names, do not even score in the top ten of the FASTA search.

The next step, after identifying other sequences that contain the *cdc10/SW16* repeats, would be to include them in the multiple sequence alignment and perhaps repeat the profile search.

Hydropathy Plot

Up to this point in the analysis, most of what has been learned about the *Notch* protein has been determined by comparison to other sequences or to itself. The following analyses look at the structural and chemical attributes of the protein.

```
NOTC$DROME  NEUROGENIC LOCUS NOTCH PROTEIN (GENE NAME:       55    41    47
ANK2$HUMAN  ANKYRIN 2.1 AND 2.2.                             50    50    50
ICEN$ERWHE  ICE NUCLEATION PROTEIN (GENE NAME: ICEE).        46    46    46
HMCU$DROME  HOMEOBOX PROTEIN CUT (GENE NAME: CUT).           45    45    45
RS10$ECOLI  30S RIBOSOMAL PROTEIN S10 (GENE NAME: RPSJ)      44    44    44
VGL1$PRV    GLYCOPROTEIN GI.                                 43    43    43
YB07$FOWPM  HYPOTHETICAL BAMHI-ORF7 PROTEIN.                 43    43    44
APB$HUMAN   APOLIPOPROTEIN B-100 PRECURSOR (APO B-100/A      42    42    46
NO27$SOYBN  NODULIN-27.                                      42    42    43
NYLB$FLASP  6-AMINOHEXANOATE-DIMER HYDROLASE (EC 3.5.1.      41    41    41
RECN$ECOLI  RECN PROTEIN (GENE NAME: RECN).                  41    41    42
VSI1$REOV3  SIGMA 1 PROTEIN PRECURSOR (HEMAGGLUTININ) (      41    41    43
SYI$ECOLI   ISOLEUCYL-TRNA SYNTHETASE (EC 6.1.1.5) (ISO      40    40    40


Consensus Sequence:    GETPLHLAAR .A..EAVKIL LD..A.R.A. DN.D
```

Figure 22: Top scores from a search of the SWISS-PROT database with a consensus generated from the multiple sequence alignment of the *cdc10/SWI6* repeats. The consensus is written below the scores.

Transmembrane Region?

An easily grasped and very useful analysis is the hydropathy plot (Kyte and Doolittle, 1982; see Chapter 2). This method measures a sequence's aversion to water by averaging the hydropathy of each residue in a sliding window along the sequence. The most hydrophobic regions should be found in an apolar environment, the interior of the protein or within a lipid bilayer, for instance. One of the features hydropathy plots are most successful at predicting is membrane spanning regions. An α helix requires about 20 residues to cross the lipid bilayer. This produces a characteristic highly hydrophobic region on a hydropathy plot. The hydropathy plot of the *Notch* protein (Figure 23) clearly shows this feature near residue 1760. This plot also shows a highly hydropathic region near the amino terminus, a feature associated with a signal peptide which is usually proteolytically removed during maturation. Towards the carboxy terminus, a highly hydrophilic region is found corresponding to the poly-glutamine, opa repeat.

This plot suggests that *Notch* may contain a transmembrane segment. If this were the case, it is possible that the approximately 1740 amino acid region containing the EGF-like and *lin12* repeats would be extracellular and that the remaining 950 amino acids including the opa and *cdc10/SWI6* repeats would be intracellular. This would be consistent with the conjecture that the EGF-like repeats are involved in cell-cell communication.

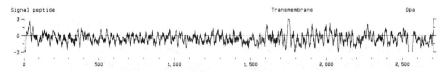

Figure 23: Hydropathy plot of the *Notch* protein. Portions of the curve above 0.0 indicate hydrophobic regions.

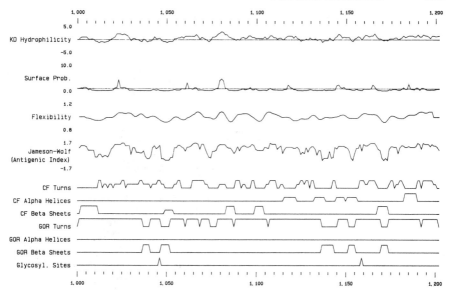

Figure 24: Structural predictions for EGF-like repeats 25, 26 and 27 of the *Notch* sequence as displayed by the GCG program PlotStructure. This program uses the methods of several researches to make its predictions (Chou and Fasman, 1978; Nishikawa, 1983; Garnier et al., 1987; Hopp and Woods, 1981; Emini et al., 1985; Janin, 1987; and Kyte and Doolittle, 1982).

Antigenic Determinants

Hydropathy plots can also help identify regions of the protein which may be antigenic. Antibodies against synthetic polypeptides are used for protein expression studies and biochemical characterization. Hydrophilic regions are often exposed on the protein's surface, making them candidates for antibody binding. Other factors in predicting antigenicity are chain flexibility, surface probability and secondary structure. The method of Jameson and Wolf (1988) calculates and plots an Antigenic Index based on a weighted sum of each of these factors (see Chapter 2). Figure 24 shows a plot of these various predictions.

The locations of conserved residues in a multiple sequence alignment is a good indicator of the location of important structural features. Heavily gapped regions in a multiple sequence alignment, in which several sequences have "extra" residues, may point to surface loops and quite possibly belong to exposed regions in the folded protein (Gribskov, personal communication). A few sites in the 36 EGF-like repeats fall into this category (Figure 18). Repeat 29 has 10 extra residues between the first and second amino acids of the consensus sequence, residues 1141 through 1150. Repeats number 8, 11 and 23 also have extra residues in this position. Note that the Jameson and Wolf antigenic index is fairly high for the extra residues in repeat 29.

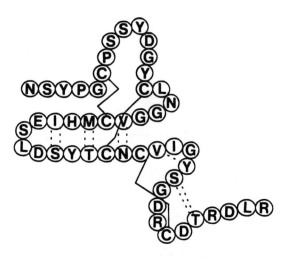

Figure 25: The structures of murine EGF. The structure of murine EGF was resolved by NMR. [Reprinted from Davis (1990), *The New Biologist*, Vol. 2, p.411, Fig. 1a].

Secondary Structure

One of the ultimate goals of computer-based sequence analysis is to predict protein structure. Although current algorithms are far from attaining this goal, secondary structure prediction programs can be useful if their limitations are understood (see Chapter 2). The most common methods calculate a probability that a given section of the sequence will form an α helix, β strand, random coil, or turn by correlating amino acids with local secondary structure, and usually achieve about 55-65% accuracy (Nishikawa, 1983). The values for each amino acid have been empirically derived from proteins with known three-dimensional structures. One problem is that these methods are based on the structure of soluble, globular proteins and may therefore be less accurate for other types of proteins. Recently, there have been some novel approaches to the secondary structure problem. One method uses a supervised learning algorithm to "teach" a neural network to recognize secondary structure patterns, with proteins of known structures as a training set. This approach has achieved a 64% accuracy rate for three-state predictions (Qian and Sejnowski, 1988).

The most intriguing structural aspect of *Notch* is its EGF-like repeats. The structure of EGF has been resolved by nuclear magnetic resonance or NMR (Carver et al., 1986) and can be useful in the analysis of the *Notch*

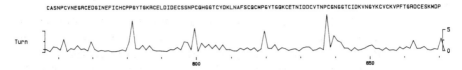

CASNPCVNEGACEDGINEFICHCPPGYTGKACELDIDECSSNPCQHGGTCYDKLNAFSCQCMPGYTGQKCETNIDDCVTNPCGNGGTCIDKVNGYKCVCKVPFTGADCESKMDP

Figure 26: Predicted turns as determined by Chou and Fasman for three EGF-like repeats.

repeats. Figure 25 shows the disulfide bonds between pairs of cysteines in soluble EGF. Note that each disulfide bond creates a turn in the protein. Turns are one of the structures most accurately predicted by computer methods. It will be interesting to compare what is physically known about EGF with the computer predicted secondary structure. Figure 26 shows the location of turns predicted by the Chou-Fasman, probability-based method (Chou and Fasman, 1978) for the *Notch* EGF-like repeats 19, 20 and 21. The spikes on the plot represent turns. This plot predicts turns between cysteine one and two, three and four, and five and six. A comparison with the secondary structure schematic in Figure 21 shows that the prediction agrees with the structure.

Protein Degradation: PEST Sequences

Protein stability is a key factor in the regulation of cell metabolism. Proteins have a wide range of degradation rates and many efforts have been made to correlate these rates with their sequences. One group has observed that intracellular proteins with half-lives of less than two hours contain at least one region which is rich in proline (P), glutamic acid(E), serine (S), and threonine (T), flanked by positively charged residues (Rogers et al., 1986). They have called these regions PEST signals (see Chapter 2).

The intracellular portion of the *Notch* sequence was scanned with a PEST search program. The algorithm identifies a possible PEST site and calculates a score based on a linear equation combining the mole percent of P, E, S and T and the hydrophobicity of the region. Scores greater than 5.0 are considered "likely," between 0 and 5.0 are "uncertain," and less than 0 are "unlikely" to be a PEST site. These cutoffs were empirically determined. Figure 27 shows that *Notch* contains two PEST-like sequences: one between the membrane spanning region and the *cdc10* repeats, the other near the carboxyl terminus.

From	To	Score	Sequence
443	460	6.09	GVDCSEDIDECDQGSPCE
1821	1831	6.04	WSDDESDMPLP
2645	2661	4.87	LVQTLDSYPTPSPESPG
2408	2421	2.28	EQGLSPPYSNQSPP

Figure 27: PEST signal sites.

PROSITE identified a casein kinase II-dependent phosphorylation site at the same position as the first PEST site (Figure 12; see Scan for Motifs with PROSITE). This is noteworthy because the conditional degradation of some proteins containing PEST sites is thought to correlate with casein kinase II-dependent phosphorylation (Rechsteiner et al., 1989).

This concludes the protein analysis section of this chapter. This section has loosely fallen into two parts: comparison-based analyses and biochemical analyses. Most of the comparison-based analyses can also be applied to DNA. Both sections have left out a number of analyses: methods to align multiple sequences, statistically evaluate similarity, determine secondary structure, and scan with profile libraries. But underlying these more advanced topics are the fundamentals such as window/stringency schemes, dynamic programming methods, and evaluating similarity, which this section has demonstrated.

GENOMIC DNA

This section will concentrate on finding simple sites and control elements within genomic DNA.

Weight Matrices

Protein expression is regulated by transcriptional and translational controls. Transcription initiation is determined by interactions between proteins and regions of the DNA. Many protein-binding sites have very degenerate sequences which makes their identification by computer difficult. Several compilations of promoter elements and other protein-binding site consensus sequences are available (Ghosh, 1990; Wingender, 1988), but scanning with a simple consensus sequences misses too many elements. A standard way to accommodate this degeneracy is to use a weight matrix to represent the element, rather than a consensus (Staden, 1984). A weight matrix is a table of values derived from the frequency of each base at a given position in the motif and is often normalized with respect to composition. It is calculated by taking the natural logarithm of the fractional base frequency at each position, although there are other methods to determine the weights (Stormo, 1984). The frequencies are determined from collections of putative or experimentally determined signal sequences. Although weight matrices offer the most accurate way of describing these elements, compiling them is no small task. Therefore, this approach has suffered from a lack of good matrices.

Several recent developments have begun to remedy this situation. One is the introduction of a new database, the Eukaryotic Promoter Database of the EMBL data library (Bucher, 1988; see Appendix VIII). This has provided a rigorously tested data set good for statistical analysis. Another is the availability of sensitive methods for compiling and scanning with weight matrices (Bucher, 1990).

Potential Cap-signals:

position	Score	0	
938	-3.1300	CCATACGG	
948	-3.5700	TCTTTTTC	
958	-3.5600	GCACCGAC	
970	-1.7100	TCACACTG	
988	-3.0900	ACAGATCG	
1003	-3.2200	CCAGTGGA	
1068	-1.7900	ACAGTTCT	
1152	-2.9600	TCAATTAC	
1160	-3.7000	ACAGCAAG	
1196	-3.6700	CCAGCGGA	
1211	-2.5600	TCAGCAAG	
1383	-3.7500	GCAATACG	
1475	-3.3900	TCTTTTTT	
1485	-1.9300	CCACTTTT	
1503	-3.6500	TCAAAACG	
1579	-3.0000	TCAAAACT	
1662	-2.5100	GCATACTA	
1681	-2.8400	GCAGTTAA	
1689	-2.9100	ACATATCC	
1791	-2.8200	GCAATCGC	
1802	-2.4000	GCAGCCGA	
1814	-1.3100	GCAGTCGC	
1829	-2.9400	ACACTTGG	
1931	-2.8600	ACACCGTT	
1971	-2.3100	TCAGAACA	
2034	-3.4500	GCACAAAC	

a

Potential TATA-boxes:

position	Score	0	10
1140	-8.1500	ATATACAAACAAATC	
1564	-8.1300	CTTTAAAGTCTGAAG	
1586	-3.5500	CTATAAAAAACAAAA	

Weak TATA-box matches (-11.00 =< Score < 8.16)

position	Score	0
982	-10.6500	ATTTGAAACAGATCG
1020	-10.7300	TTGTGAAAGCGGACG
1092	-10.5200	TTTTGAATGTGTGTG
1116	-9.9400	ACGTAAAATCGCGCT
1180	-9.0800	AAATGAAAAGGATGG
1311	-11.0000	GTGTATCTACCTCGA
1418	-10.4800	GAATTTGTGGCTCGA
1442	-10.3400	AGAGAAAAGCAAGCA
1501	-9.4400	GTTTCAAAACGGAAA
1609	-10.4900	CAAAAAAAACAACAA
1722	-10.7800	CTAAAGAAACCGAGA
1852	-10.6100	TAACAAAATGCACGC

b

Figure 28: Potential (a.) Cap-signal and (b.) TATA-box sites according to the method of Phillip Bucher (1990).

Simple Regulatory Elements

RNA transcription is controlled by the binding of certain proteins to DNA regions called promoters. The four major eukaryotic promoter elements are the CCAAT, TATA and GC boxes and the cap signal. The TATA box is thought to function to position the RNA polymerase relative to the transcription initiation site. The function of the cap box is still unclear. Both elements occur at almost fixed positions relative to the initiation site: TATA is 25 to 30 bases upstream of and the cap box surrounds the iniation site. Unlike TATA and cap, the positions of the CCAAT and GC-boxes are variable and can occur on either strand of the DNA. A number of different proteins appear to bind to these elements, and it is not clear which ones actually promote transcription.

Bucher has published weight matrices for these four promoter elements (Figure 27, see also Chapter 1). They were derived by an algorithm which takes local sequence composition into account to help specify signal location and match significance (Bucher, 1990). The *Notch* sequence was scanned with Bucher's signal search program and a portion of the results are shown in Figure 28. This table shows the position where the element was found, its score, and the sequence of the putative binding site. Figure 29 shows an annotated segment of the *Notch* promoter region with the putative binding

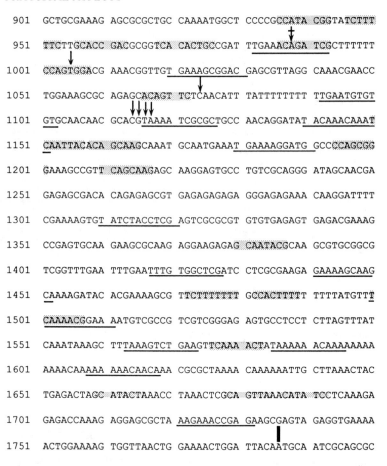

```
 901    GCTGCGAAAG AGCGCGCTGC CAAAATGGCT CCCCGCCATA CGGTATCTTT

 951    TTCTTGCACC GACGCGGTCA CACTGCCGAT TTGAAACAGA TCGCTTTTTT

1001    CCAGTGGACG AAACGGTTGT GAAAGCGGAC GAGCGTTAGG CAAACGAACC

1051    TGGAAAGCGC AGAGCACAGT TCTCAACATT TATTTTTTTT TTGAATGTGT

1101    GTGCAACAAC GCACGTAAAA TCGCGCTGCC AACAGGATAT ACAAACAAAT

1151    CAATTACACA GCAAGCAAAT GCAATGAAAT GAAAAGGATG GCCCCAGCGG

1201    GAAAGCCGTT CAGCAAGAGC AAGGAGTGCC TGTCGCAGGG ATAGCAACGA

1251    GAGAGCGACA CAGAGAGCGT GAGAGAGAGA GGGAGAGAAA CAAGGATTTT

1301    CGAAAAGTGT ATCTACCTCG AGTCGCGCGT GTGTGAGAGT GAGACGAAAG

1351    CCGAGTGCAA GAAGCGCAAG AGGAAGAGAG CAATACGCAA GCGTGCGGCG

1401    TCGGTTTGAA TTTGAATTTG TGGCTCGATC CTCGCGAAGA GAAAAGCAAG

1451    CAAAAGATAC ACGAAAAGCG TTCTTTTTTT GCCACTTTTT TTTTATGTTT

1501    CAAAACGGAA AATGTCGCCG TCGTCGGGAG AGTGCCTCCT CTTAGTTTAT

1551    CAAATAAAGC TTTAAAGTCT GAAGTTCAAA ACTATAAAAA ACAAAAAAAA

1601    AAAACAAAAA AAACAACAAA CGCGCTAAAA CAAAAAATTG CTTAAACTAC

1651    TGAGACTAGC ATACTAAACC TAAACTCGCA GTTAAACATA TCCTCAAAGA

1701    GAGACCAAAG AGGAGCGCTA AAGAAACCGA GAAGCGAGTA GAGGTGAAAA

1751    ACTGGAAAAG TGGTTAACTG GAAAACTGGA TTACAATGCA ATCGCAGCGC
```

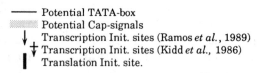

——— Potential TATA-box
▓▓▓ Potential Cap-signals
↓ Transcription Init. sites (Ramos *et al.*, 1989)
↓ Transcription Init. sites (Kidd *et al.*, 1986)
▮ Translation Init. site.

Figure 29: Annotated promoter region of *Notch*.

sites marked. Possible transcription initiation sites were determined experimentally by primer extension (Ramos et al., 1989). The only experimentally observed transcription site that has both a cap signal and a TATA box in the correct position is one at position 1005. But there are many weak TATA boxes and cap signals throughout this region. No CCAAT boxes were found. Figure 29 also includes putative translation initiation sites determined from a weight matrix compiled by Roger Staden (1984).

```
position:    15     56     93    171    194    234    266    351    436    475    496
   frame:     3      2      3      3      2      3      2      3      1      1      1
 quality: 39.28  37.28  32.94  37.50  35.61  45.56  40.56  43.50  37.56  33.50  32.44


position:   554    565    571    580    614    619    640    646    684    698    718
   frame:     2      1      1      1      2      1      1      1      3      2      1
 quality: 34.72  33.44  34.89  30.89  37.33  29.61  29.83  34.33  40.67  28.89  31.28


position:   738    763    766    769    827    830    836    851    890    894    920
   frame:     3      1      1      1      2      2      2      2      2      3      2
 quality: 29.50  33.72  33.39  31.00  36.06  30.78  30.00  31.67  34.33  32.00  33.67


position:  1054   1087   1121   1150   1173   1244   1259
   frame:     1      1      2      1      3      2      2
 quality: 35.28  33.94  33.56  37.00  41.06  29.11  40.00
```

a

```
position:    21     94    111    141    145    173    181    189    246    257    349
   frame:     3      1      3      3      1      2      1      3      3      2      1
 quality: 39.67  37.50  41.33  46.92  41.17  39.00  40.92  36.25  46.33  38.67  37.17


position:   378    391    433    442    447    485    512    525    546    571    599
   frame:     3      1      1      1      3      2      2      3      3      1      2
 quality: 38.75  38.92  38.67  41.75  46.75  36.67  41.50  38.17  41.00  42.00  43.75


position:   601    625    647    695    720    794    812    821    861    875    900
   frame:     1      1      2      2      3      2      2      2      3      2      3
 quality: 43.92  58.42  40.58  47.58  38.08  36.17  43.42  37.00  45.00  36.50  50.33


position:   951   1019   1047   1077   1093   1104   1131
   frame:     3      2      3      3      1      3      3
 quality: 42.58  43.50  36.33  40.75  41.50  43.33  39.67
```

b

Figure 30: Potential donor and acceptor sites as determined by frequency matrices. a. Acceptor sites. b. Donor sites.

Splice Junctions

Weight matrices can also be useful in locating splice junctions (intron-exon boundaries). Splice junctions are marked by characteristic consensus sequences (see Chapter 1). [C,A]AG/GT[A,G]AGT is the consensus sequence of the exon-intron boundary, or donor sequence, and [T,C]$_n$X[C,T]AG/G is found at the

```
Donor Sequences

621   CTATACAG/GTGAGT

900   ACCA/GTGAGT


Acceptor Sequences

355   ATCTTTTCCAG/A

692   TCCACAG/G
```

Figure 31: Sequences for the junction sites of the third and fourth exons of *Notch*.

intron-exon boundary, or acceptor sequence, where n is greater than 10 . A signal for lariat formation may also be present within the intron (see Chapter 1). The portion of the *Notch* DNA containing exons three and four was scanned with frequency tables created from a catalogue of splice junction sequences (Mount, 1982). Figure 30a and b show the tables of putative donor and acceptor sites. The two highest-scoring sites, positions 625 and 900, correspond to the actual exon-intron borders. Positions 366 and 699 are the actual intron-exon boundaries. Figure 31 shows these junction sequences.

To conclude, weight matrices are a sensitive way to find degenerate sites. However, until a comprehensive library of matrices is compiled, the method's usefulness is limited.

RNA Stem and Loop Structures

The secondary structure of messenger RNA plays a role in translation initiation, transcription and mRNA splicing. There are several programs available to predict secondary structure. Many find a secondary structure of minimum free energy based on experimentally determined free energy values for short RNA polynucleotide motifs. A simpler method to identify possible structures is the dotplot (see Chapter 3). Although the dotplot does not predict overall structure, it points out inverted repeats which are the basis of hairpin, bulge and internal loops.

To use the dotplot to find inverted repeats, the sequence is compared to the reverse complement of itself. A scoring table is used which gives points for identical nucleotide matches. Conversely, the sequence can be compared to its reverse, in which case the scoring table would give points for complementary nucleotides. Figure 32 shows the dotplot of bases 1001 to 1101 compared to their reverse complement. The axis of symmetry lies along the main diagonal which runs through the origin. Each of the short diagonals perpendicular to the symmetry axis represent inverted repeats. The closer the

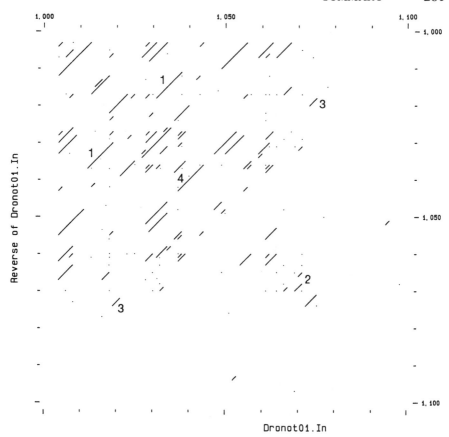

Figure 32: Dotplot of bases 1001 to 1100 to their reverse complement in the promoter region of *Notch*. The comparison was done with a window of 8 and a stringency of 14. Labelled diagonals refer to structures found and represented graphically in Figure 33.

diagonal is to the axis of symmetry, the smaller the "loop" portion of the stem-loop structure it creates. Horizontal or vertical gaps between diagonals indicate bulge loops, and non-overalpping diagonals indicate loops within loops (internal loops), or bifurcations. From this dotplot, two of several possible competing structures were selected by eye (Figure 33).

SUMMARY

This chapter has discussed the methods underlying the most common computer analyses and has given an example of how they are used. Our investigation of *Notch* has shown that much of the work in sequence analysis is in finding the best algorithm for the question at hand. Even then, programs rarely provide clear-cut "answers", but rather results that must be evaluated.

```
          A G
          A   C
          A   G
          G   G
          T-A
          G=C
      1   T~G                          A
          T-A                          C G
          G~G                          A-T
          G=C                   2   C   T
          C=G                          G=C
          A-T                          A-T
CCAGTGGACGAA-TAGGCAAACGAACCTGGAAAGCGCAG=CAACATTTATTTTTTTTTTTGAATGTGT
```

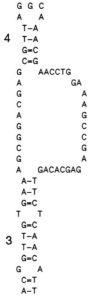

```
          G G C
          A   A
          T-A
      4   T-A
          G=C
          C=G
          G     AACCTG
          A          GA
          G           A
          C           A
          A           G
          G           C
          G           C
          C           G
          G           A
          A     GACACGAG
          A-T
          A-T
          G=C
          T   T
          G=C
      3   T-A
          T-A
          G=C
          G   A
          C=T
          A-T
CCAGTGGACGAA-TATTTTTTTTTTTGAATGTGT
```

Figure 33: Possible secondary structures for the region plotted in the dotplot of Figure 32. Stem labels refer to the labelled diagonals in the dotplot.

We hope that this chapter has pointed out the questions that need to be asked when analyzing a sequence and offered the beginner a strategy for using computer tools.

Acknowledgments: I would like to thank and Drs. Robert Duvoisin, Geri Weinmaster, Thom Hughes, Irv Edelman and Anne Marie Quinn for discussion and critical reading of the manuscript. Drs. Scott Rogers, Mark Boguski and Phillip Bucher graciously offered insights into specific programs. Dr. Clark Coffman saved me much time by providing several unpublished figures. And final thanks to the Salk Institute Biocomputing Department for allowing me the time and facilities to work on this project.

References

Abrahams, J. P., van den Berg, M., van Batenburg, E. and Pleij, C. Prediction of RNA secondary structure, including pseudoknotting, by computer simulation. 1990. Nucleic Acids Res. 18:3035-3044.

Altschul, S. F. and Erickson, B. W. 1986. Optimal sequence alignment using affine gap costs. Bull. Math. Biol. 48:603-616.

Altschul, S. F., Carroll, R. J., and Lipman, D. J. 1989. Weights for data related by a tree. J. Mol. Biol. 207:647-653.

Altschul, S. F. and Lipman, D. J. 1989. Trees, starts, and multiple biological sequence alignment. SIAM J. Appl. Math. 49:197-209.

Altschul, S. F. 1991. Amino acid substitution matrices from an information theoretic perspective. J. Mol. Biol., in press.

Altschul, S. F., Gish, W., Miller, W., Myers, E. W., and Lipman, D. J. 1990. Basic local alignment search tool. J. Mol. Biol. 215:403-410.

Altschul, S. F. and Lipman, D. J. 1990. Protein database searches for multiple alignments. Proc. Natl. Acad. Sci. USA 87:5509-5513.

Anderson, S., 1981. Shotgun DNA sequencing using cloned DNase I-generated fragments. Nucleic Acids Res. 9:3015-3027.

Ansorge, W., Sproat, B., Stegemann, J., Schwager, C., and Zenke, M. 1987. Automated DNA sequencing: ultrasensitive detection of fluorescent bands during electrophoresis. Nucleic Acids Res. 15:4593-4602.

Argos, P., Rao, J. K. M., and Hargrave, P. A. 1982. Structural prediction of membrane-bound proteins. Eur. J. Biochem. 128:565-575.

Argos, P. 1987. A sensitive procedure to compare amino acid sequences. J. Mol. Biol. 193:385-396.

Argos, P. and Vingron, M. 1990. Sensitivity comparison of protein amino acid sequences. Meth. Enzymol. 183:352-365.

Arraitia, R., Gordon, L., and Waterman, M. S. 1985. An extreme value theory for sequence matching. Ann. Stat. 14:971-973.

Artavanis-Tsakonas, S. 1988. The molecular biology of the *Notch* locus and the fine tuning of differentiation in *Drosophila*. Trends Genet. 4:95-100.

Aves, S. J., Durckacz, B. W., Carr, A., and Nurse, P. 1985. Cloning, sequencing, and transcriptional control of *Schizosaccharomyces pombe cdc10* 'start' gene. EMBO J. 4:457-463.

Bacon, D. J. and Anderson, W. F. 1986. Multiple sequence alignment. J. Mol. Biol. 191:153-161.

Bairoch, A. PROSITE: a dictionary of protein sites and patterns. In EMBL Biocomputing Technical Document 4, EMBL, Heidelberg, Germany, 1989.

Bairoch, A. 1990. PROSITE: a dictionary of protein sites and patterns. University of Geneva, Fifth release.

Ballester, R., Marchuk, D., Boguski, M., Saulino, A., Letcher, R., Wigler, M., and Collins, F. 1990. The NF1 locus encodes a protein functionally related to mammalian GAP and yeast IRA proteins. Cell 63:851-859.

Barber, A. M. and Maizel, J. V. J. 1990. Sequence editing aligner: a multiple sequence editor and aligner. Genet. Anal. Tech. Appl. 7:39-45.

Barnes, W. M. 1987. Sequencing DNA with dideoxyribonucleotides as chain terminators: hints and strategies for big projects. Meth. Enzymol. 152:538-556.

Barton, G. J. and Sternbert, M. J. 1987. A strategy for the rapid multiple alignment of protein sequences: confidence levels from tertiary structure comparisons. J. Mol. Biol. 198:327-337.

Bashford, D., Chothia, C., and Lesk, A. 1987. Determinants of a protein fold. Unique features of the globin amino acid sequences. J. Mol. Biol. 196:199-216.

Benson, D., Boguski, M., Lipman, D. J., and Ostell, J. 1990. The National Center for Biotechnology Information. Genomics 6:389-391.

Benton, D. 1990. Recent changes in the GenBank on-line service. Nucleic Acids Res. 18:1517-1520.

Berg, J. M. 1990. Zinc finger domains: hypotheses and current knowledge. Ann. Rev. Biophys. Chem 19:405-421.

Bibb, M. J., Findlay, P. R. and Johnson, M. W. 1984. The gene relationship between base composition and codon usage in bacterial genes and its uses for the simple and reliable identification of protein-coding sequences. Gene 30:157-166.

Birktoft, J. J. and Banaszak, L. J. 1984. Structure-function relationships among nicotinamide-adenine dinucleotide dependent oxidoreductases. Peptide and Protein Rev. 4:1-46.

Bishop, M. J. and Thompson, E. A. 1986. Maximum likelihood alignment of DNA sequences. J. Mol. Biol. 190:159-165.

Boguski, M. S., Elshourbagy, N. A., Taylor, J. M., and Gordon, J. I. 1984. Rat apolipoprotein A-IV contains 13 tandem repetitions of a 22-amino acid segment with amphipathic helical potential. Proc. Natl. Acad. Sci. USA 81:5021-5025.

Boguski, M. S., Elshourbagy, N. A., Taylor, J. M., and Gordon, J. I. 1985. Comparative analysis of repeated sequences in rat apolipoproteins A-I, A-IV and E. Proc. Natl. Acad. Sci. USA 82:992-996.

Boguski, M. S., Birkenmeyer, E. H., Elshourbagy, N. A., Taylor, J. M., and Gordon, J. I. 1986a. Evolution of the apolipoproteins: structure of the rat ApoA-IV gene and its relationship to the human genes for ApoA-I, C-III and E. J. Biol. Chem. 261:6398-6407.

Boguski, M. S., Elshourbagy, N. A., Taylor, J. M., and Gordon, J. I. 1986b. Rat apolipoprotein A-IV: application of computational methods for studying the structure, function and evolution of a protein. Meth. Enzym. 128:753-773.

Boguski, M. S., Freeman, M., Elshourbagy, N. A., Taylor, J. M., and Gordon, J. I. 1986c. On computer-assisted analysis of biological sequences: proline punctuation, consensus sequences and apolipoprotein repeats. J. Lipid Res. 27:1011-1034.

Boguski, M. S. 1990. The importance of repetitive protein sequences in biology and medicine: use of Medline as a primary tool for basic research in molecular biology. AMIA Proc. 1:68.

Boguski, M. S., Sikorski, R. S., Hieter, P., and Goebl, M. 1990. Expanding family. Nature 346:114.

Boguski, M. S. and States, D. S. 1991. Molecular sequence databases and their uses. Protein Engineering, in press.

Bougueleret, L., Tekaia, F., Sauvaget, I. and Claverie, J.-M. Objective comparison of exon and intron sequences by the mean of 2-dimensional data analysis methods.1988. Nucleic Acids Res. 16:1729-1738.

Breedan, L. and Nasmyth, K., 1987. Similarity between cell-cycle genes of budding yeast and fission yeast and the *Notch* gene of *Drosophila*. Nature 329:651-654.

Brendel, V. and Trifonov, E. N. 1984. A computer algorithm for testing potential prokaryotic terminators. Nucleic Acids Res. 12:4411-4427.

Brendel, V., Hamm, G. H., and Trifonov, E. N. 1986. Terminators of transcription with RNA polymerase from *Escherichia coli*: what they look like and how to find them. J. Biomol. Struct. Dyn. 3:705-723.

Brendel, V. and Karlin, S. 1989. Association of charge clusters with functional domains of cellular transcription factors. Proc. Natl. Acad. Sci. USA 86:5698-5702.

Breslow, J. L. 1988. Apolipoprotein genetic variation and human disease. Physiol. Rev. 68:85-132.

Brown, R. S., Sander, C., and Argos, P. 1985. The primary structure of transcription factor IIIA has 12 consecutive repeats. FEBS Lett. 1862:271-274.

Bucher, P. 1988. The eukaryote promoter database of the Weizmann Institute of Science. EMBL Nucleotide Sequence Data Library Release 17. Heidelberg, Germany.

Bucher, P. 1990. Weight matrix descriptions of four eukaryotic RNA polymerase II promoter elements derived from 502 unrelated promoter sequences. J. Mol. Biol. 212:563-578.

Calladine, C. R. 1982. Mechanics of sequence-dependent stacking of bases in B-DNA. J. Mol. Biol. 161:343-352.

Campos-Ortega, J. A. 1988. Cellular interactions during early neurogenesis of *Drosophila melanogaster*. Trends Neurosci. 11:400-405.

Carafa, Y. d'A., Brody, E., and Thermes, C.1990. Prediction of rho-independent *Escherichia coli* transcription terminators. J. Molec. Biol. 216:835-858.

Carillo, H. and Lipman, D. 1988. The multiple sequence alignment problem in biology. SIAM J. Appl. Math. 48:1073-1082.

Carver, J. A., Cooke, R. M., Esposito, G., Campbell, I. D., Gregory, I., and Sheard, B. 1986. A high resolution ^{1}H NMR study of the solution structure of human epidermal growth factor. FEBS Lett. 205:77-81.

Cedergren, R., Gautheret, D., Lapalme, G. and Major, F. 1988. A secondary and tertiary structure editor for nucleic acids. Comput. Appl. Biosci. 4:143-146.

Celander, D. W. and Cech, T. R. Visualizing the higher order folding of a catalytic RNA molecule. 1991. Science 251:401-407.

Chothia, C. and Lesk, A. M. 1986. The relationship between the divergence of sequence and structure in proteins. EMBO J. 5:823 -826.

Chou, P. Y. and Fasman, G. D. 1978. Prediction of the secondary structure of proteins from their amino acid sequence. Advances in Enzymology 47:45-147.

Coffman, C., Harris, W., and Kintner, C. *Xotch*, the *Xenopus* homolog of *Drosophila Notch*. Science 249:1438-1440.

Cohen, F. E., Abarbanel, R. A., Kuntz, I. D., and Fletterick, R. J. 1986. Turn prediction in proteins using a pattern matching approach. Biochemistry 25:266-275.

Cole, K. D., Fernando-Warnakulasuriya, G. J. P., Boguski, M. S., Freeman, M., Gordon, J. I., Clark, W. A., Law, J. H., and Wells, M. A. 1987. Primary structure and comparative sequence analysis an insect apolipoprotein: apolipophorin-III from *Manduca sexta*. J. Biol. Chem. 26224:11794-11800.

Collins, J. F. and Coulson, A. F. W. Molecular sequence comparison and alignment. In Nucleic Acid and Protein Sequence Analysis: A Practical Approach. Bishop, M.J. and Rawlings, C.J., eds., IRL Press, Oxford, 1987.

Collins, J. and Coulson, A. 1990. Significance of protein sequence alignment. Meth. Enzymol. 183:474-487.

Connell, C., Fung, S., Heiner, C., Bridgham, J., Chakrian, V., Heron, E., Jones, R., Menchen, S., Mordan, W., Raff, M., Recknor, M., Smith, L., Springer, J., Woo, S., and Hunkapillar, M. 1987. Automated DNA sequence analysis. Biotechniques 5:342-344.

Cornette, J. L., Cease, K. B., Margalit, H., Spouge, J. L., Berzofsky, J. A., and DeLisi, C. 1987. Hydrophobicity scales and computational techniques for detecting amphipatic structures in proteins. J. Mol. Biol. 195:659-685.

Courey, A. J. and Wang, J. C. 1983. Cruciform formation in a negatively supercoiled DNA may be kinetically forbidden under physiological conditions. Cell 33:817-829.

Cowan, S. W., Newcomer, M. E., and Jones, T. A. 1990. Crystallographic refinement of human serum retinol binding protein at 2 Å resolution. Proteins 8:44-61.

Craik, C., Sprang, S., Fletterick, R., and Rudder, W. J . 1982. Intron-exon splice junctions map at protein surfaces. Nature 299:180-1822.

Craik, C., Rutter, W. and Fletterick, R. 1983. Splice junctions: association with variation in protein structure. Science 220:1125-1129.

Crawford, I. P., Niermann, T., and Kirschner, K. 1987. Prediction of secondary structure by evolutionary comparison: application to the a subunit of tryptophan synthase. Proteins Struct. Func. Genet. 2:118-129.

Creighton, T. E. Proteins: Structures and Molecular Properties. Freeman, New York, 1984.

Davies, D. R., Sheriff, S., and Padlan, E. A. 1988. Antibody-antigen complexes. J. Biol. Chem. 263:10541-10544.

Davis, G. C. 1990. The many faces of epidermal growth factor repeats. The New Biologist 2:410-419.

Davison, D. 1985. Sequence similarity homology searching for molecular biologists. Bull. Math. Biol. 474:437-474.

Davison, D. B. and Chappelaar, J. E. 1990. The Genbank-Server at the University of Houston. Nucleic Acids Res. 18:1571-1572.

Dayhoff, M. O., and Eck, R. V. 1968. In Atlas of Protein Structure. Eds. M. Dayhoff. Silver Spring, MD: National Biomedical Research Foundation.

Dayhoff, M. O. Atlas of Protein Sequence and Structure. National Biomedical Research Foundation, Washington, D.C., 1978.

Dayhoff, M. O. 1974. Fed. Proc. 33 : 2314.

Dayhoff, M. O., Schwartz, R. M., and Orcutt, B.C. A model of evolutionary change in proteins. In Atlas of Protein Sequence and Structure, M. O. Dayhoff, ed., National Biomedical Research Foundation, Washington D.C, 1979.

De Loof, H., Rosseneu, M., Yang, C.-Y., Li, W.-H., Gotto, A. M., and Chan, L. 1987. Human apolipoprotein B: analysis of internal repeats and homology with other apolipoproteins. J. Lipid Res. 28:1455-1465.

Deininger, P. L. 1983. Random subcloning of sonicated DNA. Application to shotgun DNA sequence analysis. Anal. Biochem. 129: 216-223.

Devereux, J., Haeberli, P., and Smithies, O. 1984. A comprehensive set of sequence analysis programs for the VAX. Nucleic Acids Res. 12:387-395.

Dickerson, R. E., Drew, H. R., Conner, B. N., Wing, R. M., Fratini, A. V. and Kopka, M. L. 1982. The anatomy of A-, B-, and Z-DNA. Science 216:475-485.

Dickerson, R. E. 1983. Base sequence and helix structure variation in B and A DNA. J. Mol. Biol. 166:419-441.

Dickerson, R. E., Bansal, M., Calladine, C. R., Dieckmann, S., Hunter, W. W., Kennard, O., von Kitzing, E., Lavery, R., Nelson, H. C. M., Olson, W. K., Saenger, W., Shakked, Z., Sklenar, H., Soumpasis, D. M., Tung, C.-S., Wang, A. H.-J., and Zhurkin, V. B. 1989. Definition and parameters of nucleic acid structure parameters. EMBO J. 8:1-4.

Doolittle, R. F. 1981. Similar amino acids: chance or common ancestry? Science 214:149-159.

Doolittle, R. F., Feng, D. F., and Johnson, M. S. 1984. Computer-based character-ization of epidermal growth factor precursor. Nature 307:558-560.

Doolittle, R. F. 1986. Of URFS and ORFS: A Primer on How to Analyze Derived Amino Acid Sequences. University Science Books, Mill Valley, CA, 1986.

Drew, H. R. and Calladine, C. R. 1986. Sequence-specific positioning of core histones on an 860 base-pair DNA. J. Mol. Biol. 195:143-173.

Dumas, J. P. and Ninio, J. 1982. Efficient algorithms for folding and comparing nucleic acid sequences. Nucleic Acids Res. 10:197-206.

Edwards, A., Voss, H., Rice, P., Civitello, A., Stegemann, J., Schwager, C., Zimmermann, J., Erfle, H., Caskey, C. T., and Ansorge, W. 1990. Automated DNA sequencing of the human HPRT locus. Genomics 6:593-608.

Eisenberg, D., Weiss, R. M., and Terwilliger, T. C. 1982. The helical hydrophobic moment: a measure of the amphiphilicity of a helix. Nature 299:371-374.

Eisenberg, D., Schwarz, E., Komaromy, M., and Wall, R. 1984a. Analysis of membrane and surface protein sequences with the hydrophobic moment plot. J. Mol. Biol. 179:125-142.

Eisenberg, D., Weiss, R. M., and Terwilliger, T. C. 1984b. The hydrophobic moment detects periodicity in protein hydrophobicity. Proc. Natl. Acad. Sci. USA 81:140-144.

Eisenberg, D., Wesson, M., and Wilcox, W. Hydrophobic moments as tools for analyzing protein sequences and structures. In Prediction of Protein Structure and the Principles of Protein Conformation, G.D. Fasman, ed., Plenum Press, New York, 1989.

Elder, J. K., Green, D. K., and Southern, E. M. 1986. Automated reading of DNA sequencing gel autoradiographs using a large format digital scanner. Nucleic Acids Res. 14:417-424.

Elder, J. K. and Southern, E. M. Automatic reading of DNA sequencing gel autoradiographs. In Nucleic Acid and Protein Sequence Analysis: A Practical Approach, M.J. Bishop and C.J. Rawlings, ed., IRL Press, Oxford, 1987.

Emini, E. A., Hughes, J. V., Perlow, D. S., and Boger, J. 1985. Induction of hepatitis A virus-neutralizing antibody by a virus-specific synthetic peptide. J. Virol. 55:836-839.

Engelman, D. M., Steitz, T. A., and Goldman, A. 1986. Identifying nonpolar transbilayer helices in amino acid sequences of membrane proteins. Annu. Rev. Biophys. Chem. 15:321-354.

Farber, G. K. and Petsko, G. A. 1990. The evolution of alpha/beta barrel enzymes. Trends Biochem. Sci. 15:228-234.

Fauchere, J. L. and Pliska, V. 1983. Hydrophobic parameters of amino acid side chains from the partitioning of N-acetyl-amino acid amides. Eur. J. Med. Chem.-Chim. Ther. 18:369-375.

Felsenstein, J. 1973. Maximum-likelihood estimation of evolutionary trees from continuous characters. Am. J. Hum. Genet. 25:471-492.

Felsenstein, J. 1985. Phylogenies and the comparative method. American Naturalist 1251:1-15.

Feng, D. F., Johnson, M. S., and Doolittle, R. F. 1985. Aligning amino acid sequences: comparison of commonly used methods. J. Mol. Evol. 21:112-125.

Feng, D. and Doolittle, R. F. 1986. Progressive sequence alignment as a prerequisite to correct phylogenetics trees. J. Mol. Evol. 25:351-360.

Feng, D. and Doolittle, R. 1987. Progressive multiple sequence alignment. J. Mol. Evol. 25:351-360.

Fickett, J. W. 1982. Recognition of protein coding regions in DNA sequences. Nucleic Acids Res. 10:5303-5318.

Fichant, G. and Gautier, C. 1987. Statistical method for predicting coding regions in nucleic acid sequences. Comput. Appl. Biosci. 3:287-295.

Fields, C. A. and Soderlund, C. A. 1990. gm: a practical tool for automating DNA sequence analysis. Comput. Appl. Biosci. 6:263-270.

Finer-Moore, J., Bazan, J. F., Rubin, J., and Stroud, R.M. Identification of membrane proteins and soluble protein secondary structural elements, domain structure and packing arrangements by fourier-transform amphipatic analysis. In Prediction of Protein Structure and the Principles of Protein Conformation. G.D. Fasman, ed., Plenum Press, New York, 1989.

Fitch, W. M. 1966. An improved method of testing for evolutionary homology. J. Mol. Biol. 16:9-16.

Fitch, W. M. 1969. Locating gaps in amino acid sequences to optimize the homology between two proteins. Biochem. Genet. 3:99-108.

Fitch, W. M. 1970. Further improvements in the method of testing for evolutionary homology among proteins. J. Mol. Biol. 49:1-14.

Fitch, W. M. and Margoliash, E. 1970. The usefulness of amino acid and nucleotide sequences in evolutionary studies. Evol. Biol. 4:67-109.

Fitch, W. M., and Smith, T. F. 1983. Optimal sequence alignments. Proc. Natl. Acad. Sci. USA 80:1382-1386.

Fox, T. D. 1985. Diverged genetic codes in protozoans and a bacterium. Nature 314:132-133.

Freier, S. M., Kierzek, R., Jaeger, J. A., Sugimoto, N., Caruthers, M. H., Neilson, T. and Turner, D. H. Improved free-energy parameters for predictions of RNA duplex stability. 1986. Proc. Natl. Acad. Sci USA 83:9373-9377.

Frey, D. and Adams, R. (1989) !%@:: A Dictionary of Electronic Mail Addressing and Networks. O'Reilly and Assoc., Sebastopol, CA, USA.

Friedman, D. I., Imperiale, M. J., and Adhya, S. L. 1987. RNA 3' end formation in the control of gene expression. Ann. Rev. Genetics 21:453-488.

Fu, Y.-H. and Marzluf, G. A. 1990. nit-2, the major nitrogen regulatory gene of *Neurospora crassa*, encodes a protein with a putative zinc finger DNA-binding domain. Mol. Cell Biol. 103:1056-1065.

Fuchs, R., Stoehr, P., Rice, P., Omond, R., and Cameron, G. 1990. New services of the EMBL Data Library. Nucleic Acids Res. 18:4319-4323.

Garnier, J., Osguthorpe, D. J., and Robson, B. 1978. Analysis of the accuracy and implication of simple methods for predicting the secondary structure of globular proteins. J. Mol. Biol. 120:97-120

Geiduschek, E. P. and Tocchini-Valentini, G. P. 1988. Transcription by RNA polymerase III. Ann. Rev. Biochem. 57:873-914.

George, D. G., Barker, W. C., and Hunt, L. T. 1990. Mutation data matrix and its uses. Meth. Enzymol. 183:333-351.

Ghosh, D. 1990. A relational database of transcription factors. Nucleic Acids Res. 18:1749-1756.

Gibbs, A. J. and McIntyre, G. A. 1970. The diagram, a method for comparing sequences. Its use with amino acid and nucleotide sequences. Eur. J. Biochem. 16:1-11.

Gilbert, W. 1987. The exon theory of genes. Cold Spring Harbor Symp. Quant. Biol. 52:901-905.

Gill, S. C. and von Hippel, P. H. 1989. Calculation of protein extinction coefficients from amino acid sequence data. Anal. Biochem. 182:319-326.

Ginsberg, A. M., King, B. O., and Roeder, R. G. 1984. *Xenopus* 5S gene transcription factor IIIA: characterization of a cDNA clone and measurement of RNA levels throughout development. Cell 39:479-489.

Gotoh, O. 1986. Alignment of three biological sequences with an efficient traceback procedure. J. Theor. Biol. 121:327-337.

Grantham, R., Gautier, C., Gouy, M., Mercier, R., and Pave, 1980. Codon catalog usage and the genome hypothesis. Nucleic Acids Res. 8:r49-r60.

Gren, E. J. 1984. Recognition of messenger RNA during translational initiation in *Escherichia coli*. Biochimie 66:1-29.

Gribskov, M., Devereux, J., and Burgess, R. R. 1984. The codon preference plot: graphic analysis of protein coding sequences and prediction of gene expression. Nucleic Acids Res. 12:539-549.

Gribskov, M., McLachlan, A. D. and Eisenberg, D. 1987. Profile analysis detection of distantly related proteins. Proc. Natl. Acad. Sci. USA 84:4355-4358.

Gribskov, M., Lüthy, R., and Eisenberg, D. 1989. Profile analysis. Meth. Enzymol. 183:146-159.

Grosjean, H. and Fiers, W. 1982. Preferential codon usage in prokaryotic genes; the optimal codon-anticodon interaction energy and the selective codon usage in efficiently expressed genes. Gene 18:199-20.

Grymes, R. A., Travers, P., and Engelberg, A. 1986. GEL - A computer tool for DNA sequencing projects. Nucleic Acids Res. 14:87-99.

Hahn, S., Buratowski, S., Sharp, P. A., and Guarente, L. 1989. Isolation of the gene encoding the yeast TATA binding protein TFIID: a gene identical to the SPT15 suppressor of Ty element insertions. Cell 58:1173-1181.

Hancock, J. M. and Dover, G. A. 1988. Molecular coevolution among cryptically simple expansion segments of eukaryotic 26S/28S rRNAs. Mol. Biol. Evol. 54:377-391.

Hanks, S. K., Quinn, A. M., and Hunter, T. 1988. The protein kinase family:

conserved features and deduced phylogeny of the catalytic domains. Science 241:42-52.

Harrison, S. C. and Aggarwal, A. K. 1990. DNA recognition by proteins with the helix-turn-helix motif. Ann. Rev. Biochem. 59:933-969.

Hawley, D. K. and McClure, W. R. 1983. Compilation and analysis of *Escherichia coli* promoter sequences. Nucleic Acids Res.11:2237-2255.

Hennig, W. 1966. Phylogenetic systematics. University of Illinois Press, Urbana, IL.

Herz, J., Hamann, U., Rogne, S., Myklebost, O., Gausepohl, H., and Stanley, K. K. 1988. Surface location and high affinity for calcium of a 500-kd liver membrane protein closely related to the LDL receptor suggest a physiological role as lipoprotein receptor. EMBO J. 13:4119-4127.

Hieter, P. A., Max, E. E., Seidman, J. G., Maizel, J. V., and Leder, P. 1980. Cloned human and mouse kappa immunoglobulin constant and J region genes conserve homology in functional segments. Cell 22:197-207.

Hoeijmakers, J. H. J. 1990. Cryptic initiation sequence revealed. Nature 343:417-418.

Hoffman, A., Sinn, E., Yamamoto, T., Wang, T., Roy, A., Horikoshi, M., and Roeder, R. G. 1990. Highly conserved core domain and unique N terminus with presumptive regulatory motifs in a human TATA factor TFIID. Nature 346:387-390.

Hogan, M. E., Roberson, M. W. and Austin, R. H. DNA flexibility variation may dominate DNase I cleavage. 1989. Proc. Natl. Acad. Sci. USA 86:9273-9277.

Holland, S. K. and Blake, C. C. 1987. Proteins, exons and molecular evolution. Biosystems 20:181-206.

Holley, L. H. and Karplus, M. 1989. Protein secondary structure prediction with a neural network. Proc. Natl. Acad. Sci. USA 86:152-156.

Holm, L. 1986. Codon usage and gene expression. Nucleic Acids Res. 14:3075-3087.

Hopcroft, J. E. and Ullman, J. D. Introduction to Automata Theory, Languages, and Computation. Addison-Wesley, Reading, MA, 1979.

Hopp, T. P. and Woods, K. R. 1981. Prediction of protein antigenic determinants from amino acid sequences. Proc. Natl. Acad. Sci. USA 78:3824-3828.

Horikoshi, M., Wang, C. K., Fujii, H., Cromlish, J. A., Weil, P. A., and Roeder, R. G. 1989. Cloning and structure of a yeast gene encoding a general transcription initiation factor TFIID that binds to the TATA box. Nature 341:299-303.

Humphries, S. E. 1988. DNA polymorphisms of the apolipoprotein genes: their use in the investigation of the genetic component of hyperlipidaemia and atherosclerosis. Atherosclerosis 72:89-108.

Ikemura, T. 1981. Correlation between the abundance of *Escherichia coli* transfer RNAs and the occurrence of the respective codons in protein genes. J. Mol. Biol. 146:1-21.

Ikemura, T. 1982. Correlation between the abundance of yeast transfer RNAs and the occurrence of the respective codons in protein genes. J. Mol. Biol. 158:573-597.

Ikemura, T. 1985. Codon usage and tRNA content in unicellular and multicellular organisms. J. Mol. Evol. 2:13-34.

Jacobs, G., and G. Michaels. 1990. Zinc finger gene database. The New Biologist 2:583-584.

Jameson, B. A. and Wolf, H. 1988. The antigenic index: a novel algorithm for predicting antigenic determinants. Comput. Appl. Biosci. 4:181-186.

Johansen, K. M., Fehon, R. G., and Artavanis-Tsakonas, S. 1989. The *Notch* gene product is a glycoprotein expressed on the cell surface of both epidermal and neuronal precursor cells during *Drosophila* development. J. Cell Biol. 109:2427-2440.

Kabsch, W. and Sander, C. 1983. Dictionary of protein secondary structure: pattern recognition of hydrogen-bonded and geometrical features. Biopolymers 22:2577-2637.

Karlin, S. and Altschul, S. F. 1990. Methods for assessing the statistical significance of molecular sequence features by using general scoring schemes. Proc. Natl. Acad. Sci. USA 87:2264-2268.

Karplus, P. A. and Schulz, G. E. 1985. Prediction of chain flexibility in proteins. Naturwissenschaften 72:212-213.

Kefalas, P., Gray, F. C., and Allan, J. 1988. Precise nucleosome positioning in the promoter of the chicken beta-A globin gene. Nucleic Acids Res. 16:501-517.

Keim, P., Heinrickson, R. L., and Fitch, W. M. 1981. An examination of the expected degree of sequence similarity that might arise in proteins that have converged to similar conformational states. The impact of such expectations on the search for homology between the structurally similar domains of rhodanase. J. Mol. Biol. 151:179-197.

Kidd, S., Kelley, M. R. amd Young, M. W. 1986. Sequence of the *Notch* locus of *Drosophila melanogaster*: relationship of the encoded protein to mammalian clotting and growth factors. Mol. Cell. Biol. 6:3094-3108.

Kim, S. H., Suddath, F. L., Quigley, F. L. Mcpherson, A., Sussman, J. L., Wang, A H .J., Seeman, N. C., and Rich, A. 1974. Three-dimensional structure of yeast phenylalanine transfer RNA. Science 185:435-440.

Kneller, D. G., Cohen, F. E., and Langridge, R. 1990. Improvements in protein secondary structure prediction by an enhanced neural network. J. Mol. Biol. 214:171-182.

Konings, D. A. M., van Duijn, L. P., Voorma, H. O. and Hogeweg, P. 1987. Minimal energy foldings of eukaryotic mRNAs form a separate leader domain. J. Theor. Biol. 127:63-78.

Kozak, M. 1983. Comparison of initiation of protein synthesis in prokaryotes, eukaryotes and organelles. Microbiol. Revs 47:1-45.

Kozak, M. 1984. Compilation and analysis of sequences upstream from the translational start site in eukaryotic mRNAs. Nucleic Acids Res. 12:857-872.

Kozak, M. 1986. Regulation of protein synthesis in virus-infected cells. Adv. Virus Res. 31:229-290.

Kretsinger, R. H. 1987. Calcium coordination and the calmodulin fold: divergent versus convergent evolution. Cold Spring Harbor Symp. Quant. Biol. 52:499-507

Kristensen, T. D., Eustachio, P., Ogata, R. T., Chung, L. P., Reid, K. B. M., and Tack, B. F. 1987. The superfamily of C3b/C4b-binding proteins. Federation Proceedings 477:2463-2469.

Kroeger, M., Wahl, R., and Rice, P. 1990. Compilation of DNA sequences of *Escherichia coli* (update 1990). Nucleic Acids Res. 18:2549-2587.

Kubota, Y., Takahashi, S., Nishikawa, K., and Ooi, T. 1981. Homology in protein sequences expressed by correlation coefficients. J. Theor. Biol. 91:347-361.

Kulda, B., Caddick, M. X., Langdon, T., Martinez-Rossi, N. M., Bennett, C. F., Sibley, S., Davies, R. W., and Arst, H. N. 1990. The regulatory gene *areA* mediating nitrogen metabolite repression in *Aspergillus nidulans*: mutations affecting specificity of gene activation alter a loop residue of a putative zinc finger. EMBO J. 95:1355-1364.

Kurosky, A., Barnett, D. R., Lee, T. H., Touchstone, B., Hay, R. E., Arnott, M. S., Bowman, B. H., and Fitch, W. M. 1980. Covalent structure of human haptoglobin: a serine protease homolog. Proc. Natl. Acad. Sci. USA 77:3388-3392.

Kyte, J. and Doolittle, R. F. 1982. A simple method for displaying the hydropathic character of a protein. J. Mol. Biol. 157:105-132.

Lander, E. S. and Waterman, M. S. 1988. Genomic mapping by fingerprinting random clones: a mathematical analysis. Genomics 2:231-239.

Lehninger, A. L. Biochemistry. Worth Publishers, New York, 1977.

Lesk, A. M. Computational Molecular Biology: Sources and Methods for Sequence Analysis. Oxford University Press, Oxford, 1988.

Levitt, M. 1976. A simplified representation of protein conformations for rapid simulation of protein folding. J. Mol. Biol. 104:59-107.

Li, W.-H., Wu, C.-I., and Luo, C.-C. 1985. A new method for estimating synonymous and nonsynonymous rates of nucleotide subsitution considering the relative likelihood of nucleotide and codon changes. Mol. Biol. Evol. 22:150-174.

Li, W.-H., Tanimura, M., Luo, C. C., Datta, S., and Chan, L. 1988. The apolipoprotein multigene family: biosynthesis, structure, structure-function relationships and evolution. J. Lipid Res. 29:245-271.

Lim, V. I. 1974. Algorithms for prediction of a-helical and b-structural regions in globular proteins. J. Mol. Biol. 88:873-894.

Lim, V. I. 1978. Polypeptide chain folding through a highly helical intermediate as a general principle of globular protein structure formation. FEBS Lett. 89:10-14.

Lipman, D. J. and Pearson, W. R. 1985. Rapid and sensitive protein similarity searches. Science 227:1435-1441.

Lipman, D. J., Altschul, S. F., and Kececioglu, J. D. 1989. A tool for multiple sequence alignment. Proc. Natl. Acad. Sci. USA 86:4412-4415.

Lowe, T., Sharefkin, J., Shi Qi Yang, and Diffenbach, C.W. 1990. A computer program for selection of oligonucleotide primers for polymerase chain reactions. Nucleic Acids Res. 18:1757-1761.

Maeda, N. and Smithies, O. 1986. The evolution of multigene families: human haptoglobin genes. Ann. Rev. Genet. 20:81-108.

Mahley, R. W. 1988. Apolipoprotein E: cholesterol transport protein with expanding role in cell biology. Science 240:622-630.

Maizel, J. V. and Lenk, R. P. 1981. Enhanced graphic matrix analysis of nucleic acid and protein sequences. Proc. Natl. Acad. Sci. USA 78:7665-7669.

Margalit, H., Shapiro, B. A., Oppenheim, A. B. and Maizel, J. V. J. 1989. Detection of common motifs in RNA secondary structure. Nucleic Acids Res. 17:4829-4845.

Markopoulou, K. and Artavanis-Tsakonas, S. 1989. The expression of the neurogenic locus Notch during postembryonic development of Drosophila melanogaster and its relationship to mitotic activity. J. Neurogenet. 6:11-26.

Marshall, R. D. 1972. Glycoproteins. Annu. Rev. Biochem. 41:673-702.

Martinez, H. M. 1988. An RNA secondary structure workbench. Nucleic Acids Res. 16:1789-1798.

May, L. T., Landsberger, F. R., Inouye, M., and Sehgal, P. B. 1985. Significance of similarities in patterns: an application to beta interferon-related DNA on human chromosome 2. Proc Natl Acad Sci U S A 82:4090-4094.

McCaldon, P. and Argos, P. 1988. Oligopeptide biases in protein sequences and their use in predicting protein coding regions in nucleotide sequences. Proteins 4:99-122.

McLachlan, A. D. 1971. Tests for comparing related amino acid sequences: cytochrome c and cytochrome c551. J. Mol. Biol. 61: 409-424.

McLachlan, A. D. 1972. Repeating sequences and gene duplication in proteins. J. Mol. Biol. 72:417-437.

McLachlan, A. D. 1977. Repeating helical pattern in apolipoprotein A-I. Nature 267:465-466.

McLachlan, A. D. 1983. Analysis of gene duplication repeats in the myosin rod. J. Mol. Biol. 169:15-30.

McLachlan, A. D. and Boswell, D. R. 1985. Confidence limits for homology in protein or gene sequences: the c-myc oncogene and adenovirus E1a protein. J. Mol. Biol. 185:39-49.

McLauchlan, J., Gaffrey, D., Whitton, J. and Clements, J. 1985. The consensus sequences YGTGTTYY located downstream from the AATAAA signal is required for efficient formation of mRNA 3' termini. Nucleic Acids Res. 13:1347-1368.

Messing, J., Crea, R., and Seeburg, P. H. 1981. A system for shotgun DNA sequencing. Nucleic Acids Res. 9:309-321.

Miller, J., McLachlan, A. D., and Klug, A. 1985. Repetitive zinc-binding domains in the protein transcription factor IIIA from Xenopus oocytes. EMBO J. 46:1609-1614.

Mitchell, P. J. and Tijan, R. 1989. Transcription regulation in mammalian cells by sequence-specific DNA binding proteins. Science 245:371-378.

Mount, S. M. 1982. A catalogue of splice junction sequences. Nucleic Acids Res. 10:459-472.

Murata, M., Richardson, J. S., and Sussman, J. L. 1985. Simultaneous comparison of three protein sequences. Proc. Natl. Acad. Sci. USA 82:3073-3077.

Nagai, K. 1990. Cryptic initiation sequence revealed. Nature 343:418.

Needleman, S. B. and Wunsch, C. D. 1970. A general method applicable to the search for similarities in the amino acid sequence of two proteins. J. Mol. Biol. 48:443-453.

Nomenclature Committee of the International Union of Biochemistry (NC-IUB) 1985. Nomenclature for incompletely specified bases: recommendations 1984. Eur. J. Biochem. 150:1-5.

Nurse, P. 1985. Cell cycle control genes in yeast. Trends Genet. 1:51-55.

O'Dowd, B. F., Lefkowitz, R. J., and Caron, M. G. 1989. Structure of the adrenergic and related receptors. Ann. Rev. Neurosci. 12:67-83.

Oh, S.-K., Pavlotsky, N., and Tauber, A. I. 1990. Specific binding of haptoglobin to human neutrophils and its functional consequences. J. Leuk. Biol. 47:142-148.

Oliphant, A. R. and Struhl, K. 1988. Defining the consensus sequences of E. coli promoter elements by random selection. Nucleic Acids Res. 16:7673-7683.

Ohno, S. and Ohno, M. 1986. The all pervasive principle of repetitious recurrence governs not only coding sequence construction but also human endeavor in musical composition. Immunogenetics 24:71-78.

Ohno, S. 1988. Universal rule for coding sequence construction: TA/GC deficiency - TG/CT excess. Proc. Natl. Acad. Sci. USA 85:9630-9634.

Paabo, S., Higuchi, R. G., and Wilson, A. 1989. Ancient DNA and the polymerase chain reaction:the emerging field of molecular archeology. J. Biol. Chem. 264:9709-9712.

Pallansch, L., Beswick, H., Talian, J. and Zelenka, P. 1990. Use of an RNA folding algorithm to choose regions for polymerase chain reaction. Anal. Biochem.

185:57-62.

Patterson, C. Morphological characters and homology. In Problems of Phylogenetic Reconstruction. Van Nostrand-Reinhold, New York, 1982.

Patterson, C. 1988. Homology in classical and molecular biology. Mol. Biol. Evol. 56:603-625.

Pauling, L. and Zuckerkandl, E. 1963. Chemical paleogenetics: molecular restoration studies of extinct forms of life. Acta Chem. Scand. 17:S9-S16.

Peabody, D. S. 1989. Translation initiation at non-AUG triplets in mammalian cells. J. Biol. Chem. 264:5031-5035.

Pearson, W. R. and Lipman, D. J. 1988. Improved tools for biological sequence comparison. Proc. Natl. Acad. Sci. USA 85:2444-2448.

Pearson, W. and Lipman, D. 1988. Improved tools for biological sequence comparison. Proc. Natl. Acad. Sci. USA. 85:2444-2448.

Pearson, W. R. 1990. Rapid and sensitive sequence comparison with FASTP and FASTA. Meth. Enzymol. 183:63-98.

Peitsch, M. C. and Boguski, M. S. 1990. Is apolipoprotein D a mammalian bilin-binding protein? The New Biologist 22:197-206.

Peticolas, W. L., Wang, Y. and Thomas, G. A. 1988. Some rules for predicting the base-sequence dependence of DNA conformation. Proc. Natl. Acad. Sci. USA 85:2579-2583.

Pierce, J. R. 1980. An Introduction to Information Theory: Symbols, Signals and Noise. Dover Publications, New York.

Platt, T. 1986. Transcription termination and the regulation of gene expression. Ann. Rev. Biochem. 55:339-372.

Poncz, M., Solowiejczyk, D., Ballantine, M., Schwartz, E., and Surrey, S. 1982. "Non-random" DNA sequence analysis in bacteriophage M13 by the dideoxy chain-termination method. Proc. Natl. Acad. Sci. USA 79:4298-4302.

Posfai, J., Bhagwat, A. S., Posfai, G., and Roberts, R. J. 1989. Predictive motifs derived from cytosine methyltransferases. Nucleic Acids Res. 17:2421-2435.

Presnell, S. R. and Cohen, F. E. 1989. Topological distribution of four-alpha-helix bundles. Proc. Natl. Acad. Sci. USA 86:6592-6596.

Pringle, J. R. and Hartwell, L. H. The *Saccharomyces cerevisiae* cell cycle. In The Molecular Biology of the Yeast *Saccharomyces cerevisiae*, Life Cycle and Inheritance. Strathern, J. N. and Jones, E. W., eds., Cold Spring Harbor Laboratory, Cold Spring Harbor, N.Y., 1981.

Proudfoot, N. J. and Brownlee, G. G. 1976. 3' noncoding region in eukaryotic messenger RNA. Nature 263:211-214.

Pustell, J. and Kafatos, F. C. 1982. A high speed, high capacity homology matrix: zooming through SV40 and polyoma. Nucleic Acids Res. 10:4765-4782.

Pustell, J., and Kafatos, F. C. 1984. A convenient and adaptable package of computer programs for DNA and protein sequence management, analysis and homology determination. Nucliec Acids Res. 12:643-655.

Qian, N. and Sejnowski, T. J. 1988. Predicting the secondary structure of globular proteins using neural network models. J. Mol. Biol. 202:865-884.

Quigley, G. J., Gehrke, L., Roth, D. A., and Auron, P. E. 1984. Computer-aided nucleic acid secondary structure modeling incorporating enzymatic digestion data. Nucleic Acids Res. 121:347-366.

Ramos, R. G. P., Grimwade, B. G., Wharton, K. A., Scottgale, T. N., and Artavanis-Tsakonas, S. 1989. Physical and Functional Definition of the *Drosophila Notch* Locus by P Element Transformation. Genetics Society of America 123:337-348.

Rechsteiner, M., Rogers, S., and Rote, K. 1987. Protein structure and intracellular stability. 1987. Trends Biochem. Sci. 12:390-394.

Rechsteiner, M. 1988. Regulation of enzyme levels by proteolysis: the role of PEST regions. Adv. Enzyme Regul. 27:135-151.

Reeck, G. R., De Haen, C., Teller, D. C., Doolittle, R. F., Fitch, W. M., Dickerson, R. E., Chambon P., McLachlan, A. D., Margoliash, E., Jukes, T. H., and Zuckerkandl, E. 1987. Homology in proteins and nucleic acids: a terminology muddle and a way out of it. Cell 50:667.

Rees, D. C., Komiya, H., Yeates, T. O., Allen, J. P., and Feher, G. 1989a. The bacterial photosynthetic reaction center as a model for membrane proteins. Annu. Rev. Biochem. 58:607-634.

Rees, D. C., DeAntonio, L., and Eisenberg, D. 1989b. Hydrophobic organization of membrane proteins. Science 245:510-513.

Reich, J. G. and Meiske, W. 1987. A simple statistical significance test of window scores in large dot matrices obtained from protein or nucleic acid sequence. Comput. Applic. Biosci. 3:25-30.

Reidhaar-Olson, J. F. and Sauer, R .T. 1988. Combinatorial cassette mutagenesis as a probe of the informational content of protein sequences. Science 241:53-57.

Reisner, A. H. and Bucholtz, C. A. 1988. The use of various properties of amino acids in color and monochrome dot-matrix analyses of protein homologies. Comput. Applic. Biosci. 4:395-402.

Riedl, R. 1979. Order in Living Organisms. John Wiley & Sons, Chinchester, England.

Riordan, J. R., Rommens, J. M., Kerem, B., Alon, N., Rozmahel, R., Grzelczak, Z., Zielinski, J., Si Lok, Plavsik, N., Chou, J- L., Drumm, M. L., Ianuzzi, M. C., Collins, F. S., and Tsui, L-C. 1989. Identification of the cystic fibrosis gene: cloning and characterization of complementary DNA. Science 245:1066-1073.

Risler, J. L., Delorme, M. O., Delacroix, H., and Henaut, A. 1988. Amino acid substitutions in structurally related proteins. A pattern recognition approach. Determination of a new and efficient scoring matrix. J. Mol. Biol. 204:1019-1029.

Roberts, R. J. 1985. Restriction and modification enzymes and their recognition sequences. Nucleic Acids Res. 13:r165-r200.

Roberts, R. 1988. Restriction enzymes and their isoschizomers. Nucleic Acids Res. 16:271-313.

Robertus, J. D., Ladner, J. E., Finch, J. T., Rhodes, D., Brown, R. S., Clark, B. F. C, and Klug, A. 1974. Structure of yeast phenylalanine tRNA at 3 A resolution. Nature 250:546-551.

Rodier, F., Gabarro-Arpa, J., Ehrlick, R. and Reiss, C. 1982. Key for protein coding sequence identification: computer analysis of codon strategy. Nucleic Acids Res. 10:391-401.

Rogers, S., Wells, R., and Rechsteiner, M. 1986. Amino acid sequences common to rapidly degraded proteins: the PEST hypothesis. Science 234:364-368.

Rose, G. D., Geselowitz, A. R., Lesser, G. J., Lee, R. H., and Zehfus, M. H. 1985. Hydrophobicity of amino acid residues in globular proteins. Science 229:834-838.

Rychlik, W. and Rhoads, R. E. 1989. A computer program for choosing optimal oligonucleotides for filter hybridization, sequencing and in vitro amplification of DNA. Nucleic Acids Res. 17:8543-851.

Saenger, W. Principles of nucleic acid structure. Springer-Verlag, NY, 1984.

Sali, A., Overington, J. P., Johnson, M. S., and Blundell, T. L. 1990. From comparisons of protein sequences and structures to protein modelling and design. Trends Biochem. Sci. 15:235-240.

Sankoff, D. 1972. Matching sequences under deletion/insertion constraints. Proc. Natl. Acad. Sci. USA 69:4-6.

Sankoff, D. and Kruskal, J. B. 1983. Time Warps, String Edits and Macromolecules: The Theory and Practice of Sequence Comparison. Addison-Wesley, Reading, MA.

Sawadogo, M. and Sentenac, A. 1990. RNA polymerase B II and general transcription factors. Ann. Rev. Biochem. 59:711-754.

Schiffer, C. A., Caldwell, J. W., Kollman, P. A., and Stroud, R. M. 1990. Prediction of homologous protein structures based on conformational searches and energetics. Proteins Struct. Func. Genet. 8:30-43.

Schiffer, M. and Edmundson, A. B. 1967. Use of helical wheels to represent the structures of proteins and to identify segments with helical potential. Biophys. J. 7:121-135.

Schmidt, M. C., Kao, C. C., Pei, R., and Berk, A. J. 1989. Yeast TATA-box transcription factor gene. Proc. Natl. Acad. Sci. USA 86:7785-7789.

Schuler, G. D., Altschul, S. F., and Lipman, D. J. 1991. A workbench for multiple alignment construction and analysis. Proteins Struct. Func. Genet.9:180-190.

Schultz, J., Marshall-Carlson, L., and Carlson, M. 1990. The N-terminal TPR region is the functional domain of *SSN6*, a nuclear phosphoprotein from *Saccharomyces cerevisiae*. Mol. Cell Biol. 109:4744-4756.

Schulz, G. E. and Schirmer, R. H. Principles of Protein Structure. Springer-Verlag, New York, 1979.

Schwartz, R. M. and Dayhoff, M. O. 1979. supl. 3 ed. In Atlas of Protein Sequence and Structure. M. O. Dayhoff, ed. National Biomedical Research Foundation, Washington, D.C.

Segrest, J. P. and Feldman, R. J. 1974. Membrane protein. Amino acid sequence and membrane penetration. J. Mol. Biol. 87:853-858.

Segrest, J. P., DeLoof, H., Dohlman, J. G., Brouillette, C. G., and Ananthraramaiah, G. M. 1990. Amphipathic helix motif: classes and properties. Proteins Struct. Funct. Genet. 8:103-117.

Sellers, P. 1974. On the theory and computation of evolutionary distances. SIAM J. Appl. Math. 26:787-793.

Senapathy, P., Shapiro, M. B. and Harris, N. L. 1990. Splice junctions, branch point sites, and exons: sequence statistics, identification, and applications to the genome project. Meth. Enzym. 183:252-278.

Shapiro, B. A., Nussinov, R., Lipkin, L. E., and Maizel, J. V. 1987. An interactive dot matrix system for locating potentially significant features in nucleic acid molecules. J. Biomol. Struc. Dynamics 45:697-706.

Shapiro, B. A. and Zhang, K. 1990. Comparing multiple RNA secondary structures using tree comparisons. Comput. Appl. Biosci. 6:309-318.

Sharp, P. M. and Li, W.-H. 1987. The codon adaption index - a measure of directional synonymous codon usage bias and potential applications. Nucleic Acids Res. 15:1281-1294.

Sharp, P. M., Tuohy, T. M. F., and Mosurski, K .R. 1986. Codon usage in yeast: cluster analysis clearly differentiates highly and lowly expressed genes. Nucleic

Acids Res.:5125-5131.

Shepard, J. C. W. 1981. Method to determine the reading frame of a protein from the purine/pyrimidine genome sequence and its possible evolutionary justification. Proc. Natl. Acad. Sci. USA 78:1596-1600.

Shine, J. and Dalgarno, L. 1975. Determinant of cistron specificity in bacterial ribosomes. Nature 254:34-38.

Shulman, M. J., Steinberg, C. M. and Westmoreland, N. 1981. The coding function of nucleotide sequences can be discerned by statistical analysis. J. Theor. Biol. 88:409-420.

Sidman, K. E., George, D. G., Barker, W. C., and Hunt, L. T. 1988. The protein identification resource (PIR). Nucleic Acids Res. 16:1869-1871.

Sikorski, R. S., Boguski, M. S., Goebl, M., and Hieter, P. 1990. A repeating amino acid motif in CDC23 defines a family of proteins and a new relationship among genes required for mitosis and RNA synthesis. Cell 60:307-317.

Simpson, G. G. 1961. Principles of animal taxonomy. Columbia University Press, New York.

Smith, E. L. 1967. Evolution of proteins. Harvey Lect. 62:231-256.

Smith, L. M., Sanders, J. Z., Kaiser, R. J., Hughes, P., Dodd, C., Connell, C. R., Heiner, C., Kent, S. B. H., and Hood, L. E. 1986 . Fluorescence detection in automated DNA sequence analysis. Nature 321:674-679.

Smith, T. F. and Waterman, M. S. 1981. Comparison of biosequences. Adv. Appl. Math. 2:482-489.

Smith, T. F. and Waterman, M. S. 1981. Identification of common molecular subsequences. J. Mol. Biol. 147:195-197.

Smith, T. F., Waterman, M. S., and Fitch, W. M. 1981. Comparative biosequence metrics. J. Mol. Evol. 18:38-46.

Smith, T. F., Waterman, M. S., and Burks, C. 1985. The statistical distribution of nucleic acid similarities. Nucleic Acids Res. 13:645-656.

Sobel, E. and Martinez, H. 1986. A multiple sequence alignment program. Nucleic Acids Res. 14:363-374.

Staden, R. 1980. A new computer method for the storage and manipulation of DNA gel reading data. Nucleic Acids Res. 8:3673-3694.

Staden, R. 1982. An interactive graphics program for comparing and aligning nucleic acid and amino acid sequences. Nucleic Acids Res. 10:2951-2961.

Staden, R. and MacLachlan, A. D. 1982. Codon preference and its use in identifying protein coding regions in long DNA sequences. Nucleic Acids Res. 10:141-156.

Staden, R. 1984. Computer methods to locate signals in nucleic acid sequences. Nucleic Acids Res. 12:505-519.

Staden, R. 1988. Methods to define and locate patterns of motifs in sequences. Comput. Appl. Biosci. 4:53-60.

Staden, R. 1990a. Searching for patterns in protein and nucleic acid sequences. Meth. Enzymol. 183:193-211.

Staden, R. 1990b. An improved sequence handling package that runs on the Apple Macintosh. Comp. Applic. Biosciences 6:387-393.

Staden, R. 1990c. Finding protein coding regions in genomic sequences. Meth. Enzym. 183:163-180.

Stanley, K. K., Kocher, H.-P., Luzio, J. P., Jackson, P., Tschopp, J., and Dickson, J. 1985. The sequence and topology of human complement component C9. EMBO J. 42:375-382.

States, D. J. and Botstein, D. 1990. Evaluating the reliability for analysis of imperfect molecular sequence data. submitted.

Stormo, G. D., Schneider, T. D., and Gold, L. M. 1982a. Characterization of translational initiation sites in *E. coli*. Nucleic Acids Res. 10:2971-2996.

Stormo, G. D., Schneider, T. D., Gold, L., and Ehrenfreucht, A. 1982b. Use of the 'Perceptron' algorithm to distinguish translational initiation sites in *E. coli*. Nucleic Acids Res. 10:2997-3011.

Stormo, G. D., Schneider, T. D., and Gold, L. 1986. Quantitative analysis of the relationship between nucleotide sequence and functional activity. Nucleic Acids Res. 14:6661-6679.

Stormo, G. D. Identifying coding sequences in Nucleic Acid and Protein Sequence Analysis, A Practical Approach, M.J. Bishop and C.J. Rawlings eds. IRL Press, Oxford. 1987.

Stormo, G. D. 1990. Consensus patterns in DNA. Meth. Enzymol. 183:211-221.

Sweet, R. M. and Eisenberg, D. 1983. Correlation of sequence hydrophobicities measures similarity in three-dimensional protein structures. J. Mol. Biol. 171:479-488.

Taylor, W. and Thornton, J. 1984. Recognition of super-secondary structure in proteins. J. Mol. Biol. 173:487-514.

Taylor, W. R. 1987. Multiple sequence alignment by a pairwise algorithm. Comput. Appl. Biosci. 3:81-97.

Trainor, C. D., Evans, T., Felsenfeld, G., and Boguski, M. S. 1990. Structure of evolution of a human erythroid transcription factor. Nature 343:92-96.

Traut, T. W. 1986. Are proteins made of modules? Mol. Cell. Biochem. 70:3-10.

Travers, A. A. 1989. DNA conformation and protein binding. Ann. Rev. Biochem. 58:427-452.

Tukey, J. W. Behavioral science:quantitative methods. In Exploratory Data Analysis. Tukey, J.W., ed., Addison-Wesley, Readin g, Massachusetts, 1977.

Turner, D.H., Sugimoto, N., and Freier, S.M. 1988. RNA structure prediction.Ann. Rev. Biophys. Biophys. Chem. 17:167-192

Ukkonen, E. 1983. On approximate string matching. Proc. Int. Conf. Found. Comp. Theor. Lectures in Comp. Sci. 158:487-493.

Vingron, M. and Argos, P., 1989. A fast and sensitive multiple sequence alignment algorithm. Comput. Appl. Biosci. 5:115-121.

Velleman, P. F. Data Desk Handbook. Odesta Corporation, Northbrook, Illinois, 1988.

von Heijne, G. Sequence Analysis in Molecular Biology: Treasure Trove or Trivial Pursuit. Academic Press, San Diego, CA 1987.

Waterman, M. S. 1984. General methods of sequence comparison. Bul. Math. Biol. 464:473-500.

Waterman, M. S. Sequence alignments. In Mathematical Methods for DNA Sequences, M. S. Waterman, ed., CRC Press, Boca Raton, FL, 1989.

Weber, I.T. 1990 Evaluation of homology modeling of HIV protease. Proteins Struct. Func. Genet. 7: 172-184.

Weisbrod, S. 1982. Active chromatin. Nature 297:289-295.

Wharton, K. A., Yedvobnick, B., Finnerty, V. G., and Artavanis-Tsakonas, S. 1985a. Opa: a novel family of transcribed repeats shared by the *Notch* locus and other developmentally regulated loci in *D. melanogaster*. Cell 40:55-62.

Wharton, K. A., Johansen, K. M., Xu, T., and Artavanis-Tsakonas, S. 1985b.

Nucleotide sequence from the neurogenic locus *Notch* implies a gene product that shares homology with proteins containing EGF-like repeats. Cell 43:567-581.

Wilbur, W. J. and Lipman, D. J. 1983. Improved tools for biological sequence comparison. Proc. Nat. Acad. Sci. USA 80:726-730.

Wilbur, W. J. 1986. On the PAM matrix model of protein evolution. Mol. Biol. Evol. 2:434.

Williams, A. L.Jr., and Tinoco, I.Jr. 1986. A dynamic programming algorithm for finding alternative RNA secondary structures. Nucleic Acids Res.14:299-315.

Wingender, E. 1988. Compilation of transcription regulating proteins. Nucleic Acids Res. 16:1879-1902.

Wlodawer, A., Bott, R., and Sjolin, L. 1982. The refined crystal structure of ribonuclease A at 2.0 angstroms resolution. J. Biol. Chem. 257:1325-1532.

Yamamoto, K. and Yoshikura, H. 1985. Computer program for prediction of the optimal and suboptimal secondary structures of long RNA molecules. Comput. Appl. Biosci. 1:89-94.

Yamamoto, T., Davis, C. G., Brown, M. S., Schneider, W. J., Casey, M. L., Goldstein, J. L., and Russell, D. W. 1984. The human LDL receptor: a cysteine-rich protein with multiple Alu sequences in its mRNA. Cell 39:27-38.

Yan, S. B., Grinnel, B. W., and Wold, F. 1989. Post-translational modifications of proteins: some problems left to solve. Trends Biochem. Sci. 14:264-268.

Yang, C.-Y., Chen, S.-H., Gianturco, S. H., Bradley, W. A., Sparrow, J. T., Tanimura, M., Li, W.-H., Sparrow, D. A., DeLoof, H., Rosseneu, M., Lee, F.-S., Gu, Z.-W., Gotto, A., and Chan,L. 1986. Sequence, structure, receptor-binding domains and internal repeats of human apolipoprotein B-100. Nature 323:738-742.

Zarkower, D. and Wickens, M. 1987. Formation of mRNA 3' termini: stability and dissociation of a complex involving the AAUAAA sequence. EMBO J. 6:177-186.

Zuker, M. and Stiegler, P. 1981. Optimal computer folding of large RNA sequences using thermodynamics and auxiliary information. Nucleic Acids Res. 9:133-148.

Zuker, M. 1989a. Computer prediciton of RNA secondary structure. Meth. Enzym. 180:262-289.

Zuker, M. 1989b. On finding all suboptimal foldings of an RNA molecule. Science 244:48-52.

Zuckerkandl, E. 1975. The appearance of new structures and functions in proteins during evolution. J. Mol. Evol. 7:1-57.

Zvelebil, M. J., Barton, G. J., Taylor, W. R., and Sternberg, M. J. E. 1987. Prediction of protein secondary structure and active sites using the alignment of homologous sequences. J. Mol. Biol. 195:957-961.

Appendices

I   Nucleic Acid Codes

Code	Bases	Mnemonic
A	A	A-denine
C	C	C-ytosine
G	G	G-uanine
T (or U)	T	T-hymine (or U-racil)
R	A or G	pu-R-ine
Y	C or T	p-Y-rimidine
S	G or C	S-trong (3 H-bonds)
W	A or T	W-eak (2 H-bonds)
K	G or T	K-eto
M	A or C	a-M-ino
B	C or G or T	not-A
D	A or G or T	not-C
H	A or C or T	not-G
V	A or C or G	not-(T or U)
N (or X)	any base	a-N-y (or unknown)
.	gap	

IUPAC standard codes for nucleic acids used with
computer software programs.

II Amino Acid Codes and Properties

Residue	IUPAC Letter Code		Molecular Weight at pH7	Side chain pKa	ε_M at 280 nm
	1 letter	3 letter			
Alanine	A	Ala	89.09		
Cysteine	C	Cys	121.16	10.28	120[a]
Aspartate	D	Asp	132.10	3.65	
Glutamate	E	Glu	146.13	4.25	
Phenylalanine	F	Phe	165.19		
Glycine	G	Gly	75.07		
Histidine	H	His	155.16	6.00	
Isoleucine	I	Ile	131.17		
Lysine	K	Lys	147.19	10.53	
Leucine	L	Leu	131.17		
Methionine	M	Met	149.21		
Asparagine	N	Asn	132.12		
Proline	P	Pro	115.13		
Glutamine	Q	Gln	146.15		
Arginine	R	Arg	175.20	12.48	
Serine	S	Ser	105.09		
Threonine	T	Thr	119.02		
Valine	V	Val	117.15		
Tryptophan	W	Trp	204.22		5690
Tyrosine	Y	Tyr	181.19	10.07	1280
Water			18.01		
alpha-amino group				8.56	
alpha-carboxyl group				3.56	

[a]absorbance is for cystine, and is due to the disulfide. In addition to the one letter code, B (asx) is used to mean either aspartate or asparagine, and Z (glx) to mean either glutamate or glutamine. X is generally used to indicate any amino acid residue.

III Amino AcidComposition of Proteins in PIR Release 26

Amino acid composition (residues per 100 residues) of 25,814 sequences with a total of 7,348,950 residues. This represents all the sequences in release 26.0 of the PIR database (National Biomedical Research Foundation; see Appendix VIII).

A	ALA	7.60		M	MET	2.29
C	CYS	1.89		N	ASN	4.36
D	ASP	5.21		P	PRO	5.20
E	GLU	6.32		Q	GLN	4.17
F	PHE	3.97		R	ARG	5.23
G	GLY	7.19		S	SER	7.15
H	HIS	2.28		T	THR	5.87
I	ILE	5.29		V	VAL	6.49
K	LYS	5.81		W	TRP	1.31
L	LEU	9.17		Y	TYR	3.21

IV Log-odds Matrices

	A	B	C	D	E	F	G	H	I	K	L	M	N	P	Q	R	S	T	V	W	X	Y	Z
A	3	0	-3	0	0	-4	1	-3	-1	-2	-3	-2	0	1	-1	-3	1	1	0	-7	-1	-4	0
B	0	3	-6	3	2	-5	0	1	-2	0	-4	-3	3	-2	0	-2	0	0	-3	-6	-1	-3	1
C	-3	-6	9	-7	-7	-6	-5	-4	-3	-7	-7	-6	-5	-3	-7	-4	-1	-3	-2	-8	-5	-1	-3
D	0	3	-7	5	3	-7	0	0	-3	-1	-5	-4	2	-2	1	-3	0	-1	-3	-8	-2	-5	1
E	0	2	-7	3	5	-6	-1	-1	-3	-1	-4	-4	1	-1	2	-3	-1	-2	-3	-8	-2	-4	1
F	-4	-5	-6	-7	-6	8	-5	-2	0	-6	0	-1	-4	-5	-6	-4	-3	-4	-3	-1	-3	4	-2
G	1	0	-5	0	-1	-5	5	-4	-4	-3	-5	-4	0	-2	-3	-4	1	-1	-2	-8	-3	-6	0
H	-3	1	-4	0	-1	-2	-4	7	-4	-2	-3	-4	2	-1	3	1	-2	-3	-3	-5	-1	-1	0
I	-1	-2	-3	-3	-3	0	-4	-4	6	-2	1	1	-2	-3	-3	-2	-2	0	3	-7	-2	-2	-1
K	-2	0	-7	-1	-1	-6	-3	-2	-2	5	-4	0	1	-2	0	2	-1	-1	-4	-5	-2	-6	0
L	-3	-4	-7	-5	-4	0	-5	-3	1	-4	5	3	-4	-3	-2	-4	-4	-3	1	-5	-3	-3	-2
M	-2	-3	-6	-4	-4	-1	-4	-4	1	0	3	8	-3	-3	-1	-1	-2	-1	1	-7	-2	-4	-1
N	0	3	-5	2	1	-4	0	2	-2	1	-4	-3	4	-2	0	-1	1	0	-3	-5	-1	-2	1
P	1	-2	-3	-2	-1	-5	-2	-1	-3	-2	-3	-3	-2	6	0	-1	1	-1	-2	-7	-2	-6	-1
Q	-1	0	-7	1	2	-6	-3	3	-3	0	-2	-1	0	0	6	1	-2	-2	-3	-6	-1	-5	0
R	-3	-2	-4	-3	-3	-4	-4	1	-2	2	-4	-1	-1	-1	1	6	-1	-2	-3	1	-2	-6	-1
S	1	0	-1	0	-1	-3	1	-2	-2	-1	-4	-2	1	1	-2	-1	3	2	-2	-2	-1	-3	0
T	1	0	-3	-1	-2	-4	-1	-3	0	-1	-3	-1	0	-1	-2	-2	2	4	0	-6	-1	-3	0
V	0	-3	-2	-3	-3	-3	-2	-3	3	-4	1	1	-3	-2	-3	-3	-2	0	5	-8	-2	-3	-1
W	-7	-6	-8	-8	-8	-1	-8	-5	-7	-5	-5	-7	-5	-7	-6	1	-2	-6	-8	12	-5	-1	-3
X	-1	-1	-5	-2	-2	-3	-3	-1	-2	-2	-3	-2	-1	-2	-1	-2	-1	-1	-2	-5	0	-3	-2
Y	-4	-3	-1	-5	-4	4	-6	-1	-2	-6	-3	-4	-2	-6	-5	-6	-3	-3	-3	-1	-3	8	-1
Z	0	1	-3	1	1	-2	0	0	-1	0	-2	-1	1	-1	0	-1	0	0	-1	-3	-2	-1	0

This table is the log-odds form of the mutational distance matrix at 120 PAM (percent accepted mutation) as calculated by Dayhoff and co-workers (Dayhoff, 1978). When comparing two sequences, the value in the row corresponding to a residue in the first sequence and the column corresponding to a residue in the second sequence indicates how likely these residues are to have arisen from unrelated sequences. Specifically, the values are the log of the probability that the residues resulted from mutation of a common ancestor, divided by the probability that they are related by chance. Positive values therefore indicate residues that are more likely than chance to have a common ancestor, and negative values indicate that an evoloutionary relationship is less likely than chance.

The PAM matrices are derived using a model of evolution wherein all positions are equally mutable, and are based on a specific set of observations of mutational frequency. For more details on the calculation of PAM matrices and their limitations see chapter 3 (Scoring Systems).

Values for B and Z are the averages of values for D and N, and E and Q, respectively. X is the average value for all comparisons.

	A	B	C	D	E	F	G	H	I	K	L	M	N	P	Q	R	S	T	V	W	X	Y	Z
A	2	0	-2	0	0	-4	1	-1	-1	-1	-2	-1	0	1	0	-2	1	1	0	-6	-1	-3	0
B	0	0	-4	3	2	-5	0	1	-2	0	-3	-2	2	-1	1	0	0	0	-2	-5	0	-3	0
C	-2	-4	12	-5	-5	-4	-3	-3	-2	-5	-6	-5	-4	-3	-5	-4	0	-2	-2	-8	-3	0	-2
D	0	3	-5	4	3	-6	1	1	-2	0	-4	-3	2	-1	2	-1	0	0	-2	-7	-1	-4	1
E	0	2	-5	3	4	-5	0	1	-2	0	-3	-2	1	-1	2	-1	0	0	-2	-7	-1	-4	1
F	-4	-5	-4	-6	-5	9	-5	-2	1	-5	2	0	-4	-5	-5	-4	-3	-3	-1	0	-2	7	-2
G	1	0	-3	1	0	-5	5	-2	-3	-2	-4	-3	0	-1	-1	-3	1	0	-1	-7	-2	-5	0
H	-1	1	-3	1	1	-2	-2	6	-2	0	-2	-2	2	0	3	2	-1	-1	-2	-3	0	0	0
I	-1	-2	-2	-2	-2	1	-3	-2	5	-2	2	2	-2	-2	-2	-2	-1	0	4	-5	-1	-1	-1
K	-1	0	-5	0	0	-5	-2	0	-2	5	-3	0	1	-1	1	3	0	0	-2	-3	-1	-4	0
L	-2	-3	-6	-4	-3	2	-4	-2	2	-3	6	4	-3	-3	-2	-3	-3	-2	2	-2	-1	-1	-1
M	-1	-2	-5	-3	-2	0	-3	-2	2	0	4	6	-2	-2	-1	0	-2	-1	2	-4	-1	-2	-1
N	0	2	-4	2	1	-4	0	2	-2	1	-3	-2	2	-1	1	0	1	0	-2	-4	-1	-2	1
P	1	-1	-3	-1	-1	-5	-1	0	-2	-1	-3	-2	-1	6	0	0	1	0	-1	-6	-1	-5	0
Q	0	1	-5	2	2	-5	-1	3	-2	1	-2	-1	1	0	4	1	-1	-1	-2	-5	-1	-4	0
R	-2	0	-4	-1	-1	-4	-3	2	-2	3	-3	0	0	0	1	6	0	-1	-2	2	-1	-4	0
S	1	0	0	0	0	-3	1	-1	-1	0	-3	-2	1	1	-1	0	2	1	-1	-2	-1	-3	0
T	1	0	-2	0	0	-3	0	-1	0	0	-2	-1	0	0	-1	-1	1	3	0	-5	-1	-3	0
V	0	-2	-2	-2	-2	-1	-1	-2	4	-2	2	2	-2	-1	-2	-2	-1	0	4	-6	-1	-2	-1
W	-6	-5	-8	-7	-7	0	-7	-3	-5	-3	-2	-4	-4	-6	-5	2	-2	-5	-6	17	-3	0	-2
X	-1	0	-3	-1	-1	-2	-2	0	-1	-1	-1	-1	-1	-1	-1	-1	-1	-1	-1	-3	0	-2	0
Y	-3	-3	0	-4	-4	7	-5	0	-1	-4	-1	-2	-2	-5	-4	-4	-3	-3	-2	0	-2	10	-1
Z	0	0	-2	1	1	-2	0	0	-1	0	-1	-1	1	0	0	0	0	0	-1	-2	0	-1	0

This table is the log-odds form of the mutational distance matrix at 250 PAM (percent accepted mutation) as calculated by Dayhoff and co-workers (Dayhoff, 1978). This scoring table is probably the most commonly used in protein sequence comparisons and is also known as the MDM_{78} table. When comparing two sequences, the value in the row corresponding to a residue in the first sequence and the column corresponding to a residue in the second sequence indicates how likely these residues are to have arisen from unrelated sequences. Specifically, the values are the log of the probability that the residues resulted from mutation of a common ancestor, divided by the probability that they are related by chance. Positive values therefore indicate residues that are more likely than chance to have a common ancestor, and negative values indicate that an evolutionary relationship is less likely than chance.

The PAM matrices are derived using a model of evolution wherein all positions are equally mutable, and are based on a specific set of observations of mutational frequency. For more details on the calculation of PAM matrices and their limitations see chapter 3 (Scoring Systems).

Values for B and Z are the averages of values for D and N, and E and Q, respectively. X is the average value for all comparisons.

V
A Partial List of Software Suppliers

Below is a partial list of software suppliers and the means to reach them. In many cases, a specific contact person is given who can help you in your software selection. Specific programs have not been listed because of the rapid change in this area. However, we have provided the systems each supplier's software will run on to limit your search.

Beckman Instruments
2500 Harbor Boulevard
Mailstop E26C
Fullerton, CA 92634
1-800-742-2345
Systems: IBM and IBM-compatible

DNASTAR, Inc.
1228 South Park Street
Madison, WI 53715 USA
(608)258-7420
Contact: Sandra M. Maples
in Europe:
105-113, The Broadway, West Ealing
London W139BL UK
(081)566-1200
Contact: Dr. Patricia M. Hoyle
Systems: IBM, IBM-compatible and Macintosh

European Molecular Biology Laboratory (EMBL)
Meyerhofstrasse 1
Postfach 10.2209
D-6900 Heidelberg
Federal Republic of Germany
(49)6221-3870
Contact: Graham Cameron

Genetics Computer Group, Inc. (GCG)
University Research Park
575 Science Drive, Suite B
Madison, WI 53711 USA
(608)231-5200
Contact: Dina Beers
Systems: VAX, Sun and Silicon Graphics

Hitachi DNASIS
Hitachi America Ltd.
2000 Sierra Point Parkway
Brisbane, CA 94005 USA
1-800-624-6176 (outside California)
1-800-225-9925 (in California)
Contact: Kathy Padgett
Systems: IBM, IBM-compatible

Intelligenetics, Inc.
700 E. El Camino Real
Mountain View, CA 94040 USA
(415)962-7300
Contact: Murray Summers
Systems: Sun, VAX, IBM, IBM-compatibles and Macintosh

International Biotechnologies, Inc. (IBI)
Subsidiary of Eastman Kodak Company
P.O. Box 9558, 25 Science Park
New Haven, CT 06535 USA
(203)786-5600; 1-800-243-2555
Contact: Mark Cortelyou
Systems: Macintosh, IBM, and IBM-compatible

National Center for Biotechnology Information (NCBI)
National Library of Medicine
8600 Rockville Pike

Bethesda, MD 20894 USA
(301)496-2475
or E-mail: finzel@ncbi.nlm.nih.gov

Protein Identification Resource (PIR)
National Biomedical Research Foundation
Georgetown University Medical Center
3900 Reservoir Road N.W.
Washington D.C. 2007-2195 USA
Contact: Dr. David G. George

Staden's Package
Laboratory of Molecular Biology, MRC,
University Medical School, Hills Road,
Cambridge CB2 2QH, England
Contact: Dr. Roger Staden
Systems: VAX and Sun

VI Hardware

It is difficult to make specific recommendations about computer hardware because of the constant rapid improvements being made. At this time one can expect that the cpu performance of computers will improve about two-fold per year for a given price. In three or four years therefore your money will buy you ten times the computer that it will today, or another way to look at is that the computer you spend $5000 for today may cost $500 in 3 or 4 years. Rather than making a specific recommendation, here are some factors to consider in shopping for a computer system.

First of all consider your needs. If you are looking for a computer for general use such as word processing, and simple sequence analyses such as restriction enzyme digests, and you expect to have no more than one person using it at a time, you should strongly consider a personal computer. There are many available software packages for IBM clones and for Macintosh computers. Because the sequence databases now provide free database searches and sequence retrieval by electronic mail, you may not even need to worry about databases.

If you intend to do some of the more time consuming analyses such as RNA folding, molecular dynamics, high quality graphics, frequent database searching, or program development, you will need to consider more powerful machines in the workstation class. Large sequencing projects (50kb) should also consider this class of machine. These computers come in many configurations ranging from something like a high end personal computer to very sophisticated machines for special functions (such as interactive graphics). Many of the machines in this class run a version of the UNIX operating system, and before buying one you should make sure that you can get the software for the analyses you want to perform (or be able to write it yourself).

Until recently, there has not been much molecular biology software for UNIX machines but you can expect this to change rapidly since these machines are now very popular. Workstations, depending on whether they are low end or high end, often begin to show performance losses when more than a handful of people use the same one simultaneously. You can also expect that one person will spend a substantial part of their time learning to manage the machine, since most UNIX system manuals are difficult to master. Most UNIX workstations come with the software and capabilities to handle network communication (see Appendix VII), a definite advantage to having this kind of machine.

The largest class of computers (of general interest to individual laboratories), large VAXes, Convexes, the high end machines from Sun, SGI, HP, IBM, etc., are intended for departmental or center use. These machines typically require a minimum of one person to keep them running and show people how to use them. On the other hand, they allow up to hundreds of people to use them simultaneously without losing performance.

To give a better feeling for the options, the following section describes four common kinds of general hardware setups that people might use. The scenarios described below are extremes and there is obviously a continuum of choices between the scenarios described.

1) The complete local scenario. A typical configuration would involve a PC clone or Macintosh. A printer and plotter will be required. The best option, if the software supports it, is to fulfill both needs with a laser printer. Complete copies of the database will be available on the computer on either CD-ROM, floppy disk, or hard disk. The rapid growth of the databases will probably make maintaining the databases on floppy disks impossible in the near future. CD-ROM is probably the method most sites will use in the future. This option will require a continuing investment to purchase the databases as they are updated. All analyses will be performed on the local computer using locally available software. This computer in this configuration will usually have a modem, but may or may not have access to electronic mail.

2) PC connected to a server. This option is very much like scenario 1, but the PC is connected to a larger computer such as a departmental or computer center (I will call this other computer the server). Again a local printer or plotter is most convenient, although you may have the option of printing from the server. Analysis will probably be a combination of local software and software available on the server (probably a major commercial package). The databases, and searches of the databases, will most likely be performed on the server to take advantage of the high speed and large storage space available. The server will provide connections for electronic mail so a second option is to perform the searches by electronic mail (see Appendix VII). Although you will not have to purchase databases in this scenario, you will most likely pay for server computer time. The ability to communicate by electronic mail is so useful, that scenario 2 strongly recommend, even if you intend do most analysis on your local computer.

3) Terminal connected to a server. This option is somewhat like scenario 2 except you will have no ability to do analysis locally. However, if you have a good local area network connection to the server, you may not notice the difference. Many inexpensive terminals have printer port, allowing you print from the terminal, but it may be more difficult to attach a plotter. The big advantage of this option is that it is inexpensive to set up, requiring as little as $500. The disadvantage is that you will probably have to pay for the computer time on the server, and that you will probably have little control over the software or databases. In this scenario, you should have

Things to consider

1) What is everyone else in your department (or field) using? If the entire building is buying Macintoshes, and you buy an IBM, you are going to have to solve every problem that comes up on your own.

2) Talk to your local computer center and see if they have any recommendations. You will probably need their help if you want to connect to electronic networks.

3) Make sure that the make and model of computer you buy will actually run the software you want to use. If at all possible test the software on the actual configuration you are considering. Sure this is a pain, but so is spending $10,000 on a high-tech dust collector. You should especially note that in spite of its vaunted portability, there are many differences between UNIX systems. A program will not necessarily run on all UNIX machines just because it runs on one. Also, beware of "vaporware", software that has been announced as being in development, or even available, that may never become available.

4) Unless your needs are special, stay with the crowd. If you have the same hardware as thousands of others, you will have a wider selection of software and be much less likely to be stranded with a machine no one else in the world uses.

5) Beware of older (3-5 years) machines that are suddenly available at reduced prices. This is often the sign that the model may be discontinued, possibly leaving you in an awkward situation.

6) Keep in mind that if you substantially change the class of machine you are considering, you may have to get new quotes on software prices as well. Software and maintainence charges are often based on the class of the machine, with higher prices for machines capable of supporting more users.

7) The aggregate of the above advice may lead to a condition known as "analysis paralysis", where you don't feel you can make a decision until you have examined all the possibilities. This may be impossible in the rapidly changing computer market, indeed you may fall steadily farther behind.

complete   access to electronic communication allowing databases searches to be done by mail and therefore reducing your computer costs. In general, I would recommend scenario 2 over scenario 3 because of the advantages of having the ability to do some analyses in your own lab (as well as a PC to use as a word processor, etc.).

4) Local workstation connected to network. This is basically a high-powered version of scenario two, but instead of a PC you would have a workstation, probably a system running the UNIX or VMS operating system, in your laboratory. Depending of the exact configuration of your system, you might maintain the sequence databases locally, or use a server to access them. One possibility in this scenario is to get the databases and weekly updates by ftp (see Appendix VII), although you would probably have to purchase the quarterly updates as well. Most analysis would probably be performed locally in this scenario. Although workstations give high performance, often with full color and interactive graphics capability, they are more complex to take care of, and this option will work best if there is someone available to help with maintaining the machine. You will also have the continuing expense of maintenance support for the computer. The big advantage of this scenario is that it provides a computer with true multiuser capability. It should be considered by labs involved in large sequencing projects, frequent database searches, and software development. A networked group of workstations and terminals is also a good option for departments and larger laboratories.

VII   Electronic Communication

It is sad, but true, that "electronic communication" is a concept out of a science fiction novel for most molecular biologists. Electronic communication has the same speed advantage as the FAX, but the additional advantages of reaching a wider audience and of being a more interactive medium.

The simplest kind of electronic communication is electronic mail or E-mail. E-mail is an almost exact analog of a FAX; you sit at your desk and compose a message at the terminal, and then use the computer's mail facility to send the message to an electronic address. In my experience, messages crossing the U.S. or going from the U.S. to Europe are usually delivered in less than a half hour (but this will depend on your connection to the network). Notice that to send your E-mail message, you did not have to print out the message, get up, walk down the hall to the FAX machine, call the other FAX machine, and send the message. All you had to do was type the address, push return and the message was on the way. Electronic mail is a very low overhead means of communication, and for this reason, it is often more successful than trying to get a written or telephone response.

FTP

Another common mode of electronic communication involves interactive use of other computers that are also attached to a network. FTP (file transfer protocol) allows one to connect to a remote computer and transfer files. Many computers have accounts with very limited privileges that can be logged into using the user name "anonymous", hence the term "anonymous FTP". This is a very common way of transferring computer software and, in molecular

243

and in molecular biology, databases. Some anonymous FTP sites of interest to molecular biologists are shown in Table 1.

Table 1: FTP and server sites of interest to molecular biologists
The address for each site is shown in the left column, with the numerical internet address below, if it was available. For FTP sites, the directory containing the relevant material is shown in parentheses if it is other than the default directory. Note that the larger FTP sites have a great deal of material of general interest in åddition to what is shown here. For bulletin boards, the subscription address is shown in the left column, and the address for actual message in parentheses in the center column.

* indicates that the contact person is the author of the database or program
(1) for information on this server send the message "help" in subject
(2) for information on this server send the message "help" as the first line of the message
(3) Genetics Computer Group Sequence Analysis Package
(4) The GCG (3) program QUICKSEARCH with enhancements added at EMBL is used to check if a new sequence has been previously se quenced. The search is much faster than FASTA, but is will only find nearly identical sequences.
Abbreviations used:
db = database
bb = bulletin board (or discussion group)
DDBJ = DNA Data bank of Japan db
EMBL = European Molecular Biology Laboratory DNA sequence db
GENBANK = GenBank nucleic acid db
GENPEPT = GenBank translated protein db
PIR = Protien Identification Resource (NBRF protein sequence db)
SWISS-PROT = SWISS-PROT protein sequence db
AIMB = AI and molecular biology researchers db (L. Hunter, NLM)
ALU = Alu sequence db (Jurka)
DROMAP = *Drosophila* Genetics Maps db (M. Ashburner, Cambridge)
ECD = *Escherichia coli* db (M. Kroeger, Giessen)
ENZYME = Enzymes nomenclature db (A. Bairoch, Geneva)
EPD = Eukaryotic promoter db (P. Bucher, Stanford)
LiMB = Listing of Molecular Biology databases (C. Burks, Los Alamos)
NGDD = Normalized gene maps for *E. coli, S. typh.*, etc. (Y. Abel, Montreal)
PDB Protein Data Bank (3D structures) (E. Abola, Brokhaven)
PROSITE = Dictionary of Protein Sites and Patterns (A. Bairoch, Geneva)
PRF = Protein Research Foundation
REBASE Restriction Enzyme database (Richard Roberts)
SEQANALREF = Sequence analysis reference list (A. Bairoch, Geneva)
TFD Transcription Factor Database (D.Ghosh, NCBI)

Table 1: FTP and server sites

SOFTWARE PACKAGES AND SMALLER FTP SITES

address	contents	responsible person/more information
evolution.genetics.washington.edu 128.208.128.1 anthro.utah.edu 128.110.192.93	PHYLIP phylogeny package v3.3	Joe Felsenstein*, joe@genetics.washington.edu Alan Rogers, rogers@anthro.utah.edu
haywire.nmsu.edu 128.123.001.032	gm (gene modeler) package	Chris Fields*, cfields@nmsu.edu
mcclb0.med.nyu.edu	USENET genbank software	Ross Smith, smith@mcclb0.med.nyu.edu
ncifcrf.gov (/pub/delila)	Delila system (150 programs)	Tom Schneider*, toms@ncifcrf.gov
uvaarpa.virginia.edu (/public_access/fasta.shar)	FASTA database search program	William Pearson*, wrp@virginia.bitnet

LARGER FTP SITES

address	contents	responsible person/more information
embl-heidelberg.de 192.54.41.20	EMBL server EMBL (updated daily) SWISS-PROT (& updates), PDB, DROMAP, ECD, ENZYME, EPD, LiMB, NGDD,PROSITE, SEQANALREF, TFD PC, UNIX Mac &VAX Software	Rainer Fuchs, fuchs@embl.bitnet

LARGER FTP SITES (cont.)

address	contents	responsible person/more information
flat.nig.ac.jp 133.39.128.2	GENBANK, EMBL, DDBJ, PIR, SWISS-PROT, GENPEPT, LiMB	Sanzo Miyazawa, smiyazaw@flat.nig.ac.jp
genbank.bio.net 134.172.1.160 (/Public)	Genbank GENBANK(quarterly,weekly&nightly) GENPEPT & updates EMBL & updates SWISS-PROT ALU, ENZYME, PROSITE, REBASE, SEQANALREF On-line services software	Dave Kristofferson, kristoff@genbank.bio.net consultant@genbank.bio.net
iubio.bio.indiana.edu 129.79.1.101	IUBIO archive Mac, VAX, Atari, DOS software DROMAP, EPD,LiMB,PROSITE, REBASE, TFD, Phylip Authorin program	Don Gilbert, gilbertd@iubio.bio.indiana.edu
mbcrr.harvard.edu 134.174.51.4	Mol. Bio. Computer Research Resource software PLSEARCH pattern db * MASE 3.1 multiple sequence editor	Temple Smith, tsmith@mbcrr.harvard.edu

address	contents	responsible person/more information
menudo.uh.edu 129.7.1.6	U Houston archive GENBANK, PIR UNIX, DOS, VMS, Mac software Cray software (future) BioMatrix archive Molecular evolution bb archive	Dan Davison, dbd@theory.bchs.uh.edu
modl.unibas.ch 131.152.1.2 (/biology/EMBnet) (/biology/database)	Biocomputing server Biozentrum, Universitaet Basel EMBL (updated daily) ALU, DROMAP, ECD, ENZYME, EPD, LiMB, NGDD, PROSITE, REBASE, SEQANALREF, TFD codon usage tables	Reinhard Doelz, doelz@urz.unibas.ch
ncbi.nlm.nih.gov 130.14.20.1 (/repository)	Nat'l Center for Biotech. Information NCBI software Geninfo db documentation ENZYME, EPD, LiMB, NGDD, PROSITE, REBASE, SEQANALREF, TFD metabolism, mol-model	Scott Federhen,federhen@ncbi.nlm.nih.gov (help and informatiom)

LARGER FTP SITES (cont.)

address	contents	responsible person/more information
ncbi.nlm.nih.gov (cont.)	Transcription factor database (TFD)	D. Ghosh*, ghosh@ncbi.nlm.nih.gov
(/toolbox) (/pub)	assorted public domain software more software-BLAST, FASTA, MACAW, etc.	
(/pub/aimb-db)	AI and mol. biology researchers db	Lawrence Hunter*, hunter@nlm.nih.gov
nic.funet.fi 128.214.6.100 (pub/misc/molbio)	Finnish State Supercomputer Center VAX, UNIX, DOS, Mac software many non-biological applications	Rob Harper, harper@csc.fi

SERVER SITES

address	contents	responsible person/more information
bioserve%genome@lanl.gov (2)	Los Alamos National Laboratory server Genbank documentation software archive (future)	Michael Cinofsky, michael%domain@lanl.gov
fileserv@gunbrf.bitnet (2)	PIR server PIR, NBRF nucleic, GENBANK, EMBL	Dr. John S. Garavelli, garavell@gunbrf.bitnet Ms. Kathryn Sidman, pirmail@gunbrf.bitnet
gene-server@bchs.uh.edu (1)	U Houston gene server GENBANK, PIR	gene-server-management@bchs.uh.edu

address	contents	responsible person/more information
gene-server@bchs.uh.edu (1) (cont.)	UNIX, DOS, VMS, Mac software Cray software (future) BioMatrix archive Molecular evolution bb archive FASTA searches	gene-server-management@bchs.uh.edu
listserv@irlearn.bitnet (2)	IRLEARN list server BIOSCI newsgroups & archives Newsgroups: AGEING, AG-FOREST, BIO-NAUT, BIONEWS, BIO-JNRL, BIOMATRIX, BIO-SOFT, CHROM-22, EMBL-DB, BIOJOBS, GENBANKB, GENE-ORG, GNOME-PR, METHODS, MOL-EVOL, POP-BIO, PROTEINS, SCI-RES	Rob Harper, harper@csc.fi
listserv@taunivm.bitnet(2)	photosynthesis researchers bb (photosyn@taunivm.bitnet)	Jonathan Marder, marder@hujiagri.bitnet
listserv@utoronto.bitnet (2)	U Toronto list server GCG (3) software discussion group (info-gcg@utoronto.bitnet)	John Cargill, cargill@utoroci.bitnet cargill@galen.oci.utoronto.ca

SERVER SITES (cont.)

address	contents	responsible person/more information
netserv@embl.bitnet (2)	EMBL server EMBL updated (daily) SWISS-PROT (& updates), PDB, DROMAP, ECD, EPD, LiMB, NGDD, PROSITE, SEQANALREF, TFD PC, UNIX, Mac, VAX software	Rainer Fuchs, fuchs@embl.bitnet
search@embl.bitnet (2) quick@embl.bitnet (2)	FASTA searches Quicksearch (4) searches	
netserv@flat.nig.ac.jp (2)	FLAT DB E-mail network server DDBJ , GENBANK, EMBL (updated 2X daily), GENPEPT, SWISS-PROT, PIR, PRF keyword searches by author, journal, accession and description	Sanzo Miyazawa, smiyazaw@flat.nig.ac.jp
pythia@cis.ucsc.edu	Alu sequence identification server	AleksanderMilosavljevic pythia-admin@cis.ucsc.edu milosav@cis.ucsc.edu

address	contents	responsible person/more information
search@genbank.bio.net	Genbank server	genbank@genbank.bio.net
retrieve@genbank.bio.net	FASTA searches	consultant@genbank.bio.net (FASTA help)
	Sequence retrieval	request@genbank.bio.net (help with retrieval)

ANTICIPATED AVAILLIBILITY: FALL OF 1991

address	contents	responsible person/more information
	Biology Software Info. Clearinghouse	Kenneth Kidd, genmln@yalevm.bitnet
	On-line software database	Martin Mader, genmln@yalevm.bitnet
	peer reviews	
	software archive	
	bug reports	

TELNET/RLOGIN

Even more interactive modes of electronic communication are becoming common. Telnet allows one to log in to a remote computer connected to the network, and use it just as if it was in the next room. This is probably the most common way for researchers to contact the five National Supercomputer Centers[1]. Telnet and the UNIX program "rlogin" are also used in local networks to allow connections between two computers on the same local network.

BULLETIN BOARDS/NEWS

Electronic "bulletin boards" are one of the most powerful means of electronic communication. To use these systems, you sign up for bulletin boards devoted to topics interesting to you. For molecular biologists, many of the most immediately interesting topics are covered by one of the BIOSCI bulletin boards (Table 2 and 3). When anyone sends a message to one of the bulletin board addresses, it is immediately rebroadcast to everyone who is signed up for the bulletin board.

A somewhat similar system, known as USENET news (or more commonly as "news") is found primarily on UNIX systems. In the news system, local computers receive regular updates (newsfeeds) of postings to all newsgroups for which they have signed up.

The power of the bulletin board and newsgroup system lies in the fact that you have virtually instant contact with thousands of people who might be able to help you. For instance, suppose that you have run out of a reagent critical to your experiment, but to your dismay find that the manufacturer no longer produces it. Posting a message to the BIOSCI board , Methods-Reagents (see Table 2) is quite likely to produce a response from someone who knows of another source, or may even be willing to share with you. Many messages are posted asking for the sequences of cloning vectors or for sources of free software for particular purposes, usually generating a useful response in one or two days at the most. Bulletin boards are also used for substantive discussions of scientific topics. For example some recent topics included: the future of the Human Genome Initiative; will electronic journals become common; the best methods to determine statistical significance of sequence alignments; and the future directions and responsibilities of the sequence databases. The addresses of some bulletin boards and servers of interest are shown in Table 1.

---

[1] The five supercomputing centers, their location and phone numbers are: Cornell National Supercomputing Facility, Ithaca, NY (607/255-8686); John Von Neuman National Supercomputing Center, Princeton, NJ (609/520-2000); National Center for Supercomputing Applications, Champaign, IL (217/244-0074); Pittsburgh Supercomputing Center, Pittsburgh, PA (412/268-4960); and San Diego Supercomputing Center (619/534-5000).

Your geographical location	BIOSCI node location	Subscription address
Scandinavia & Continental Europe	Sweden (Internet)	BIOSCI@bmc.ua.USAse
United Kingdom	UK (JANET)	BIOSCI@uk.ac.daresbury
North & South America	USA (Internet/BITNET)	BIOSCI@genbank.bio.net
Ireland & Continental Europe	Ireland (EARN/BITNET)	listserv@irlearn

Table 2: Subscription to BIOSCI bulletin boards. To subscribe to a bulletin board, send a message containing your name, electronic mail address, and the board to which you wish to subscribe to one of the first three address. Automatic subscription is available at the fourth site, listserv@irlearn.bitnet, by sending a message such as "SUBSCRIBE+BIONEWS John A. Doe" or "SUBSCRIBE BIO+SOFT John A. Doe", using your own name of course. The boardnames are derived from those in Table 1 by changing the hyphen, if present to '+', or adding a '+' to the beginning of the name (e.g. BIONEWS becomes +BIONEWS).

INFO-SERVERS

Info-servers are also referred to as file-servers or just servers. These are computers that run software that allows the computer to automatically respond to electronic mail messages requesting files. Some info-servers are also sites of bulletin boards and may be called list-servers. Most info-servers will respond to a message containing the single word "help" with the details on how to use the server. Note that if you want to join a bulletin board, you must send a message to the server address, not the bulletin board itself. A message to the bulletin board will just irritate 90% of the people who get your message "help" (or even worse, "testing, please ignore"). If you are unable to get the address for the server controlling a bulletin board, you may have to send a message to the bulletin board address to get help. Don't forget to include your E-mail address!

Of particular interest to molecular biologists are the GenBank, EMBL, PIR, and UH servers which offer both retrieval of sequence entries and FASTA database searches by electronic mail. Most of the servers allow searching GenBank, EMBL, PIR and Swiss-Prot databases at a single site. The PIR server allows access only to PIR, GenBank and EMBL, but allows searches by keyword, species, author and other fields, in addition to FASTA searches for similar sequences. The details of how these servers work vary from server to server. Try sending a "help" message (see notes 1 and 2 of Table 1) to get details, or if that doesn't work, contact the responsible person shown in Table 1. Note that searches done by electronic mail will be done using the most up-to-date versions of the databases, although you may not the

Table 3: Bulletin boards

Board Name	Bitnet/EARN Board Name	USENET Newsgroup Name	Topic
AGEING	AGEING	bionet.molbio.ageing	Scientific Interest Group
AGROFORESTRY	AG-FORST	bionet.agroforestry	Scientific Interest Group
BIONAUTS	BIO-NAUT	bionet.users.addresses	Address & other info about biologists on networks
BIONEWS	BIONEWS	bionet.general	General announcements of widespread interest to biologists
BIO-JOURNALS	BIO-JRNL	bionet.journals.contents	Tables of contents of biological journals
BIO-MATRIX	BIOMATRX	bionet.molbio.bio-matrix	Applications of computers to biological databases
BIO-SOFTWARE	BIO-SOFT	bionet.software	Information on software for the biological sciences
EMBL-DATABANK	EMBL-DB	bionet.molbio.embldatabank	Messages to/from the EMBL database staff
EMPLOYMENT	BIOJOBS	bionet.jobs	Job opportunities
GENBANK-BB	GENBANKB	bionet.molbio.genbank	Messages to/from the GenBank database staff

GENOMIC-ORGANIZATION	GENE-ORG	bionet.molbio.gene-org	Scientific Interest Group
HUMAN-GENOME-PROGRAM	GNOME-PR	bionet.molbio.genome-program	NIH-sponsored newsgroup on human genome issues
METHODS-AND-REAGENTS	METHODS	bionet.molbio.methds-reagnts	Requests for information and lab reagents
MOLECULAR-EVOLUTION	MOL-EVOL	bionet.molbio.evolution	Scientific Interest Group
POPULATION-BIOLOGY	POP-BIO	bionet.population-bio	Scientific Interest Group
PROTEIN-ANALYSIS	PROTEINS	bionet.molbio.proteins	Scientific Interest Group
SCIENCE-RESOURCES	SCI-RES	bionet.sci-resources	Information from/about the funding agencies
@bmc.ua.se (Sweden)	@irlearn.ucd.ie (Ireland)	@genbank.bio.net (USA)	@uk.ac.daresbury (UK)

Table 3: BIOSCI bulletin boards. Messages can be sent to the bulletin boards by sending electronic mail to the name in column one or two, followed by one of the node names shown at the bottom of the table, e.g. bionews@genbank.bio.net or bionaut@irlearn.ucd.ie. To subscribe to a bulletin board use the addresses in Table 2.

have full control over the parameters of the search.

NETWORKS AND ADDRESSES

Electronic mail addresses are similar to postal addresses in many ways. Postal addresses are hierarchically organized first to get the message to the right area, then to progressively more defined geographical areas until finally it reaches your house on a specific street. Network addresses are similar with two exceptions. The entire address is compressed so that it can be read on a single line (this is a convenience for computers), and more importantly, the information in the address is not necessarily geographical.

The most general part of the address is called the domain. The domain is frequently the country code, e.g. ".uk" for the United Kingdom or ."ca" for Canada, but for historical reasons it may be an organizational code such as ".edu" (U.S. NSFnet educational site), ."gov" (U.S. government site), or ".bitnet" (BITNET network site). Some of these less obvious domain codes are shown in Table 4. Most networks are converging on the use of the domain addressing system adopted by INTERNET. An INTERNET address looks something like:

gribskov@fcrfv1.ncifcrf.gov

or more generally   user@site.subdomain.domain

Where *fcrfv1* is the local computer, *ncifcrf* is a subdomain specifying the National Cancer Institute computer facility in Frederick, MD and *gov* is the U.S. government domain code.

There are two main exceptions to the domain addressing system. In the U.K. JANET addresses reverse the order of the items following the'@'. If you have trouble with an electronic mail address for someone in the United Kingdom, check to see if the domain ".uk" is shown immediately following

Table 4: Some internet domains

Suffix	Type of site
.com	commercial
.edu	educational
.gov	U.S. government
.mil	U.S. military
.net	network organization
.org	organization
.bitnet	BITNET site (includes EARN and NetNorth)
.uucp	UUCP network site (include EUnet and USENET)

"@", and if so reverse the address like so:

change   user@uk.ac.ucl.cs to user@cs.ucl.ac.uk
                          JANET   INTERNET

The other exception is for the UUCP networks which may still use addresses that look like uunet!site!user or mcvax!domain!user.

GETTING A NETWORK CONNECTION

If you are located at a university, the easiest way to get a network connection is to contact your local computer center and see if you can connect directly through them. Non-academic users will probably have to connect directly to the network, but it is worth contacting a nearby university or research lab first for advice. Alternatively, you can contact the networks directly; addresses are provided in Frey and Adams (1989).

VIII Sequence and Structural Databases

The following list contains some of the commonly used databases for sequence analysis, a description of their contents and availability.

CCSD

Contents:

Complex Carbohydrate Structural Database containing complex carbohydrate, glycolipid, and glycopeptide sequences and annotations from published articles.

Sponsors:

University of Georgia; U.S. Department of Energy; NIH; European Economic Community.

Availability:

IBM PC floppy diskettes, CD-ROM
carb@uga.bitnet

EMBL

Contents:

Nucleic acid sequences from published articles and by direct submission from authors.

Sponsor:

European Molecular Biology Laboratory

Availability:

Network, CD-ROM, magnetic tape
datalib@embl.bitnet

259

GenBank

Contents:
Nucleic acid sequences from published articles and by direct submission from authors. Translations of coding regions separately available (GenPept).

Sponsor:
National Institute of General Medical Sciences, NIH by contract to Intelligenetics, Inc., and Los Alamos Laboratory

Availability:
Network, CD-ROM, magnetic tape
gos@genbank.bio.net gb-sub%life@lanl.gov (for direct submission)

GenInfo

Contents:
Nucleic acid and protein sequences with MEDLINE abstracts from published articles and by direct submission from authors; GenBank and NBRF/PIR data incorporated in ASN.1.

Sponsor:
National Center for Biotechnology Information, NIH.

Availability:
Network, CD-ROM
geninfo@ncbi.nlm.nih.gov

NRL_3D

Contents:
Protein sequence and structure database derived from PDB and searchable in the PIR/NBRF environment.

Sponsors:
Office of Naval Research; U.S. Army Medical Research and Development Command.

Availability:
Network, CD-ROM, magnetic tape
pirmail@gunbrf.bitnet

PDB

Contents:
Protein and nucleic acid three-dimensional structures by direct submission from authors of crystallographic and NMR data as well as models.

Sponsors:
U.S. National Science Foundation and National Library of Medicine, NIH by contract to Brookhaven National Laboratory.

Availability:
Network, magnetic tape
pdb@bnlchm.bitnet

PIR/NBRF

Contents:
Protein sequences from published articles.

Sponsors:
National Library of Medicine, NIH by grant to the National Biomedical Research Foundation/Protein Identification Resource.

Availability:
Network, CD-ROM, magnetic tape
pirmail@gunbrf.bitnet

OWL

Contents:
Protein sequences consolidated from NBRF/PIR, SWISS-PROT, GenBank (translation), NEWAT86, PSD-Kyoto, NRL_3D and PDB.

Sponsors:
University of Leeds; Science and Engineering Council, U.K.; Protein Engineering Initiative.

Availability:
Network, CD-ROM, magnetic tape
uig@daresbury.ac.uk

SWISS-PROT

Contents:
Protein sequences from published articles and translations of coding regions from EMBL.

Sponsors:
Amos Bairoch, University of Geneva

Availability:
Network, CD-ROM, magnetic tape
bairoch@cgecum51.bitnet

IX Data Submission

Most biological journals strongly recommend or require that sequences be submitted to the appropriate sequence database before publication of the related paper. It is highly preferable that the sequences be submitted in electronic form since this avoids the introduction of errors during manual transcription, and allows the databases to more efficiently use their limited resources. Sequence data are shared among the following databases: EMBL Data Library (Heidelberg, FRG); GenBank (Los Alamos, NM, U.S.A. and Mountain View, CA, U.S.A), DNA Data Bank of Japan (DDBJ; Mishima, Japan); National Biomedical Research Foundation Protein Identification Resource (NBRF-PIR; Washington, D.C., U.S.A.); Martinsried Institute for Protein Sequence Data (MIPS; Martinsried, FRG) and International Protein Information Database in Japan (JIPID; Noda, Japan).

A software package for the preparation of sequence data for submission to the databases is available, and its use is encouraged. The AUTHORIN software runs on IBM PC and Macintosh computers and can be obtained by sending your name and postal address to authorin@genbank.bionet. The AUTHORIN package is free. A second alternative for submitting sequences is to get the sequence submission form by electronic mail from the databases. A single form is used by all of the databases for both protein and nucleic acid sequences. The data submission form can be obtained by sending the message "DATASUB" to retrieve@genbank.bio.net, the message "SEND SUBFORM" to fileserv@gunbrf.bitnet, or the message "GET DOC:DATASUB.TXT" to netserv@embl.bitnet. The form (Figure 1) can then be filled in with a simple text editor and sent to the database either on disk, or by electronic mail. Only as a last resort, should typed sequence be submitted. The completed form should be sent to the appropriate postal or electronic address shown in Table 1.

Table 1: Addresses for sequence submission.

GenBank Submissions
Mail Stop K710
Los Alamos National Laboratory
Los Alamos, NM 87545 U.S.A.
Telephone: (505) 665-2177
Electronic mail: gb-sub%life@lanl.gov

EMBL Data Submissions
Postfach 10.2209
D-6900, Heidelberg
Federal Republic of Germany
Telephone (+49) 6221-387-258
Telefax (+49) 6221-387-306
Electronic mail: datasubs@embl.bitnet

PIR Submissions
National Biomedical Research Foundation
3900 Reservoir Road, NW
Washington, DC 20007 U.S.A.
Telephone: (202) 687-2121
Electronic mail: fileserv@gunbrf.bitnet

Figure 1: (starting on next page) Electronic Data Submission Form. This form is printed for information only. Do not use it for actual data submission The form should be filled out in a plain-text (ASCII) format without embedded word processing characters. If the sequence is to be submitted by electronic mail, lines should not exceed 80 characters since these are often truncated during E-mail transmission. Each sequence should include the names of the authors. Each distinct sequence should be listed separately using the same number of bases (residues) per line. The length of each sequence in bases or residues should be clearly indicated. Enumeration should begin with a "1" and continue in the direction 5' to 3' (or amino- to carboxy- terminus). Amino acid sequences should be listed using the one-letter code. Translations of protein coding regions in nucleotide sequences should be submitted in a separate computer file from the nucleotide sequences themselves. The code for representing the sequence characters should conform to the IUPAC-IUB standards, which are described in: Nucl. Acids Res. 13: 3021-3030 (1985) (for nucleic acids) and J. Biol. Chem. 243: 3557-3559 (1968) and Eur. J. Biochem 5: 151- 153 (1968) (for amino acids) (see also Appendices I and II).

I. GENERAL INFORMATION

Your last name   first name   middle initials

Institution

Address

Computer mail address   Telex number

Telephone   Telefax number

On what medium and in what format are you sending us your sequence data?
(see instructions at the beginning of this form)
  [ ] electronic mail
  [ ] diskette
     computer: operating system: editor:
  [ ] magnetic tape
     record length: blocksize: label type:
     density   [ ] 800   [ ] 1600   [ ] 6250
     character code [ ] ASCII [ ] EBCDIC

II. ACCESSION NUMBER

An accession number is permanently assigned to every sequence in the
database. If an accession number has not already been assigned to this work,
a number will be assigned upon receipt of the data. We strongly recommend
that all references to this data cite the assigned accession number.

ACCESSION NUMBER_____

III. CITATION INFORMATION

These data are [ ] published [ ] in press [ ] submitted [ ] in preparation
          [ ] no plans to publish

authors

---

title of paper

---

journal   volume, first-last pages, year

Do you agree that these data can be made available in the database before they appear in print?
[ ] yes   [ ] no, they should be made available only after publication.

===

Does the sequence which you are sending with this form include data that does NOT appear in the above citation?
[ ] no
[ ] yes, from position _____ to _____ [ ] base pairs OR
                        [ ] amino acid residues
  (If your sequence contains 2 or more such spans, use the feature table in section IV to indicate their positions)
If so, how should these data be cited in the database?
[ ] published [ ] in press [ ] submitted [ ] in preparation
[ ] no plans to publish

---

authors

---

address (if different from that given in section I)

---

title of paper

---

journal   volume, first-last pages, year

===

List references to papers and/or database entries which report sequences overlapping with that submitted here.

1st author   journal, vol., pages, year and/or database, accession number

---

===

IV. DESCRIPTION OF SEQUENCED SEGMENT

Wherever possible, please use standard nomenclature or conventions. If a question is not applicable to your sequence, answer by writing N.A. in the appropriate space; if the information is relevant but not available, write a question mark (?).

What kind of molecule did you sequence?   (check all boxes which apply)

[ ] genomic DNA   [ ] genomic RNA   [ ] virus or [ ] provirus
[ ] cDNA to mRNA   [ ] cDNA to genomic RNA
[ ] organelle DNA [ ] organelle RNA   please specify organelle:
[ ] tRNA   [ ] rRNA   [ ] snRNA   [ ] scRNA
[ ] other nucleic acid. please specify:
[ ] peptide [ ] sequence assembled by [ ] overlap of sequenced fragments
                          [ ] homology with related sequence
                          [ ] other. please specify:

          [ ] partial: [ ] N-terminal
                              [ ] C-terminal
                              [ ] internal fragment

length of sequence   [ ] base pairs or [ ] amino acid residues

gene name(s) (e.g., lacZ)

gene product name(s) (e.g., beta-D-galactosidase)

Enzyme Commission number (e.g., EC 3.2.1.23)

gene product subunit structure (e.g., hemoglobin alpha-2 beta-2)

The following items refer to the original source of the molecule you have
sequenced.
   organism (species) name (e.g., *Escherichia coli*; *Mus musculus*)

sub-species   strain (e.g., K12; BALB/c)

name/number of individual/isolate (e.g., patient 123; influenza virus A/PR/
8/34)

developmental stage   [ ] germ line [ ] rearranged

haplotype   tissue type   cell type

The following items refer to the immediate experimental source of the
submitted sequence.
   name of cell line (e.g., HeLa; 3T3-L1)

library (type; name)   clone(s)

The following items refer to the position of the submitted sequence in the genome.

chromosome (or segment) name/number

| map position | units: [ ] genome % [ ] nucleotide number |
| | [ ] other: |

===

Using single words or short phrases, describe the properties of the sequence in terms of:
  - its associated phenotype(s);
  - the biological/enzymatic activity of its product;
  - the general functional classification of the gene and/or gene product
  - macromolecules to which the gene product can bind (e.g., DNA, calcium,other proteins);
  - subcellular localization of the gene product;
  - any other relevant information.

Example (for the viral *erbB* nucleotide sequence): transforming capacity; EGF receptor-related; tyrosine kinase; oncogene; transmembrane protein.

===

V. FEATURES OF THE SEQUENCE

Please list below the types and locations of all significant features experimentally identified within the sequence. Be sure that your sequence is numbered beginning with "1."

In the column marked   fill in

feature	type of feature (see information below)
from	number of first base/amino acid in the feature
to	number of last base/amino acid in the feature
bp	an "x" if numbering refers to position of a base pair in a nucleotide sequence
aa	an "x" if numbering refers to position of an amino acid residue in a peptide sequence
id	indicate method by which the feature was identified. E = experimentally; S = by similarity with known sequence or to an established consensus sequence; P = by similarity to some other pattern, such as an open reading frame
comp	an "x" for a nucleotide sequence feature located on strand complementary to that reported here

Significant features include:

- regulatory signals (e.g., promoters, attenuators, enhancers)
- transcribed regions (e.g., mRNA, rRNA, tRNA).(indicate reading frame if start and stop codons are not present)
- regions subject to post-transcriptional modification (e.g., introns, modified bases)
- translated regions
- extent of signal peptide, prepropeptide, propeptide, mature peptide
- regions subject to post-translational modification (e.g., glycosylated or phosphorylated sites)
- other domains/sites of interest (e.g., extracellular domain, DNA-binding domain, active site, inhibitory site)
- sites involved in bonding (disulfide, thiolester, intrachain, interchain)
- regions of protein secondary structure (e.g., alpha helix or beta sheet)
- conflicts with sequence data reported by other authors
- variations and polymorphisms

The first 2 lines of the table are filled in with examples.

Numbering for features on submitted sequence [ ] matches manuscript [ ] does not match manuscript

	feature	from	to	bp	aa	id	comp
EXAMPLE	TATA box	1	8	x		S	
EXAMPLE	exon 1	9	264	x			

VI.   SEQUENCE DATA

Please enter the nucleotide sequence data here:

Please enter the translated amino acid sequence here:

X   Glossary

The following glossary contains many of the terms used in this book and the sequence analysis field. The number in parentheses after each entry refers to the chapter where more information can be found on the topic.

alignment (3) 1. A one-to-one matching of two sequences so that each character in a pair of sequences is associated with a single character of the other sequence or with a null character (gap). Alignments are often displayed as two rows with an optional third row in between pointing out regions of similarity, for example:

```
Human     GAPLEPVYPGDNATPEQMAQYAADLRRYINMLTRPRYGKR
          :|  :|  ||||:|  |::   :   :|  |:|::||  ||
Chicken   GPSQPTYPGDDAPVEDLIRFYDNLQQYLNVVTRHRY..
```

2. The process of making an alignment of two or more sequences.

assembly (1, 4) The process of correctly joining together the DNA sequence from individual sequencing experiments into a contiguous segment. See CONTIG.

antigenic index (2) A prediction of the antigenicity of a sequence based on the hydrophilicity, predicted side chain flexibility, surface probability, and predicted turns.

codon preference (1,4) The preferred codon usage in highly expressed genes

codon usage (1,4) The observed usage of the amino acid codons in a particular gene, tissue, or organism.

271

consensus sequence (1) A single sequence that represents the content of a group of aligned sequences. The consensus sequence character is often the residue that is the plurality at any position. A WEIGHT MATRIX is a more informative way to represent a group of sequences.

contig (1) DNA sequence read from several separate gels that has been merged or "assembled" into a longer contiguous segment.

diagonal (3) In a dot matrix comparison a row of dots along a diagonal (sometimes shown as a connected diagonal line) represents a region of high local similarity between two sequences.

directional information values (2) In the Garnier-Osguthorpe-Robson secondary structure prediction method, a table of scores for each of the twenty amino acid residues in a window of 8 residues in each direction around the current position. The scores indicate the influence of the residues in the window on the secondary structure observed at the central position.

domain (2) An independently folding portion of a protein. Often used less precisely to mean any distinguishable region of a sequence.

end gap (3) Gaps which include the first or last positions in an alignment. End gaps may be weighted, i.e. penalized, or unweighted, depending on the program.

extinction coefficient (2) The degree to which a molecule absorbs light. Often given in terms of the absorbance of a 1M solution (molar extinction coeficient, ε) or of a 1 % (10mg/ml) solution ($\varepsilon^{1\%}$). Extinction coefficients are usually measured for absorption peaks: 280 nm for protein, 260 nm for DNA.

gap (1, 2, 3, 4) A space inserted into a sequence to enhance the its alignment with another sequence. Gaps are often represented by a '.' or '-' character.

gap extension penalty (3) The length-dependent term, l, of a gap penalty of the form $w = g + lx$. Where w is the gap penalty, g the length-independent term, l the length-dependent term, and x the length of the gap.

gap opening penalty (3) Also known as the gap creation penalty. The length-independent term, g, of a gap penalty of the form $w = g + lx$. (see gap extension penalty).

genetic code matrix (3) Also known as minimum base change scoring. A scoring system for protein sequences where the distance between any pair of residues is the minimum number of substitutions required to change the codon for the first residue to that of the second.

global alignment (3) An optimal alignment that includes all characters from each sequence. Global alignments may miss short regions of high local similarity. Global alignments are most useful for closely related sequences of known homology.

hash table (3) A listing of the positions at which all words of a fixed length (word size or ktup) occur in a query sequence. The FASTA database searching program uses a hash table approach.

helical wheel (2) A graphical view of the asymmetry of the distribution of hydrophobic side chains in (potential) alpha-helices.

homology (3) Similarity attributable to descent from a common ancestor. Homology is an all or none relationship. As with pregnancy, it is difficult to be only slightly homologous. In molecular biology, homology is often inferred from a high degree of sequence similarity.

hydropathic (2) Hating water. An amino acid residue with an aliphatic or aromatic side chain.

hydrophilic (2) Liking water. An amino acid residue with a polar side chain.

hydrophobic (2) Fearing water. An amino acid residue with an aliphatic or aromatic side chain.

hydrophobic moment (2) A quantitative measure of the asymmetry of the distribution of hydrophobic side chains in α-helices and β-strands.

identity diagonal (3) In an intrasequence dot matrix comparison, the identity diagonal represents the one-to-one matching of the sequence with itself. Compare MAIN DIAGONAL.

identity matrix (3) Also known as a unitary matrix. A scoring system in which only identical characters received a positive similarity score.

indel (3) An insertion/deletion. When two sequences are aligned, it is impossible to tell whether a gap is actually an insertion in the first sequence or a deletion from the second. The term indel indicates that either is possible.

information content (3) The number of bits needed to uniquely specify a message, where one bit is able to distinguish between two equally likely things. When the base frequencies are equal, it takes one bit to distinguish a purine from a pyrimidine, and two bits of information to uniquely specify a single base.

isoelectric point (2) The pH at which a protein or peptide is uncharged.

ktup or ktuple (3) The word size used to make the hash table in the FASTA program.

local alignment (3) An optimal alignment that includes the most similar local regions or regions. Local alignments may include only short portions of the sequences that were used to calculate the alignment. Local alignments are especially useful for distantly related sequences, although they work equally well for closely related ones.

log-odds (3) A scoring system in which the values are the logarithm of the relative probability (odds) of a comparison being due to homology or being due to chance.

main diagonal (3) In an intersequence dot matrix comparison, the main diagonal is a diagonal or diagonals that predominate over the others. The main diagonal is often inferred to represent the homologous matching of the two sequences. Compare IDENTITY DIAGONAL.

metric distance (3) A scoring system that has the following properties:
- no distance is less than 0
- identical sequence characters have a distance of 0
- the distance is symmetric; that is, the distance from A to B is the same as the distance from B to A.

The scoring system as a whole obeys the triangle inequality; if you consider any three distances, the distance from A to C must be less than or equal to the distance from A to B plus the distance from B to C.

MDM$_{78}$ (3) Mutation Data Matrix, 1978. The most common scoring system for proteins. MDM$_{78}$ is the log-odds form of the PAM-250 mutation probability matrix. See Scoring Systems in Chapter 3 for a discussion of the derivation of this scoring system.

minimum base change (3) See GENETIC CODE MATRIX.

Monte Carlo simulation (3) A method of calculating significance where the analysis in question is repeated using randomized or permuted sequences, in order to determine the expected scores for unrelated (random) sequences.

neighborhood table (3) A listing of the positions at which all words of fixed length and within a certain threshold of similarity occur in a sequence. Compare HASH TABLE.

optimal alignment (3) The best possible alignment of two sequences under specific conditions. Optimal alignments are sensitive to the scoring system, penalties for gaps, and to the algorithm (local or global) used.

overlaps (1) Segments of sequence that are common to sequences derived from separate sequencing experiments.

PAM (3) Percent accepted mutations. 1 PAM means there has been 1 mutation per 100 residues, 250 PAM would be 2.5 mutations per residue. See Scoring Systems in Chapter 3.

path graph (3) A figure showing the locations of the pointers in a dynamic programming alignment. See also POINTER.

pointer (3) In a dynamic programming alignment, a pointer that defines the position of the best "previous" alignment is set for each position in the score matrix. The best previous alignment must lie in either the previous row or column. See Chapter 3.

profile (2) A profile is a position specific scoring table that represents the information from a family of related sequences. A profile can be used much like a sequence for alignment and database searching, in effect aligning to the consensus of an entire family. A profile is a special kind of WEIGHT MATRIX.

progressive alignment (3) A multiple alignment algorithm in which the sequences are first clustered and then added one by one, in order of decreasing similarity, to the growing multiple alignment.

propensity (2) In the Chou and Fasman secondary structure prediction, the measure of a residue's tendency to assume a given structure.

PROSITE (2, 4) A database of "signatures" (regular expressions) specific for various protein motifs. An example of a PROSITE pattern is the epidermal growth factor (EGF) signature $C-X-C-X_5-G-X_2-C$ which is equivalent to cys-any residue-cys-any 5 residues-gly-any 2 residues-cys. PROSITE patterns are examples of REGULAR EXPRESSIONS.

regular expression (2) A string of characters specifying a pattern. Usually, wildcards (match to anything) and variable positions (match to one of the following) are allowed. A consensus sequence is a restricted form of a regular expression that allows only one possiblity at each position.

score matrix (3) In a dynamic programming alignment, the score matrix indicates the quality of the alignment ending at each possible pair of residues. For instance $S_{10,15}$ is the score for the alignment that ends with residue 10 of sequence 1 aligned with residue 15 of sequence 2.

stringency (3, 4) When a statistic or score is calculated for a window of residues, the term stringency is used to refer to the minimum score which will be saved or considered to be a match. For example, with a window of 10 and a stringency of 6, 6 out of 10 bases must be identical.

traceback (3) The second stage of a dynamic programming alignment, in which the alignment is found by following the pointers back from the highest scoring position in the score matrix.

unitary matrix (3) See IDENTITY MATRIX.

variation moment (2) A quantitative measure of the asymmetry of the distribution of mutational changes in a family of sequences. Similar to the hydrophobic moment, but it describes regions or sides of a helix where changes are evolutionarily tolerated.

weight matrix (1, 4) A two-dimensional representation of a sequence pattern where one axis represents the position in the pattern, and the other every possible sequence character that could occur in the sequence. A PROFILE is a special type of weight matrix that includes information about the positions of gaps and can therefore be used in alignment procedures.

Z score (3) Also known as a z value, standard normal deviate, or standardized score. The Z score measures the distance of a value from the mean of a distribution in standard deviation units, $Z = (\text{value} - \text{mean}) / \sigma$. In sequence analyses, the mean and standard deviation are usually those of unrelated or randomized sequences — see Monte Carlo Simulation.

Index